ς

An Introduction to Acarology

THE MACMILLAN COMPANY
NEW YORK · BOSTON · CHICAGO
DALLAS · ATLANTA · SAN FRANCISCO

MACMILLAN AND CO., LIMITED
LONDON · BOMBAY · CALCUTTA
MADRAS · MELBOURNE

THE MACMILLAN COMPANY
OF CANADA, LIMITED
TORONTO

Cunaxa taurus (Kramer)

THOMAS M. EVANS

An Introduction to

ACAROLOGY

Edward W. Baker

BUREAU OF ENTOMOLOGY AND PLANT QUARANTINE
AGRICULTURAL RESEARCH ADMINISTRATION
UNITED STATES DEPARTMENT OF AGRICULTURE

G. W. Wharton

DEPARTMENT OF ZOOLOGY, DUKE UNIVERSITY
DURHAM, NORTH CAROLINA

THE MACMILLAN COMPANY

New York

To Our Friend and Teacher

DR. HENRY ELLSWORTH EWING

1883–1951

PREFACE

I N THE past few years there has been a growing demand for an elementary and comprehensive work on mites, both from the professional acarologist and from students and investigators in related fields such as entomology, zoology, and parasitology. In the United States before 1940 there were only a few scattered workers in the field. Now, the interest created by the recognition of mites that carry human diseases and the problems created in agriculture by the use of DDT which causes heretofore unknown and undescribed species to become serious pests of plants have resulted in a growing list of both students and professional workers who have become interested in learning something about the Acarina. It is for these people that this book has been written.

The German acarologist, Vitzthum, completed the section on Acari in Bronns' "Klassen und Ordnungen des Tierreichs" in 1942. While this work is comprehensive it is also exhaustive and does not present a digest of available knowledge for the beginner. Vitzthum's masterpiece has been extremely helpful to us, and we have followed his classification except in cases where our studies have indicated necessary changes. One of the most apparent deficiencies of Vitzthum's monograph for the beginner is its complete lack of keys and the absence of discussion of the Acarina family by family.

The present book consists of a short introduction to the general structure, development, and ecology of mites in general and then each family is considered as a unit. We have prepared keys to the group that are designed to enable the reader to place any acarine in its proper family. In the discussion of each family the following information is given if it is known: a diagnosis, a list of genera and their type species (the reader is referred to S. A. Neave, 1939, "Nomenclator Zoologicus,"

vii

for the citations to the genera), a discussion which includes the biology, the economic or medical importance with emphasis on the species involved, and a series of references to pertinent literature. In addition line drawings of the representatives of the families are included.

The Acarina are still poorly known even by specialists in the group. Therefore, it is anticipated that many changes will have to be made before a definitive work on the group is achieved. In many cases very little is known about certain families. When it is realized that the Acarina represent an area for investigation in systematics, ecology, and economic zoology that is practically virgin territory, we can see that we are truly on the threshold of a new and exciting field.

The authors wish to thank Drs. R. E. Beer, G. M. Kohls, H. H. J. Nesbitt, A. E. Pritchard, and R. W. Strandtmann for their helpful advice and criticism.

Edward W. Baker and G. W. Wharton

TABLE OF CONTENTS

Chapter I PAGE 1

Introduction

Chapter II PAGE 36

The Suborder Onychopalpida Wharton, 1947

Chapter III PAGE 40

The Suborder Mesostigmata G. Canestrini, 1891

Chapter IV PAGE 137

The Suborder Ixodides Leach, 1815

Chapter V PAGE 146

The Suborder Trombidiformes Reuter, 1909

Chapter VI

Hydrachnellae Latreille, 1802

Chapter VII

The Suborder Sarcoptiformes Reuter, 1909

Chapter VIII PAGE 387

Oribatei Dugès, 1833

Index PAGE 439

xiii

CHAPTER I

Introduction

THE Acarina are to be found in almost every habitat available to animal life. Careful examination of the nearest handful of soil will surely uncover several (Figure 1), and in many localities literally thousands of specimens will be found. The feathers of birds are frequently alive with mites as are the pelts of animals. Many people carry a colony of follicle mites in their facial pores. Fresh water streams, lakes, and ponds have their mite faunas. The oceans are not free from them. Some mites are adapted to live in the hot water of springs that occur in certain volcanic regions. Insects, whatever their habitat, act as hosts for many species. Mites invade the internal organs of man and animals, both vertebrate and invertebrate. Most plants produce suitable quarters, and examination of the debris from the fork of any tree will yield specimens. This world of life remains unknown to most men. Some zoologists and even some entomologists have never seen mites in their native haunts. Few of them appreciate the wealth of species that are at hand everywhere.

Some of the Acarina, however, are known to the layman, and others frequently call attention to themselves by their activities. Ticks are well known to most people of the world because they are large enough to be seen readily with the naked eye and because frequently they attack man and his domestic animals. In the southern United States most people have had the misfortune to make the acquaintance of chiggers although few of them would recognize one as the larva of a mite. Fruit growers know the spider mites at first hand, and the eriophyids, another group of mites, are familiar to them. Many dog owners owe their introduction to the Acarina to mange-producing mites that attack their pets. People who work with stored food products, such as grain or copra, are at times aware of some of the mites that infest these products because they produce an irritating itch. During periods of over-crowding such as occurred in England during World War II the human-itch mite becomes prevalent and causes much suffering. While the activities of a few species are well known, people acquainted with their ravages can rarely recognize the mites if they see them.

The small size of mites is responsible for the lack of information

Figure 1 Mites removed from a small sample of litter and soil collected behind the Biology building at Duke University. This collection is representative of the acarid fauna found in humus. (Photo by Haliburton)

available on them. The one suborder of the Acarina—the ticks—that is readily visible to the unaided eye is well studied. Students of ticks know them as well as the entomologists know the larger insects. They can be studied effectively without special techniques. A dissecting microscope or even a high-powered hand lens will reveal the important taxonomic features. With other Acarina this is not the case. Techniques foreign to the entomologist must be used, and special methods of collecting are required. Specimens must be mounted on microscopic slides and studied under magnifications as high as one thousand diameters. Furthermore, the techniques are not the same as those used in various zoological sciences, although many special methods are borrowed from both zoology and entomology. The Acarina are not small enough to be handled like protozoans or soft-bodied enough to be treated as worms and they are too small to be studied like insects. Therefore they have been ignored by zoologists and entomologists alike.

Many individuals would explain our lack of information on the mites on the basis of their relatively insignificant importance. This is *not* the case. At present many groups of mites that are of known economic importance are poorly understood. As knowledge of mites increases the vital, practical significance of many species will be recognized. The science of acarology holds the same position today that entomology held fifty or one hundred years ago.

History: Mites and ticks have been recognized for a long time. The early Greek writers were familiar with ticks and a few mites. In fact, Acari is the Latinized form of the Greek word for mite. By the time of Linnaeus, however, only about ninety species had been discussed in the literature, and the tenth edition of the "Systema Naturae" included only some twenty-nine species of mites in the genus *Acarus.* By 1850, however, many species were recognized. Oudemans 1926–1937 in his "Kritisch Historisch Overzicht der Acarologie" covers the literature up to and including 1850. Oudemans' work is invaluable to anyone desiring information on early publications concerned with mites.

From 1850 to the present time most work of a general nature has been done in Europe. Nalepa, G. and R. Canestrini, Berlese, Trouessart, Hirst, Michael, Oudemans, Vitzthum, Thor, Trägårdh, and others have made valuable contributions. André, Grandjean, Lundblad, Sellnick, Willmann, and Viets are still publishing important works. In the United States only two general acarologists have been active during most of the present century, although several have contributed extensively on water mites, red spiders, oribatid mites, or other groups. Nathan Banks ranks as the first American acarologist, while his successor at the United States National Museum, the late Dr. Henry Ellsworth Ewing, contributed more on the Acarina than any other American.

At present some twenty or thirty investigators in the United States are actively engaged in the study of the Acarina and the number is rapidly increasing. The United States government through its agencies, especially the Departments of Agriculture, Army, Navy, and United States Public Health Service, is becoming more interested in acarinids so that rapid development may be expected in the near future.

Collecting: Mites are easy and at the same time difficult to collect. Because of their small size many are invisible in their natural habitats. For this reason, special techniques are required to capture them. Frequently the environment of the mites is collected in the field, and the mites themselves are apprehended in the laboratory; however, there are certain phases of the work that are the same for all.

Collections are of little value unless records are made at the time of collection. The record should include the date, locality, name of the collector, a description of the habitat, and any pertinent remarks about temperature, humidity, and associated animals or plants that seem important. In making an entry in a notebook it is well to remember that it is an easy matter to ignore irrelevant information that is recorded but practically impossible to recall relevant information that was not recorded because it did not seem important at the time. Each collection must be clearly labeled so that the collector can easily correlate it with the appropriate notations in his notebook.

Mites collected in the field may be preserved indefinitely in 85 per cent ethyl alcohol. They should be placed in small vials. Vials with over-all dimensions of 5 mm. by 28 mm. are obtainable from scientific supply companies. After alcohol, specimens, and label have been added to a vial it should be firmly stoppered with a cotton plug and put in a bottle of 85 per cent alcohol. When a vial has been filled it can be dropped into the stock bottle of alcohol for safekeeping. Another convenient method is to use rubber-stoppered novacaine tubes (such as used by a dentist) that have been refilled with 85 per cent alcohol. Most dentists discard large numbers of these tubes, and they are usually willing to save them for a collector.

Because of their small size, mites are difficult to handle. A moistened camel's-hair brush will be found helpful in the field. Water-color brushes sizes 0 to 2 are best. Larger brushes are difficult to use. Although mites are small and fragile little injury to them results when they are picked up on the point of a brush. Iris forceps and dissecting forceps are helpful in manipulating the larger specimens and the small specimen vials. In picking up a mite with a pair of forceps it is desirable to avoid using the tips of the forceps. If the mite is grasped between the prongs of the forceps a few millimeters from the tip, usually no harm will come to the specimen since the tips of the forceps will come together first and thus protect the specimen when only light pressure is applied.

Free-living terrestrial mites are usually found in collections of organic debris, such as the upper layers of the soil. Many specimens will be found in the litter and litter-like accumulations found in cavities or forks of trees and bushes. Rotten logs and the soil beneath them are favored by some mites. The soil beneath rocks frequently produces soil-inhabiting species. Many plant feeders are to be found near the roots, leaves, and buds of plants or in the gills of many mushrooms. Beds of moss are usually very productive. Plants or parts of plants that appear abnormal should be particularly investigated. Most mites require a moist environment. For this reason damp soil and debris will yield more specimens than dry. During wet weather many species that ordinarily live in the upper layers of the soil will be found in the litter.

A white or black enamel or porcelain saucer or tray is helpful in examining material in the field. A small portion of the material to be examined is placed on the tray. It is then picked over bit by bit. Many mites will fall onto the tray where they will be visible against its shiny, smooth surface. Once detected, the specimen should be chased away from the debris and after it has cleaned itself it can be picked up with a camel's-hair brush and placed in a vial. Any mites seen on the material in the tray should be forced out on a clean portion so that no debris is added to the vial. This precaution should be heeded especially when soil is being examined. Once a mite that has soil adhering to it is placed in alcohol it is practically impossible to cleanse it. The tray can be used in another manner also. Many mites, especially chiggers, will investigate any new object brought into their environment. Therefore, if the tray is placed on the ground and left for several minutes it will frequently acquire specimens that can be removed and placed into vials.

Mites will frequently adhere to flannel that is dragged past them. This method is particularly useful for collecting unattached ticks. The usual tick drag (Figure 2) is one yard square. It is made of flannel and its anterior end is tacked to a stick one yard long. A rope of convenient length is tied to the ends of the stick and the collector then pulls the drag slowly over the area to be investigated. At intervals the cloth is examined and the specimens removed with forceps or fingers.

Figure 2 A tick drag in operation.

By far the most efficient method of collecting terrestrial mites is that of bringing the environment into the laboratory for study. Number 5 paper bags are useful. The environment to be studied is placed in a bag; the top of the bag is then twisted and sealed with a rubber band. When very moist material such as damp moss is collected, oilsilk or rubberized cloth bags should be used. Once in the laboratory the material can be examined with the aid of a dissecting microscope or it can be run through a modified Berlese funnel.

The modified Berlese funnel is the most useful tool available for separating mites and small insects from the debris in which they are found. Berlese funnels of many types have been designed (Figure 3). A suitable one for general collecting can be made simply. The funnel itself consists of a cone of sheet metal open at each end. The large opening should be about one foot in diameter while the small opening should not be greater than an inch in diameter. Such a cone should have an over-all length of eighteen inches. Three legs should be fastened to the cone so that it will stand upright with the small opening at the bottom. The legs should be sufficiently long so that a jar can be placed under the small opening. It is helpful to solder a metal screw

Figure 3 A battery of Berlese funnels in use at Duke University. In the foreground are small funnels that are used to collect ectoparasitic mites. Two of them are in operation. The hosts are placed in small cages and the parasites are recovered from the water beneath the funnel. In the background are large funnels used to collect mites from debris. Notice the lights above each funnel for desiccating the material. (Photo Duke University by Whitley)

cap to the cone at the lower end so that the collecting jar can be screwed into place. This reduces the chances of contamination of the collection from outside sources and prevents the escape of animals in the sample. A cover for the large upper opening should be made and fitted with an electric light bulb. Reflectors made to fit light sockets make excellent covers. Larger or smaller funnels may be found more useful for special purposes.

Debris is wrapped in cheesecloth and placed in the funnel. The funnel is then tapped lightly to bring down any loose material before the collecting jar is in place. Once the jar is in place turn on the light and wait for the desiccation of the debris to force the mites to the bottom of the funnel. At times as many as three days will elapse before the debris in the funnel becomes completely desiccated. In this case specimens will continue to drop into the collecting jar for three days. When extensive collections are made a battery of Berlese funnels is required. Many species of mites and other arthropods will be found in the collecting jars. It is necessary to sort the specimens under a dissecting microscope.

In order to collect parasitic mites it is first necessary to collect their hosts. Almost all animals larger than mites are parasitized by them. Not only terrestrial but aquatic animals serve as hosts. While most parasitic mites are ectoparasites, some are endoparasites, and still others are social parasites. It is not possible to discuss at length procedures for collecting all types of hosts. For this information the "Collectors' Manual" published by the Smithsonian Institution is recommended. When collecting parasitic mites it must be remembered that proper identification of the host species is as important as identification of the mite. In order to identify the host properly it must be preserved so that it can be submitted to a specialist for study. In collecting hosts of parasitic mites, large numbers of hosts should be obtained if a satisfactory survey is to be achieved. Fortunately mites do not leave their hosts upon their deaths as rapidly as do such insects as some fleas. For this reason snap traps are satisfactory for capturing mammals and other small, terrestrial vertebrates which serve as hosts for mites. The only satisfactory method of collecting birds is shooting. A double-barreled shotgun is to be preferred for this purpose so that both light and heavy shot will be available instantaneously. Hosts must be placed in mite-proof bags as soon as collected, so that parasites cannot crawl from one host to another.

Examination of hosts in the laboratory is greatly facilitated by the use of a dissecting microscope. In examining a host the external surface should be thoroughly studied first. In the case of mammals and birds the fur and feathers make this difficult. With a little experience, however, it will be found that the skin can be exposed by careful manipulation of the fur or feathers. In examining insects the wings, and the elytra in the case of beetles, must be unfolded. The areas of the body covered by the wings are favored by many ectoparasitic mites. Before investigating the internal organs the ear, eye, anal, and genital openings should be examined. Few mites are parasitic in the digestive tract of animals, but some are associated with the respiratory systems of both vertebrates and invertebrates.

When animals suspected of harboring mites are brought into the laboratory alive, many of the ectoparasites can be collected without examining the host. Live hosts can be placed in cages that have wire or hardware cloth bottoms so that mites that fall off will drop through the floor of the cage. A suitable tray is placed beneath the cage from which the parasites can then be collected. Feces and urine of the host interfere frequently with this method but judicious feeding and frequent examination and cleaning can overcome this difficulty.

Figure 4   A Birge net. (Photo by Parker)

There are two useful tools for collecting free-living water mites. One is a small dip net with a narrow mesh bag with which mites that are visible in the water can be scooped up and the other is a Birge net (Figure 4). Water mites are to be found in practically all waters, but the best collecting sites for them are small lakes, streams, and ponds. In using the Birge net care should be exercised so that the bag remains expanded in the water. The net is designed to be used in weedy areas so that it snags infrequently. It is in the weedy areas along the shores that most water mites live.

Preparation for Study: Ticks can be studied satisfactorily without mounting them on a glass slide. The taxonomic characters of ticks can best be made out if the tick is studied with the aid of a fairly high-powered dissecting microscope.

Mites, on the other hand, must be prepared for examination by transmitted light and a compound microscope. Therefore they must be cleared and mounted on a glass slide. Many methods have been used in the past and can be found in the literature. Recently a new method has been evolved that is satisfactory for many mites. The directions for preparing and using polyvinyl alcohol (PVA) mounting medium follow:

1. Dissolve "Elvanol" 71-24 (Du Pont polyvinyl alcohol) in four volumes of water by stirring at about 90 C.
2. Filter the solution until it is no longer murky.
3. Concentrate the clear filtrate on a water bath until it has the viscosity of Karo syrup. (A scum will form on the surface during the process of evaporation but will redissolve when stirred into the solution.)
4. Add 22 parts of lactic acid to 56 parts of the PVA concentrate to make the finished mounting medium.
5. Use like any mountant. Materials may be mounted directly from life, any aqueous solution, or alcohol.

The large amount of shrinkage of PVA causes it to shrivel the soft-bodied mites (Tetranychidae) and to crush some of the larger, brittle ones (Oribatei). The solution should be used with discretion.

In most cases, however, other methods are more useful. Temporary mounts may be made in any clearing agent such as glycerin, mineral oil, phenol, lactic acid, etc. Satisfactory permanent mounts can be made with aqueous solutions of gum arabic, chloral hydrate, and glycerin. One of the best of the modified Berlese solutions is Hoyer's. At the United States National Museum specimens have been preserved in this for twenty years without deteriorating. It is an excellent medium for the Tetranychidae which are one of the more difficult groups to mount. The formula is:

        50 grams distilled water
        30 grams gum arabic (clear crystals)
    200 grams chloral hydrate
        20 grams glycerin

The ingredients should be mixed at room temperature in the above sequence. In the more humid areas, such as the Gulf States, the cover glass should be ringed to prevent absorption of moisture. Other excellent Berlese mixtures are published but as yet the perfect mounting medium has not been found.

Workers at the University of California have developed a methocellulose formula which has proved to be excellent for many mites. Their formula is:

> 5 grams methocellulose
> 2 grams carbowax 4,000
> 1 milliliter diethylene glycol
> 25 milliliters 95 per cent ethyl alcohol
> 100 milliliters lactic acid
> 25 milliliters distilled water

They found the best procedure was to clear thoroughly in lactophenol before mounting, although some of the more delicate mites needed no special preparation as the lactic acid in the medium cleared the specimens sufficiently.

Newell 1947 has devised a method for making permanent glycerin mounts. Untreated mites cannot be mounted satisfactorily in oil-soluble resins because the refractive indices of these substances are too close to those of the ectoskeletal elements of mites. If mites are mounted in such materials as damar or balsam they must first be cleared in lactic acid or mild caustic to remove the soft tissues. Their exoskeletons must then be stained so that they will contrast with the mounting medium. If a phase-contrast microscope is available, however, unstained specimens can be studied satisfactorily in such mounting media.

As soon as slides have been made they should be labeled. It is conventional to put the collection data on the right-hand label and reserve the left-hand label for the name of the mite.

Terminology: Acarology has been developed largely as an outgrowth of entomology. Therefore the terms used in describing the anatomy of mites and ticks have been borrowed from entomology. Unfortunately entomological terms when applied to mites frequently have entirely different meanings from the term as originally used. Analogy rather than homology has been the usual criterion for transferring a term from one group to the other. It would be possible to create an entirely new vocabulary that applied properly to the Acarina, but this would create more confusion than now exists. Consequently names which have more or less general acceptance among acarologists will be used and will be defined as they apply to the Acarina without regard for their original entomological meaning. In most cases Vitzthum 1940 will be followed.

Metamerism: Many acarinids appear to consist of a single segment. Others have the body apparently divided into a cephalothorax and abdomen, and in some the abdomen appears to be segmented. Evidence of primary segmentation is found in the primitive Notostigmata. Some of the tarsonemids appear to have posterior segments but these are probably secondary rather than primary.

Vitzthum 1940 divides the body of acarinids according to the following chart (Figure 5):

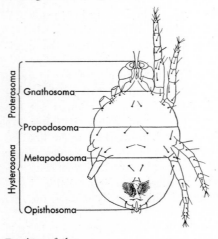

Figure 5 *Schizotetranychus schizsopus* (Zacher), 1913 showing the arbitrary divisions of the body. (After Vitzthum 1940)

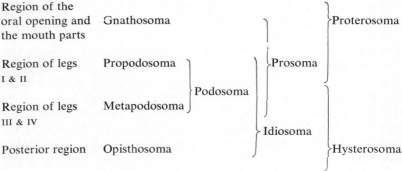

André and Lamy 1937 review the opinions on the primary metamerism of the acarinids and following Henking 1882 and Oudemans 1909 state that there are thirteen metameres in most of the mites. The ventral parts of three segments are fused to form the gnathosoma. The first or pre-oral segment bears no appendages, the second bears the chelicerae, and the third the pedipalps. The podosoma consist of the dorsal parts of the first three segments and all of the next four segments, each one of which bears a pair of legs. The opisthosoma is usually composed of six segments. Variation in the number of opisthosomal segments is found and this accounts for variation in the total number of segments suggested above. The Notostigmata may have as many as ten or eleven opisthosomal segments. *Pachygnathus* may have eight or nine and *Parhypocthonius* has seven.

The gnathosoma is usually set off from the rest of the body at least dorsally; but in some groups (Uropodina, Spelaeorhynchidae, Crypto- stigmatina, and others), the segments of the propodosoma extend over the gnathosoma and enclose it in a cavity or camerostome. In one family of the Prostigmata (Smaridiidae) the gnathosoma is protrusible on a long, narrow, trunklike stalk that may be as long as the mite itself. The gnathosoma is narrow and in no way can be said to correspond to the head of other arthropods. It is frequently called the capitulum, but the term gnathosoma is to be preferred since it bears only the mouth and mouth parts.

The propodosoma with the first two pairs of legs is frequently separated from the metapodosoma by a deep furrow. The Trombiculidae exhibit this separation very well. It is for this reason that the gnathosoma and propodosoma together are referred to as the proterosoma while the metapodosoma and opisthosoma which are usually fused insensibly with one another are designated as the hysterosoma.

The prosoma corresponds to the cephalothorax of other arachnids but in no case are the anterior segments so fused that they form a distinct body region that can be designated as a cephalothorax in contradistinction to a posterior abdomen. However, *Speleorchestes* is exceptional in that the gnathosoma, propodosoma, metapodosoma, and opisthosoma are apparently each distinct from the others.

The podosoma is that portion of the body that bears the walking legs. The idiosoma includes the body of the mite posterior to the gnathosoma. In many mites and all the ticks the only clearly recognizable body divisions are gnathosoma and idiosoma.

Integument: As is the case with other arthropods the integument of the Acarina consists essentially of a single layer of epithelial cells, the hypodermis, and sclerotized layers which they secrete. The cuticle (Figure 6) can be subdivided into four distinct layers which are characterized by Vitzthum 1940 as follows:

1. Tectostracum—the outermost covering which is always very thin and never pigmented

2. Epiostracum—the upper layer
3. Ectostracum—the middle layer, usually pigmented with acid dyes
4. Hypostracum—the inner layer, usually pigmented with basic dyes

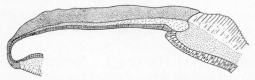

Figure 6 A section through the integument of *Hyalomma marginatum brionicum* Schulze and Schlottke, 1929 showing the two inner sclerotized layers, the ectostracum and hypostracum, with the hypodermis beneath them. (After Vitzthum 1940)

The four layers are not recognizable in all acarinids. One or more of the chitinous layers may be absent or so combined with others that they are unrecognizable. In some cases the hypodermis itself may be so expanded by swelling of the opisthosoma, such as occurs in *Pyemotes,* that it is impossible to demonstrate it.

Although the fundamental structure of the integument is similar in all species, the appearance, texture, and physical properties of the sclerotized coverings are varied and widely different from one group to the next. The Notostigmata possess a leathery, thin, granular cuticle. Many mites are completely or partially enclosed in heavy, armor-like sheaths. The Holothyroidea, many of the Mesostigmata, and the majority of the Oribatei are provided with hard, protective plates that enclose the entire body. The Trombidiformes and the Acaridiae have an elastic, transparent cuticle that may have hardened regions in the form of plates or setal bases.

Much of the beauty of form and design resident in the structure of the Acarina is to be found in the ornamentation of the cuticle which is produced by pores, ridges, folds, or pigment found

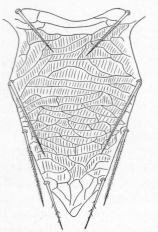

Figure 7 The sternal plate of the nymph of *Parasitus fucorum* (DeGeer), 1778. (After Vitzthum 1940)

in its various layers (Figure 7). The ornamentation of the cuticle is usually constant within species and is used in some groups to distinguish them.

Many special structures are derived from the cells of the hypodermis. There are various glands, setae, dyes, and special sensory organs formed wholly or in part by specialized portions of the hypodermis and its secretions (Figure 8). With the exception of the setae and hypodermal glands integumental derivatives will be considered under the organ systems to which they belong.

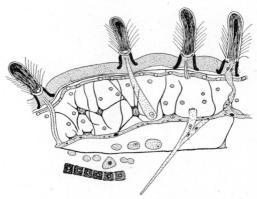

Figure 8   Transverse section through the integument of *Trombidium holosericeum* (Linnaeus), 1758. (After Vitzthum 1940)

The integument of many acarinids is provided with glands. Enlarged cells of the hypodermis pour their secretions directly out on the surface of most ticks. The water mites are well provided with glands that open in specialized areas over the body (Figure 9). These glands are more complicated than those of the ticks. Most of the Sarcoptiformes have a pair of oil glands that produce an oily fluid that is light yellow to deep brown in color. Similar glands have been found in a few of the Mesostigmata, e.g., *Eulaelaps stabularis* and *Euhaemogamasus horridus*.

The forms of setae are legion. As in most arthropods the setae serve many functions. They are tactile organs in that the nerves are so arranged as to pick up pressure exerted on the setae. Some setae must also serve as organs of chemo-reception. Others actually protect their owners from attacks of predators in the same manner as the quills of a porcupine protect it. In many mites two fundamentally different types of setae are recognizable: the setae proper, and the sensory setae which are obviously different from the majority of body setae.

The setae proper ("Eigentliche Haare" of Vitzthum 1940, "Poils proprement dits" of Grandjean 1935) are of many types (Figure 10). They may be simple, pilose, plumose, capitate, spatulate, cordate, palmate, pilidiform, pinnate, chambered, dentate, furcate, or may be so irregular that only a careful description will suffice for their identi-

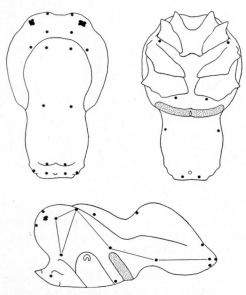

Figure 9 The arrangement of the integumental glands of *Megaluracarus globator* (Müller), 1776. (After Vitzthum 1940)

fication. It is difficult to grasp the significance of the diversity of form exhibited by the setae. Their form and number in any species are usually constant. For this reason they are very useful as taxonomic characters.

The primitive type of seta was most likely attenuate and pilose. The primitive arrangement of the setae corresponded with the primary segmentation of the animal, each segment being provided with a row of from two to six dorsal setae at its posterior margin. This primitive arrangement is maintained with little modification in certain of the Trombidiformes and Sarcoptiformes. In all of the larger groups, however, reduction or multiplication of the setae has occurred many times so that the primitive arrangement is obscured in many species.

The type of sensory seta most frequently seen is a striated sensory seta that is probably a chemo-receptor. They are called "solenidien" by Vitzthum and "solenidions" by Grandjean. They are hollow and a living extension of the cells associated with them fills their lumen. They are directly connected with the peripheral nervous system. They are most commonly found on the distal segments of the appendages.

Figure 10 Types of body setae found on various mites. Top row; simple, pilose [*Neocheyletiella rohweri* Baker, 1949], plumose [*Euschöngastia peromysci* (Ewing), 1929], capitate [*Spathulathrombium southcotti* (Womersley), 1935]; middle row: spatulate, cordate [*Spathulathrombium maximum* Womersley, 1945], palmate [*Cheletogenes ornatus* (Canestrini and Fanzago, 1876)], pilidiform [*Holcotrombidium securigerum* (Canestrini), 1897]; bottom row: furcate [*Hiotrombidium tubbi* (Womersley), 1937], chambered [*Camerotrombidium opulentum* (Womersley), 1945], and dentate [*Acaropsis docta* (Berlese), 1886].

In addition to the striated sensory setae, microsensory setae ("famulus" of Grandjean 1935), are regularly found on the genu, tibia, and tarsi of the legs. Their function is not known but it is unlikely that such small structures would be tactile in nature. Whiplike setae ("acanthoides" of Grandjean 1935), are also common on the legs. They differ from ordinary setae in being longer and nude. These setae might function as tactile organs.

Certain setae are frequently associated with particular structures. Sensillae are setiform organs that arise from specialized pits, pseudostigmata, or sensillae bases, usually found on the propodosoma. The sensillae may be of almost any form but almost invariably they are readily distinguishable from the body setae. A specialized forked seta is found on the palpal tarsus of most of the Mesostigmata.

Grandjean made a study of the nature of the chitin found in the setae of the different groups of mites. He found that certain of the setae of the Trombidiformes and Sarcoptiformes were optically active. The setae of these two groups were readily stained with iodine. The setae of the Mesostigmata and Holothyroidea were found to be optically inactive and resistant to iodine. He designated the active chitin as actinochitin and included the Trombidiformes and Sarcoptiformes in one group, the Actinochitinosi; the Mesostigmata and Holothyroidea are combined as the Anactinochitinosi. Further study is required to determine the significance of a classification based upon the optical activity of the setae.

Plates: The integument of most acarinids is not uniform in thickness. Certain areas are covered by much thicker layers than others and these heavy areas are the plates or shields. They correspond to the sclerites of insects but differ from them in that they usually extend over more than a single segment and in some cases may encompass the entire idiosoma. Furthermore, in most cases the plates found in the Acarina are not modifications of the primary sclerites but secondarily developed structures.

None of the primary sternites remains unmodified. A vestige of the tritosternum remains, however, in the Notostigmata and the Mesostigmata as a peculiar seta-like structure in front of the sternal plate (Figure 11). It consists of a basal portion that is usually unpaired from which a pair of pilose lacinae originate. In the Notostigmata the basal portion is paired while in the Uropodina the lacinae are fused basally but may be trifurcate distally. All other plates on the venter of the acarinids are secondary structures and not formed from the primary sternites.

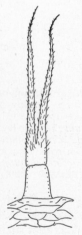

Figure 11 The tritosternum of *Haemolaelaps traubi* (Strandtmann), 1948. (After Strandtmann 1948)

In a few mites all of the dorsal plates are in reality the modified tergites. They are readily recognizable in the Tarsonemini (Figure 12) and the hysterosomal plates of the Protoplophoridae and Mesoplophoridae can be traced back to the primary tergites. In the remainder of the mites only the propodosomal plate is a remnant of the primary tergites. It is formed by a fusion of the tergites of the segments of the first two pairs of legs; that is, segments IV and V.

The propodosomal plate has been known under a variety of names in the different groups of mites. In the ticks and in larvae of the Trombidiidae, Trombiculidae, and related groups it is known as the scutum. In the adults of many of the Prostigmata it is called the crista metopica. In the oribatids that are capable of withdrawing the gnathosoma and legs into a cavity in the hysterosoma the propodosomal plate closes the opening like a trap door. In this group, the Ptyctima, the propodosomal plate is known as the aspis. The anterior portion of the dorsal plates or shield of other mites, or in some cases the entire dorsal plate, is in reality the propodosomal plate.

Figure 12   *Resinacarus resinatus* Vitzthum, 1927. A lateral view that shows the tergites. (After Vitzthum 1940)

The secondary plates or shields are formed in a number of ways. In the Pterygosomidae the setal bases become enlarged and fuse to form plates. The cuticle in the region of the genital and anal openings frequently thickens and thus anal and genital plates are formed. At times the cornea of the eyes will be supported at the periphery by a sclerotized ring that becomes enlarged to form an ocular plate. The integument may harden without apparent reason. Areas where glands open or muscles attach frequently develop into plates. In some groups sternal plates are formed by a fusion of the coxae, parts of which may sink below the surface to form internal apodemata. The arrangement of the secondary plates is quite different in different groups of mites and thus discussion of them must be considered separately for each group.

Gnathosoma: The gnathosoma bears the mouth parts, the chelicerae, and the pedipalps. The mouth is hidden by the pedipalps and chelicerae. The gnathosoma is reduced in size and appears to consist only of its appendages and their projections. It is constructed in different ways in the different groups of mites; since fusion, expansion, and degeneration of its component parts have progressed in many ways, its relation to the rest of the body is not the same in all groups. At times the gnathosoma may be enclosed in a camerostome or cavity in the idiosoma, or it may form a prominent snout or beak.

Dorsally the gnathosoma is usually covered, at least in part, by a tectum (Snodgrass 1948) or epistome as other authors call it. The tectum is an anterior projection. It consists of a thin, chitinous plate that is usually toothed at its free end (Figure 13). The tectum may be so reduced in some mites as to be entirely lacking.

The chelicerae originate below the tectum although they are at times covered by dorsal extensions of the pedipalps. These organs are so important that they will be considered later under a separate section.

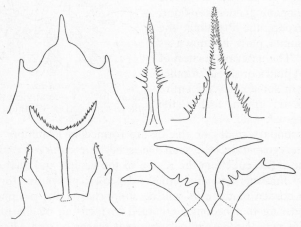

Figure 13   Tecta of various mites. Upper row, from left to right, *Pergamasus olivaceus* Vitzthum, 1927; *Discopoma regia* Vitzthum, 1921; *Neopodocinum coprophilum* Vitzthum, 1926: lower row *Trigonholaspis salti* Vitzthum, 1930; *Cyrtolaelaps capreolus* Berlese, 1904. (After Vitzthum 1940)

Between and below the chelicerae is the mouth. The mouth is ventral to the labrum and dorsal to the hypostome. These structures may be elaborately developed, but they are seldom seen because their presence is overshadowed by the pedipalps and chelicerae. Laterally the oral opening may be flanked by paralabra which may assist in closing the mouth and probably aid in directing food into the opening. In the Notostigmata and the Holothyroidea a toothed, radula-like organ derived from the labrum is associated with the oral opening.

The pedipalps form the lateral-ventral surface of the gnathosoma. In some groups the basal expansions of the pedipalps extend medially and dorsally and fuse in the midline to form a tube in which the chelicerae are found.

The hypostome forms the ventral-median wall of the gnathosoma. In most groups it is insensibly fused with the pedipalps but in the ticks it can be seen as a toothed structure between the pedipalps (Figure 14). The so-called hypostome of the ticks is not homologous to the hypostome of the other groups but is in reality formed largely from the pedipalps although its basal portion is formed in part by the true hypostome.

Chelicerae: The chelicerae of the Acarina usually terminate in a chela that is composed of a dorsal, fixed digit and a ventral, movable digit. In all of the suborders such chelate chelicerae are to be found. In the Notostigmata, Holothyroidea, and the Tetrapodili only chelate chelicerae are known. The chelicerae of the Tetrapodili are modified, however, in that the movable digit has become stylet-like and is the sole effective piercing element (Figure 15). The chela is formed from the tibia and tarsus.

Fundamental segmentation of the chelicerae is obscure. In most arachnids the chelicerae consist of three segments. In some of the younger stages of certain mesostigmatids the chelicerae have six segments. In most other acarinids, however, the chelicerae are divided into two or three segments.

Figure 14 The hypostome of *Ixodes rasus* Neumann, 1899.

The primitive type of chelate chelicera is superficially similar in structure to the chelae of many decapod crustaceans. Each digit is provided with teeth which may or may not oppose each other. This type of chela is used for grasping prey or crushing other types of food (Figure 16). In the males of many of the mesostigmatids the movable digit is modified as an accessory copulatory organ (Figure 17). It is used to transfer the spermatophores from the genital opening of the male to that of the female. Even though the movable digit is greatly modified the fixed digit is unchanged.

The primitive chelate type is modified in many ways. Both elements may become minute and needle-like and together form a piercing structure such as is found in *Dermanyssus* (Figure 18). The fixed digit may disappear and the movable digit

Figure 15 The chelicera of *Eriophyes pini* (Nalepa), 1887.

Acarology

may become terminal rather than lateral in position. The movable digit may become long and threadlike as it is in the spider mites. In the ticks the chelicerae are chelate but the movable digit is lateral rather than ventral and the teeth are on the outer surface of the chelae, not on the inner. The chelicerae of the ticks function as anchors and their structure is well adapted for this purpose (Figure 19).

Special sense organs and setae are found on the chelicerae of many mites. At the base of the movable digit in some mesostigmatids an

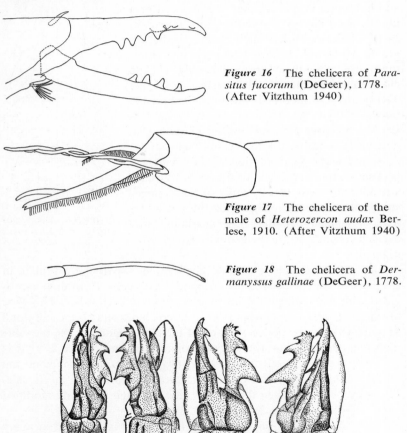

Figure 16 The chelicera of *Parasitus fucorum* (DeGeer), 1778. (After Vitzthum 1940)

Figure 17 The chelicera of the male of *Heterozercon audax* Berlese, 1910. (After Vitzthum 1940)

Figure 18 The chelicera of *Dermanyssus gallinae* (DeGeer), 1778.

Figure 19 The chelicerae of *Ixodes reduvius* (Linnaeus), 1758. Left, dorsal and ventral views of the male; right, dorsal and ventral views of the female. (After Vitzthum 1940)

extension of the synarthrodial membrane produces a pulvillus which resembles a cluster of setae in some cases or a coronet in others. There is frequently a seta at the tip of the fixed digit but not on the movable digit. Setae and sensory pores are found on the chelicerae of other groups as well.

Pedipalps: The pedipalps are the second appendages in the arachnids. In the Acarina they originate laterally from the palpal coxae which are probably homologous to the fused, basal segments of a primitive, biramous appendage. In recent Acarina the pedipalps are never divided into more than six segments, but in the Devonian *Protacarus crani* Hirst there are seven segments. The segments of the pedipalps are named as are those of the legs, beginning with the proximal element, as follows: coxa, trochanter, basifemur, telofemur, genu, tibia, and tarsus. The reduction in the apparent number of segments from the primitive seven to the maximum of six in living acarinids is accomplished by fusion of the basifemur and telofemur to form an undivided femur.

A relatively unmodified palp is found in the Onychopalpida, Mesostigmata, Cryptognathidae, Sarcoptiformes, Limnocharidae, and Eylaidae. In some of the above groups the palp is six-segmented but in all the tarsus and tibia are similar to those of the legs. The palpal tarsi of the Onychopalpida are provided with claws as are the tarsi of the legs (Figure 20).

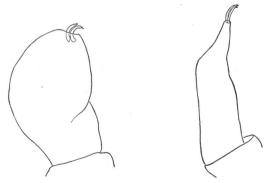

Figure 20   Right, the palpal tarsi of *Neocarus texanus* Chamberlain and Mulaik, 1942 and left, the palpal tarsi of *Holothyrus australasiae* Womersley, 1935 to show the palpal claws. The setae have been omitted so that the claws are apparent.

In addition to the simple, leglike pedipalps there are several important modifications. In some of the parasitic groups the pedipalps are reduced to vestigial knobs with specialized spines or angular projections adapted to their parasitic habit. In the Trombidiformes the palpi may become enlarged and function as accessory chelicerae.

Figure 21   The last two segments of the pedipalps of *Euschöngastia indica* (Hirst), 1915.

Figure 22   The pedipalp of a cheyletid mite.

In some of the Trombidiformes the relationship between the palpal tarsus and palpal tibia is modified. The tibia is frequently provided with a terminal stout claw which displaces the palpal tarsus to a ventral position. A chelate pedipalp results from this displacement (Figure 21). In its unmodified form the chelate pedipalp serves as a hand. The dorsal claw is opposed by the palpal tarsus or thumb and the mite is capable of picking up and holding not only its food but other objects as well.

In the Cheyletidae the chelate type of pedipalp is enormously developed (Figure 22). The tibia is provided with a stout claw and the tarsus which has moved medially is also provided with cteniform or falcate, clawlike setae. In this group the right and left pedipalps oppose each other and form a powerful grasping organ with which to press the prey against the relatively minute chelicerae. The pedipalps of the Cunaxidae and Bdellidae function in a similar fashion but these lack the palpal thumb.

Legs: The majority of the Acarina possess three pairs of walking legs in the larval stage and four pairs in all subsequent stages. The erio-

phyids have only two pairs of legs in all stages, and some of the Podapolipodidae and Phytoptipalpidae have either only three pairs of
legs as adults or in some cases only a single pair.

The legs, like the palps, are usually divided into six segments which
extend from the body in the following order: coxa, trochanter, femur,

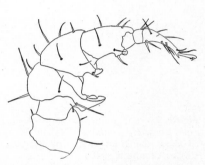

Figure 23 A dorsal view of the tarsus
I of *Haemolaelaps glasgowi* (Ewing),
1925.

Figure 24 Leg II of the male of *Parasitus bombophilus* Vitzthum, 1930.
(After Vitzthum 1940)

genu, tibia, and tarsus. Frequently the femur is divided into two segments, the basifemur and the telofemur, so that seven segments are
present. Fusion of the segments also occurs so that a five-segmented
leg may occur or even a two-segmented leg as is found in *Schizocarpus.*
In *Chirodiscus* legs I and II consist of a single segment. In *Tarsotomus,*
on the other hand, the tarsus may be divided into as many as eighteen
segments.

The tarsi of the walking legs characteristically bear a pair of well-
developed claws. In addition to the claws a delicate, transparent,
sucker-like structure (the caruncle) may be present. A caruncle is
regularly found on the tarsi of the Mesostigmata and Ixodides (Figure
23). In the Trombidiformes an empodium is frequently found between
the two claws and in some cases the median empodium develops into
a claw while the paired claws are reduced or modified to form tenent

hairs. When the legs are modified so that they are no longer used for walking the claws are vestigial or absent. For example, the anterior pair of legs in the Macrochelidae are used as tactile rather than ambulatory organs and the claws are either minute or absent. Many of the water mites that are active swimmers have no tarsal claws.

Figure 25   An outline diagram of the male of *Analges nitzschii* Haller, 1878 to show the enlargement of legs III. (After Vitzthum 1940)

Figure 26   A ventral view of leg I of *Protomyobia claparèdei* (Poppe), 1896 to show the roughened hair-grasping prominences.

The legs are used primarily for walking and running but in certain groups they have other functions. The tactile and swimming legs have been discussed. Frequently the legs are used as graspers during copulation. The second pair of legs of many of the Parasitidae are strongly modified especially in the male (Figure 24). The males of the Analgesidae have exceptionally developed posterior legs (Figure 25). They are so massive as to be useless as locomotor organs. The legs of water mites have many long, closely set setae that increase their surface in such a way as to make them efficient paddles. Some mites have certain pairs of legs modified as hair-grasping organs (Figure 26). The posterior legs of mites of the genera *Spelorchestes* and *Nanorchestes* have specialized muscles that enable the mites to jump quite effectively. *Eupodes* with its enlarged femur IV is thought to be an effective jumper also.

The coxae of the walking legs of many mites are immovable and so imbedded in the skin that they frequently form an endoskeleton.

Muscles: Acarinids have striated muscles similar to those of other arthropods. The muscles extend into the appendages from the body and each leg is furnished with extrinsic as well as intrinsic muscles. The body musculature is well developed in many groups. The body muscles are responsible for the movement of the genital armature, the anal plates, and the gnathosoma. Muscles may originate or insert on plates, apodemata, epimera, or on the unspecialized, soft cuticle between the plates. The origins and insertions of muscles can be detected externally because they frequently produce visible scars on the plates and dimple-like concavities in the softer integument. In the soft-bodied mites the muscles are capable of changing the shape of the idiosoma.

Digestive System: The digestive system of the Acarina is essentially a simple tube. The anterior portion or fore-gut is derived from the stomadaeum and consists of a muscular pharynx and tubular esophagus. The mid-gut or ventriculus is endodermal in origin and is characterized by a large lumen and a well-developed digestive epithelium. The hind-gut develops from the proctodaeum and can frequently be divided into an anterior, thin-walled, tubular intestine that in turn empties into a muscular rectum which opens to the outside through the anus.

There are three fundamental types of digestive systems:

1. A mesostigmatid type that is characteristic of the Onychopalpida, Mesostigmata, and Ixodides
2. A trombidiform type that is characteristic of the Trombidiformes
3. A sarcoptiform type that is characteristic of the Sarcoptiformes

The mesostigmatid type has a typical fore-gut composed of a muscular pharynx and a long, narrow esophagus that enters a small, central portion of the mid-gut. The mid-gut is characterized by a relatively small ventriculus from which large lateral diverticula arise. The intestine is long, except in the ticks, and it opens directly into a spherical rectum which connects with the anus. An ill-defined colon is present in the Notostigmata. Excretory tubules enter the hind-gut between the intestine and colon.

The trombidiform type is characterized by the lack of colon and rectum. The fore-gut is typical in that the pharynx and esophagus are well developed. The ventriculus is large and its diverticula are broadly attached to it. The hind-gut in the Trombidiformes has been modified to form an excretory organ. Until recently most authors reported that there was no opening into the hind-gut from the ventriculus. Blauvelt 1945 has demonstrated such an opening in a *Tetranychus* (Figure 27).

The sarcoptiform type is more nearly like the parasitiform than the trombidiform. All of the divisions—pharynx, esophagus, ventriculus, intestine, colon, and rectum—are usually distinguishable. The body of the ventriculus is usually larger than its pair of posterior caeca. In this respect it differs widely from the mesostigmatid type.

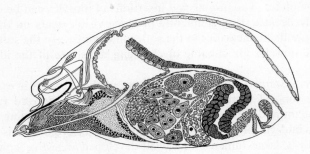

Figure 27   A longitudinal section through the body of a *Tetranychus*. (After Blauvelt 1945)

A number of salivary glands empty on the gnathosoma near the mouth. These glands probably produce secretions which contain digestive enzymes. The larvae of many of the Trombidiformes can digest the cuticle of their hosts. In the spider mites certain of the glands produce silk. The cells of the epithelial wall of the ventriculus and its caeca are glandular. They probably secrete digestive enzymes and it is probable that digestion and absorption occur principally in the lumen and cells of the mid-gut. The feces are formed in the intestine and are usually voided with the excretory products as tiny spheres. A secretion is used by the deutonymphs of certain uropodids to form an anal pedicel by which they attach themselves to larger arthropods, usually beetles.

Excretory System: Three types of excretory organs are found in the Acarina. The most primitive is the coxal gland. Excretory tubules that open into the hind-gut but which are endodermal in origin are the most usual type. As previously mentioned the hind-gut of the Trombidiformes becomes modified to form an excretory organ. In addition to these organs, the cells of the mid-gut are excretory in function. During digestion the cells become filled with excretory products that are cast off into the lumen of the mid-gut from whence they pass into the intestine. Mites excrete their nitrogenous wastes in the form of guanin. The Notostigmata have two excretory tubules and a pair of coxal glands that open on coxae I or II. The Holothyroidea have two pairs of excretory tubules and a pair of coxal glands that open on coxae I.

The Mesostigmata have one pair of excretory tubules and from one to four pairs of coxal glands.

The Trombidiformes have no excretory tubules of the usual type but the hind-gut is modified as an excretory organ in many of them. Coxal glands are present in some of the Trombidiformes.

The Sarcoptiformes have a pair of small excretory tubes. Coxal glands have been found in the oribatids.

Circulatory System: The circulatory system of most Acarina consists only of the blood, which is colorless and bathes all of the organs of the body. Amoeboid leucocytes are present and can best be demonstrated during the quiescent stages that precede ecdysis. A simple heart is present in the Holothyroidea and some of the Mesostigmata.

Respiratory System: Of all the anatomical features of the Acarina, those associated with the respiratory system are most important to the systematics of the group. The suborders are established largely on the basis of this system. In those mites that have tracheae the number and placement of the stigmata are of first importance. In function the respiratory system is similar to that of most terrestrial arthropods. The main tracheae are subdivided into tracheoles that run through most of the tissues and provide for the gaseous exchanges required by the metabolism of the cells. Some mites have no tracheal system. These mites are usually small, and respiration must be either carried on through the cuticle or by means of anaerobic reactions.

The Notostigmata have four pairs of stigmata situated on the dorsal surface of the first four segments of the opisthosoma. They open through the leathery cuticle and are not supported by stigmal plates. Tracheal trunks branch out from each pair of stigmata but they do not anastomose.

The Holothyroidea have two pairs of stigmata. The anterior pair is situated laterally above coxa III. It communicates with a vestibule from which many tracheae extend out into the body tissues. The posterior pair of stigmata open into a pair of atria from which many thin-walled diverticula extend.

The Mesostigmata and Ixodides have a single pair of stigmata in the adults, but in larval ticks there may be found several pairs of stigmata. The stigmata open into an atrium from which the tracheal trunks arise. Associated with the stigmata and trachea there is a chitinous tube, the peritreme. In the Mesostigmata the stigmata are situated ventrally lateral to the coxae and at the level of or in front of coxae III. The peritremes are usually long and anteriorly directed. They may be extended posteriorly for some distance as well and they may be almost straight or strongly bent. In the Ixodides the peritreme is never tubelike and is confined to the area adjacent to the stigmata that are placed behind or lateral to coxae IV.

The stigmata of the Trombidiformes are usually situated on the gnathosoma or between the gnathosoma and the propodosoma. The females of the Tarsonemini have a pair or two pairs of stigmata on the proterosoma. Many males lack a respiratory system entirely. The Prostigmata have the stigmal openings on the gnathosoma and frequently stigmal horns or peritremes are present (Figure 28). The peritremes of the prostigmatids give rise to tracheal trunks and are not similar to the peritremes of the Mesostigmata. Many of the bdellids have a genital tracheal system in addition to the usual prostigmatic type. In a number of the smaller trombidiform mites stigmata and tracheae are reduced or wanting.

The Sarcoptiformes lack tracheae and stigmata or have minute tracheae. The Acaridiae lack a specialized respiratory system. Most Oribatei are remarkable in that they have developed a system of tracheae that opens through stigmata and porose areas in many regions of the body. In this group even the pseudostigmata are associated with the respiratory system. Grandjean 1934 describes in detail the structure of the respiratory system of this group. Some of the oribatids, however, lack respiratory openings and tracheae.

Nervous System: Consolidation of the segmental ganglia has progressed in the Acarina to such an extent that the central nervous system is an integrated mass surrounding the esophagus. In the embryonic and larval stages fusion of the ganglia is not as complete as in the nymphs and adults. The portion of the brain dorsal to the esophagus gives rise to the nerves that supply the pharynx, chelicerae, and eyes. The nerves that run to the pedipalps, legs, and posterior internal organs all originate from that portion of the brain that is ventral to the esophagus (Figure 29). The nerves that run to the appendages do not supply other portions of the body. Apparently motor and sensory fibers are incorporated in all the nerves.

Sense Organs: As with other arthropods the setae of the Acarina are primarily sensory in function. They have been discussed under the section on the integument with one exception. Many of the Trombidiformes and Sarcoptiformes possess specialized setiform, pseudostigmatic organs or sensillae. They usually arise from a specialized

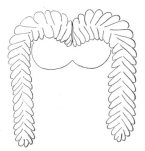

Figure 28 The emergent peritremes of *Allothrombium* sp.

Figure 29 The brain of a *Tetranychus.* (After Blauvelt 1945)

depression in the propodosomal plate or in the region of this plate if it is lacking. This depression is known as a pseudostigma and in the Oribatei is connected with air sacs that aid in respiration. The function of the pseudostigma and its sensilla is unknown. That it is sensory is probably correct since the sensillae are directly connected to the nervous system. The terrestrial mites that possess them usually have them well developed, but closely related aquatic groups have them reduced or lacking. Sensillae may vary in structure as widely as the body setae (Figure 30). They can be readily recognized in any one species because they are always considerably different from the ordinary setae.

The palps and legs of all acarinids are more or less thickly clothed with setae and in many cases are provided with striated, sensory setae. At times the palps or one or more pairs of legs are modified as tactile organs. The tarsi are usually well provided with special sensory setae and in the ticks and Rhagidiidae special organs have developed on the anterior tarsi. Haller's organ is characteristic of all stages of all ticks with the exception of Ceratixodes that lack it in the nymphal and perhaps also in the larval stage. Haller's organ is associated with the olfactory responses of ticks. It is situated on tarsus I and usually con-

sists of a pit containing specialized setae (Figure 31). The Notostigmata have a similar organ and the Mesostigmata have a concentration
of setae on tarsus I similar to the setae of Haller's organ. The Rhagidiidae have well-developed "Rhagidia organs" on tarsi I and II, and
related groups have similar though not as highly modified structures.

In the integument of most mites special areas consisting of pores,
longitudinal clefts, or depressions that are supplied by nerves or are
indirectly connected with the nervous system will be found. The func-

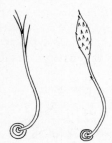

Figure 30 Sensillae of *Trombicula* (*Eutrombicula*) *alfreddugèsi* (Oude-mans), 1910 and *Galumna* sp.

Figure 31 A section through Haller's organ of *Dermacentor venustus* Banks, 1908.

tion of these structures is unknown but they are probably sensory in
nature. Mites respond to a number of stimuli for which no organs of
special sense have yet been demonstrated. It is possible that these
obscure organs respond to such stimuli.

Eyes are present in many of the mites and many mites that lack
them probably respond to changes in light intensity. The eyes of mites
are never developed beyond the ocellus stage. Compound eyes are
unknown in the Acarina. Mites that lack eyes usually have thin, transparent areas on the dorsal surface so that changes in light intensity will
penetrate to the tissues below. The simplest eye consists of a concentration of pigment granules associated with an optic nerve. The pigment is frequently red but at times black or blue. Lenslike corneas are
associated with the pigment granules in many cases. The most complicated eyes are found in certain of the water mites. Mites may have a
single median eye or one or two pairs of propodosomal eyes or all five
as is the case with many of the hydracarinids. Even the most complicated of eyes probably do no more than detect light intensity. It is
doubtful that images are formed.

Reproductive System: The Acarina are all dioecious. In most groups the males can be distinguished from the females even though males and females are similar to each other. Fertilization is internal, but the methods by which the spermatophores are introduced into the female reproductive system vary considerably. Some mites develop young parthenogenetically but none has been shown to be exclusively parthenogenetic. Mites may be oviparous or ovoviviparous. Only sexual reproduction is known.

The male reproductive system consists of a testis or pair of testes, vasa deferentia, accessory gland or glands, an ejaculatory duct, and a penis. The penis is lacking in the Mesostigmata where the spermatophores are introduced into the female by the chelicerae. Many males have one or more pairs of legs modified as organs for grasping the female during copulation.

The female reproductive system consists of an ovary or pair of ovaries, an oviduct, uterus, seminal receptacle, accessory glands, and in some cases a vagina. There is a specialized ovipositor in some groups (Oribatei), but usually the eggs are laid through the genital opening without the aid of an ovipositor.

The genital openings of both males and females are usually closed by specialized plates that frequently have genital suckers associated with them or near them. In most mites examination of the genital opening is sufficient to distinguish the sexes but in some the presence or absence of a penis is the only reliable criterion, while in others examination of the gonads is required.

The spermatozoa are frequently immature when transferred to the female and mature only after copulation is completed. Most mites develop one or a few eggs at any time but the ticks and some of the tarsonemids develop numerous eggs concurrently.

Most eggs are provided with an eggshell that protects the developing embryo. In some cases eggs can be transported by wind currents for great distances.

Life Cycle: The primitive life cycle consists of an egg in which the blastula develops, a deutovum formed by a chorion that is secreted by the blastoderm, a six-legged larva, a protonymph, deutonymph, tritonymph, and adult males and females. So many families deviate from this primitive life cycle, however, that it is the exception rather than the rule. The life cycle of many of the mites is still to be determined.

In most mites the larvae, except for the absence of the genital openings and the posterior pair of legs, are similar to the adults. In some prostigmatid mites the larva is quite different from the adult and in reality metamorphoses into the nymph. The nymphs are usually similar to the adults. In the oribatids, uropodids, and the acarids, however, certain of the nymphs differ markedly from the adults.

Classification:　　Most acarologists, entomologists, and zoologists consider the Acarina to be an order of the class Arachnida. As long as the Arachnida are subdivided primarily into orders this course reflects the relationships of the Acarina as well as any other. However, when certain of the orders are grouped together into subclasses as is done by Petrunkevitch 1949 and others, it might seem desirable to consider the Acarina as a separate subclass. The Acarina are readily separable from other arachnids in that they possess a distinct gnathosoma. Furthermore they are never divided so that a distinct cephalothorax and abdomen are clearly recognizable. The phylogeny of the Acarina is obscure and most students of the group consider them to be polyphyletic in origin. In the present work the Acarina will be considered as an order.

A diagnostic classification of the Acarina follows:

Phylum Arthropoda: Metameric animals with an exoskeleton and jointed appendages.

Subphylum Chelicerata: Arthropods without antennae or mandibles. Mouth parts consist of pedipalps and chelicerae.

Class Arachnida: Chelicerates that lack gill books.

　　Order Acarina: Arachnids with the mouth parts more or less distinctly set off from the rest of the body on a false head, capitulum, or gnathosoma. Posterior segmentation is greatly reduced or absent. Primary sclerites are largely replaced by secondary plates of divers origins. Larval stages normally have three pairs of legs; nymphal and adult stages usually have four pairs of legs. Usually minute except for ticks and a few mites.

　　　　Suborder Onychopalpida (Chapter II): Acarina with typical ambulacral claws on the pedipalps and more than one pair of idiosomal stigmata.

　　　　Suborder Mesostigmata (Chapter III): Acarina with a single pair of stigmata lateral to the legs that is usually associated with an elongated peritreme, or if absent degenerate parasites of the respiratory tract of vertebrates. Haller's organ absent. Hypostome not developed for piercing.

Suborder Ixodides (Chapter IV): Acarina with a pair of stigmata posterior or lateral to the coxae associated with a stigmal plate rather than an elongated peritreme. Haller's organ present. Hypostome modified as a piercing organ and provided with recurved teeth.

Suborder Tromibidiformes (Chapters V and VI): Acarina with a pair of stigmata on or near the gnathosoma or absent. Palpi usually free and highly developed. Chelicerae usually modified for piercing. Anal suckers never present.

Suborder Sarcoptiformes (Chapters VII and VIII): Acarina without stigmata or with a system of tracheae opening through stigmata and porose areas on various parts of the body. Coxae forming apodemes beneath skin on venter of body. Mouth parts usually for chewing, with strong chelae; a few parasitic forms with specialized chelicerae. Palpi simple. With or without pseudostigmata and pseudostigmatic organs. Anal suckers often present.

References:

Banks, N. 1915. The Acarina or mites. U.S. Dept. Agric. Rpt. 108:1–153.

Berlese, A. 1882–1903. Acari, Myriopoda, et Scorpiones hucusque in Italia reperta. Fasc. 1–101. Padua.

Ewing, H. E. 1929. A manual of external parasites. 1–225 + xiv. Baltimore.

Oudemans, A. C. 1926–1937. Kritisch Historisch Overzicht der Acarologie. (Volumes 1 and 2 supplements to Volumes 69 and 72 of Tijdschr. Ent. Leiden. Volume 3 published in six parts independently.)
1926. 850 V.C.–1758. 1:1–500 + vii.
1929. 1759–1804. 2:1–1097 + xvii.
1936–37. 1805–1850. 3:1–3379 + ci.

Petrunkevitch, A. 1949. A study of Palaeozoic Arachnida. Trans. Conn. Acad. Art. Sci. 37:69–315.

Radford, C. D. 1950. Systematic check list of mite genera and type species. Union Internat. des Sci. Biol., ser. C (sec. Ent.) 1:1–252.

Reuter, E. 1909. Zur Morphologie und Ontogonie der Acariden. Acta Soc. Sci. Fenn. 36, No. 4:1–288.

Snodgrass, R. E. 1948. The feeding organs of Arachnida including mites and ticks. Smithsonian Misc. Coll. 110, No. 10:1–93.

Vitzthum, H. G. 1929. Acari. Die Tierwelt Mitteleuropas 3, No. 7:1–112.

——. 1931. Acari. Kükenthals Handbuch der Zoologie. 3, 2 half:1–160.

——. 1940–1942. Acarina. Bronns' Klassen und Ordungen des Tierreiches. 5, Sect. 4, Book 5:1–1011 + xi.

CHAPTER II

The Suborder Onychopalpida Wharton, 1947

MOST mites have such specialized pedipalps that there are no palpal claws on the palpal tarsi, although some may have secondarily developed tibial claws. The groups Notostigmata and Holothyroidea, that comprise the Onychopalpida are unique in that they possess reduced ambulacral claws on the pedipalps and a radula-like organ on the labrum. Although it is far from clear that these two represent a monophyletic group, their inclusion in a single suborder helps to emphasize their primitive nature and does set them apart as possibly representing living remnants of a former extensive fauna of primitive mites.

Morphology: The palpal claws have already been mentioned. The suborder is also unique in that its members have at least four lateral stigmata. Because of the paucity of species no general account of the morphology of the group will be required to explain the key characters and is therefore omitted. For an account of the morphology With 1904 and Grandjean 1938 are recommended.

Key to the Onychopalpida

1. With tritosternum, at least four pairs of dorso-lateral stigmata, two pairs of eyes, and leathery cuticle   Notostigmata

   Without tritosternum, two pairs of lateral stigmata; no eyes, and sclerotized cuticle   Holothyroidea

NOTOSTIGMATA WITH, 1903

Chamberlain and Mulaik 1942 erected the family Neocaridae to accommodate a new species of Notostigmata that they found in Texas.

While there is much justification for their action on the basis of morphology, it seems undesirable to recognize the familial separation that they suggest when so few species are represented in the group, as a whole. Therefore, only the single family Opilioacaridae is recognized here.

Opilioacaridae With, 1902

Figure 32

Diagnosis: These are medium-sized mites about 1 mm. long, and oval in shape. The hysterosoma has indications of segmentation dorsally, the cuticle is striated with numerous minute pores, a divided tritosternum is present, two eyes are located on each side of the propodosoma, and the setae are simple or feathered. The pedipalps have reduced ambulacral claws while the chelicerae are unmodified and a radula-like organ with recurved teeth is situated between and hidden by the chelicerae. The legs are segmented secondarily, trochanters III and IV are divided, the coxae are freely movable, and a pair of unmodified ambulacral claws is present on each tarsus. The genital openings of each sex are ventral between coxae III, the females have an ovipositor, and the males have specialized areas

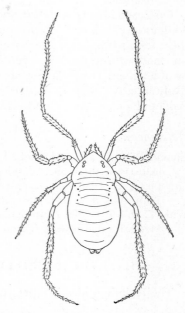

Figure 32 *Opilioacarus segmentatus* With, 1902. Dorsal view of female showing the four pairs of opisthosomal stigmata. (After With 1903)

lateral to the opening. On the dorsal-lateral aspect of the hysterosoma four pairs of stigmata are present, while a median stigma is present in *Neocarus*.

Genera:

1. *Opilioacarus* With, 1902 (= *Eucarus* With, 1903)
   Type. *Opilioacarus segmentatus* With, 1902
2. *Neocarus* Chamberlain and Mulaik, 1942
   Type. *Neocarus texanus* Chamberlain and Mulaik, 1942

3. *Paracarus* Chamberlain and Mulaik, 1942
   Type. *Opilioacarus hexopthalmus Redikorzer,* 1937

Discussion: Although opilioacarids are primitive, they, like so many other primitive animals, have specialized characteristics. The radula-like structure in the gnathosoma, the secondary segmentation of the legs, and the divided tritosternum are all considered to be evidence of specialization.

Opilioacarids are secretive and live under stones and other debris. Chitinous remnants of other arthropods have been found in the gut of these mites. It appears likely therefore that they feed, at least in part, on small arthropods. These mites have been found in the Mediterranean area and Texas. So few specimens have been collected that relatively little is known of their life cycle. They are not known to be of economic or medical importance.

References:

Chamberlain, R. and S. Mulaik. 1942. On a new family in the Notostigmata. Proc. Biol. Soc. Washington. 55:125–131.
Grandjean, F. 1936. Un acarien synthetique: *Opilioacarus segmentatus* With. Bull. Soc. Hist. Nat. Afr. Nord. 27:413–444.
With, C. J. 1904. The Notostigmata a new suborder of Acari. Vidensk. Medd. fra den Naturk. Foren. i. Kbhvn. 1904:137–192 + Pls. iv–vi.

HOLOTHYROIDEA REUTER, 1909

The Holothyroidea is represented only by the family Holothyridae.

Holothyridae Thorell, 1882

Figure 33

Diagnosis: The holothyrids are large (up to 7 mm. long) and hemispherical in shape but distinctly longer than broad. Evidence of primary segmentation is lacking, and the body is divided into gnathosoma and idiosoma. The deep brown, smooth cuticle is heavily sclerotized in adults, eyes are absent, and the setae are of relatively unmodified form. Tarsal claws and five movable segments are located on the pedipalps. The chelicerae are chelate. A radula-like organ is present on the tip of the labrum. The legs are all provided with paired ambulacral claws. In the midline between coxae iii and iv is located the genital opening which is closed by two plates in the male and four in the female.

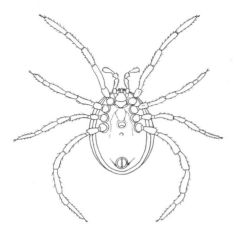

Figure 33 *Holothyrus longipes* Thorell, 1882. Ventral view of the male. (After Hirst 1922)

Genus:

> *Holothyrus* Gervais, 1842
> Type. *Holothyrus coccinella* Gervais, 1842

Discussion: Species of *Holothyrus* are found in New Guinea, Ceylon, Australia, and islands in the Indian Ocean. The habits and life history of holothyrids are unknown. On Mauritius, Hirst 1922 records the fact that a *Holothyrus* is fairly common and that the irritant poison that they secrete is reported to cause the death of ducks and geese that swallow them. He also mentions that children suffer ill effects from the poison of these mites.

References:

Hirst, S. 1922. Mites injurious to domestic animals. Econ. Ser. British Mus. (Nat. Hist.). 13:1–107.

Thon, K. 1906. Die aüssere Morphologie und die Systematik der Holothyriden. Zool. Jahrb., Syst. 23:677–724 + Pls. 28-29.

Womersley, H. 1935. A species of Acarina of the genus Holothyrus from Australia and New Zealand. Ann. Mag. Nat. Hist. 16:151–154.

CHAPTER III

The Suborder Mesostigmata G. Canestrini, 1819

THE Mesostigmata and Ixodides are usually combined to form a single suborder, the Parasitiformes. The evidence for this arrangement is good on morphological grounds, especially when the position of the stigmata and the structure of the gnathosoma are considered. However, two other suborders—the Trombidiformes and Sarcoptiformes—are apparently more closely related to each other than are the Mesostigmata and Ixodides. The relationship among these suborders, however, is not expressed in the classification. It seems desirable for simplicity to omit the term Parasitiformes from the classification. This omission is not intended to deny relationship between the suborders but is made to increase the utility of the classification.

The Mesostigmata are readily recognized by their gnathosoma, lateral stigmata, tritosternum, dorsal plates, ventral plates, genital openings, and legs. They are diverse in the details of their structure but are nevertheless a fairly compact group. Vitzthum 1931 estimated that there were 1,290 species at that time, but since 1931 numerous new species have been described. Even at present almost every small collection of mites contains a few new species of Mesostigmata. Since so many forms await discovery and description, the classification is of course in a state of flux.

In a recent series of papers Trägårdh has investigated the comparative anatomy of their sclerotized structures and has succeeded in obtaining some degree of order out of the previous chaos. This has been achieved largely by studying the ventral plates of the females and the structures associated with the genital openings. Although his groups are established on the basis of the structure of females, his more recent investigations show that the ventral plates of the males may also be useful in demonstrating relationships. Despite Trägårdh's excellent

40

work much information concerning the Gamasides is needed before a satisfactory understanding of that group will be achieved. Of the 1,290 species reported by Vitzthum 1939, 889 or more than 75 per cent belonged to the Gamasides.

Trägårdh follows the more commonly accepted classification of the Acarina and assigns the Mesostigmata to the rank of supercohort. In the present discussion Trägårdh's supercohort will be considered a suborder. Trägårdh's classification will be followed in spirit except that the names of the categories and some of his subdivisions will be omitted.

Morphology: Mesostigmatid mites are usually well armored with brown to deep brown sclerotized plates or shields. In almost every case (*Rhodacarus* is an exception) the body consists of two distinct regions: an anterior, minute gnathosoma and a posterior idiosoma. In the Uropodina, one of the groups, the gnathosoma is frequently enclosed in a cavity (camerostome) in the idiosoma.

With a little experience the general facies of mesostigmatid mites will enable the student to recognize more than 90 per cent of the species. However, all species that have either a tritosternum or one pair of lateral stigmata with a sinuate peritreme or both may be safely placed in the Mesostigmata. Of particular importance in the classification of the suborder is the distribution of the ventral plates, ventral setae, and ventral pores. Since Trägårdh's classification is to be used his nomenclature for the structures will be used where applicable.

The gnathosoma of mesostigmatid mites is a complicated apparatus. The chelicerae and the distal segments of the pedipalps are relatively unmodified, but the fused basal segments of the pedipalps that form the ventral wall are extended anteriorly and dorsally as several projections and sheaths about the chelicerae. Dorsally an anterior projection extends over the gnathosoma and is called a tectum by Snodgrass 1948 or epistome by other authors. In the midline of the gnathosoma there is usually a groove that has markings reminiscent of recurved teeth. Lateral to the gnathosomal groove are the two main sections of the ventral wall of the gnathosoma. Anteriorly these are differentiated into a median hypostome, lateral cornua, and more medial paralabra.

The legs of the mesostigmatids are usually well sclerotized. They typically have six or seven movable segments. The tarsi end in pretarsi that usually bear sucker-like caruncles and a pair of ambulacral claws. Tarsus I is frequently provided with a tuft of sensory setae on the dorsal surface of the apex, but no pitlike Haller's organ, such as is found in the ticks, is present. (Haarlov 1943).

The idiosoma is armored with sclerotized plates. On the dorsal surface there is usually a single plate, but this may be completely or partially divided into two or more plates. Laterally there may be plates that connect the dorsal plate to the ventral plates, or lateral plates may be entirely lacking in which case soft, striated integument connects dorsal and ventral sclerites.

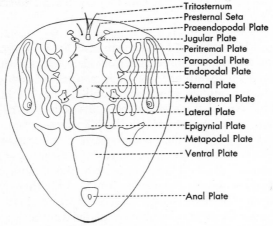

Tritosternum
Presternal Seta
Praeendopodal Plate
Jugular Plate
Peritremal Plate
Parapodal Plate
Endopodal Plate
Sternal Plate
Metasternal Plate
Lateral Plate
Epigynial Plate
Metapodal Plate
Ventral Plate

Anal Plate

Figure 34 A diagrammatic arrangement of the ventral plates that may be encountered in the Mesostigmata. A median plate, if present, will have the same position as the epigynial plate.

The ventral plates are of extreme importance in recognizing the suborders (Figure 34). Just posterior to the gnathosoma in the midline there is the tritosternum. The tritosternum consists of a basal portion and two or three setiform distal processes. The tritosternum is a modified remnant of the sternal plates of the third segment and is the only relic of the primary sternites. Flanking the tritosternum there may be a pair of presternal setae and/or praeendopodal plates that always lack setae. These plates are called jugular plates by Ewing 1928, but Trägårdh reserves the term jugular for plates anterior to the sternal plate that bear sternal setae and may or may not have pores. Posterior to the tritosternum lies the so-called sternal plate. In some genera this plate bears four pairs of setae and three pairs of pores. The sternal plate is thought to have been formed by the fusion of coxal plates with the ventral body wall. The presence of four pairs of setae on some sternal plates supports this hypothesis. At the other extreme the sternal plate may bear only two pairs of setae. In this case one pair of setae will be found on the jugular plates, while the fourth pair is on the metasternal plates just posterior and lateral to the sternal plate between coxae III and IV. The most common arrangement is to have three pairs of setae and two pairs of pores on the sternal plate and the fourth pair of setae and third pair of pores on the metasternal plates. In the female the genital opening usually lies posterior to the sternal plate and between the metasternal plates. The female genital opening may be guarded by a median epigynial plate that may or may not bear setae; it may be flanked by setal-bearing lateral plates, or it may have both or neither of the plates. A median plate formed by sclerotization of the dorsal wall of the vagina may be present beneath the epigynial plate, or when the epigynial plate has been lost secondarily the median plate may be apparent on the surface as it is in the genus *Fedrizzia*. Posterior to the female genital opening is the ventral plate. The ventral plate bears setae and it may be found fused with either the epigynial plate or anal plate. Endopodal plates frequently occur between the coxae and the sternal plates. Parapodal plates occur lateral to the coxae. The stigmata and peritremes are sometimes located on special peritremal plates. Posterior to coxae IV and lateral to the ventral plate, metapodal plates are to be found. In the males the genital opening may be in the middle of the sternal plate or at its anterior border. As a rule much fusion is exhibited in the ventral plates of the males.

Larvae of mesostigmatid mites have only three pairs of legs and reduced plates. Nymphs have four pairs of legs and can be readily recognized by the absence of genital openings. The dorsal plate of the nymphs is frequently broken into several platelets. The sternal and ventral plates, however, are usually fused to form a single ventral plate.

Trägårdh 1946 has achieved a sufficiently clear understanding of the comparative morphology of the group to be able to explain some of the relationships among the groups. Three of the groups lack an epigynial plate and show no evidence of a secondary loss of the plate. These three—the Megisthanina, Liroaspina, and Microgynina—comprise one group. The other group in which either an epigynial plate or lateral plates or both are associated with the female genital opening is divided into eight groups: the Gamasides, Celaenopsina, Fedrizziina, Zerconina, Thinozerconina, Trachytina, Diarthrophallina, and Uropodina.

A key to the groups of the Mesostigmata modified from Trägårdh 1946 follows:

Key to the Mesostigmata

1. Well-developed epigynial plate present in females, or if reduced or lacking its function taken over by median plate or lateral plates   2

    Epigynial plate primitively absent in females; median and lateral plates not closing genital opening   8

2. Lateral plates present   3

    Lateral plates absent   4

3. Discrete metasternal plates present   Celaenopsina

    Metasternal plates combined in sternal plate   Fedrizziina

4. Epigynial plate hinged or fused to ventral plate along transverse suture, or peritreme ventral, or both   5

    Epigynial plate not articulated at base, peritreme dorsal
                                                                                          Thinozerconina

5. Epigynial plate with one pair of genital setae   6

    Epigynial plate without setae   7

6. Male genital aperture surrounded by sternal plate; metasternal plates reduced so that only metasternal setae apparent; chelicerae of males not modified for copulation   Zerconina

    Male genital aperture in front of sternal plate; metasternal plates varied; chelicerae of males more or less modified to transfer spermatophores during copulation   Gamasides

7. Metasternal plates distinct   Trachytina

    Metasternal plates greatly reduced or lacking   10

8. Presternal setae not present; female genital opening transverse slit   9

    Presternal setae flanking tritosternum; female genital opening crescentic fissure between sternal and ventral plates   Megisthanina

9. Female genital opening large, between sternal and ventral plates
                                                                                          Liroaspina

    Female genital opening small, with no connection with either sternal or ventral plates   Microgyniina

10. Presternal setae flanking tritosternum   Diarthrophallina

    Presternal setae not present   Uropodina

MEGISTHANINA TRÄGÅRDH, 1946

Only a single family is contained in the Megisthanina. There is little doubt, however, that it deserves group rank. Mites that belong to this group have a unique genital opening in that the sternal plate appears to function as an epigynial plate.

Megisthanidae Berlese, 1914

Figure 35

Diagnosis: Megisthanids are large (from 1 to 4 mm.) mites, oval in shape, and their bodies are divided into a gnathosoma and idiosoma. The cuticle is present with a single dorsal plate over the entire dorsum. The venter has an elongated ventral plate, and the sternal plate is divided into two parts, the posterior part of which resembles an epigynial plate. No eyes are present. A pair of presternal setae flank the tritosternum, the palps are unmodified, and the chelicerae are chelate and stout with strong teeth. Legs are stout with toothlike projections sometimes present on leg IV but there are no claws on leg I. The female genital opening is a crescent-shaped fissure placed just posterior to

Figure 35 *Megisthanus floridanus* Banks, 1904. Ventral view of female.

the sternal plate, while the male genital opening is located in the sternal plate aperture and is closed by two plates between which there is a transverse fissure. The stigmata are opposite the posterior legs and have elongated peritremes.

Genera:

1. *Megisthanus* Thorell, 1882
   Type. *Megisthanus caudatus* Thorell, 1882
2. *Celaenogamasus* Berlese, 1901
   Type. *Celaenogamasus hirtellus* Berlese, 1901
3. *Cyclothorax* v. Frauenfeld, 1868
   Type. *Cyclothorax carcinicola* v. Frauenfeld, 1868
4. *Hoplomegistus* Berlese, 1903
   Type. *Megistanus armiger* Berlese, 1888 (*Megistanus* is a *lapsus* of *Megisthanus*)

5. *Stenosternum* Kramer, 1898

Type. *Stenosternum bipilosum* Kramer, 1898

Discussion: The diagnosis given above is based on the genus *Megisthanus*. Vitzthum 1942 suggests that all of the genera may not agree with a diagnosis based on *Megisthanus,* but knowledge of the other genera is too limited for a definite statement to be made. Only the genus *Megisthanus* has been examined in preparing this work.

Species of *Megisthanus* are commonly found on large beetles in moist environments. The best source of *Megisthanus* in the United States is the patent leather beetle, *Popilius disjunctus* Illiger. The species found on this beetle is *Megisthanus floridanus* Banks. As far as is known, megisthanids are of little economic or medical importance.

References:

Trägårdh, I. 1943. Further contributions towards the comparative morphology of the Mesostigmata (Acarina) the Antennophoridae and the Megisthanidae. Arkiv. för Zoologi. 34A. N:o 20:1–10.

——. 1946. Outlines of a new classification of the Mesostigmata (Acarina) based on comparative morphological data. Lunds Universitets Arsskrift. N.F. Avd. 2. 42: No. 4:1–37.

——. 1946. Contributions towards the comparative morphology of the Mesostigmata (Acarina) VII. The praesternal hairs and the male genital aperture. Särtryk ur Entomologsk Tidskrift. Arg. 67. Häft. 3:88–108.

LIROASPINA TRÄGÅRDH, 1946

The Liroaspina contains only two families of small mites that are similar to the Megisthanina and the Microgyniina in that they lack an epigynial plate.

Trägårdh 1946 in a study of the male genital openings recommends that the two families originally placed in the Liroaspina be further separated so that each is to be placed in a separate group. There is some justification for such a step since the male genital openings differ considerably. However, Trägårdh's original plan of basing the classification on the ventral plates of the females will be followed and thus the Liroaspina will not be split.

Key to the Liroaspina

1. Sternal shields III and IV fused to narrow, transverse shield; sternal shields I and II free or fused in females; male genital aperture closed by nude, circular disk   Liroaspidae

   Sternal shields II, III, and IV fused in female, I free; male genital aperture closed by two-piece circular disk bearing single pair of setae   Epicriidae

Liroaspidae Trägårdh, 1946

Figure 36

Diagnosis: The characteristic distribution of the dorsal plates of liroaspids is diagnostic for the family. A single, large plate covers most of the dorsal surface of the podosoma. At the posterior end there is an entire or divided pygidial plate that may or may not have posterior, setal-bearing projections. Between these two plates is a series of smaller plates and platelets. The sternal plates of the females are divided or partially fused. No epigynial plate is present. The male genital aperture is covered by a nude circular disk. It is situated near the anterior margin in the sternal shield. All tarsi are provided with pretarsi and claws.

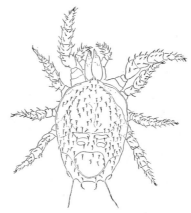

Figure 36   *Liroaspis armatus* Fox, 1947. Dorsal view of female.

Genera and subgenera:

1. *Liroaspis* Banks, 1902 (= *Dwigubskyia* Oudemans, 1936)
   Type. *Liroaspis americana* Banks, 1902
2. *Berlesiana* Turk, 1943
   Type. *Epicrius cirratus* Berlese, 1917
3. *Epicroseius* Berlese, 1904
   a. *Epicroseius* s. str.
      Type. *Epicroseius angelioides* Berlese, 1904
   b. *Iphidinychus* Berlese, 1913
      Type. *Echinoseius (Iphidinychus) manicatus* Berlese, 1913. (*Echinoseius* is apparently only a *lapsus* for *Epicroseius*)

4. *Willmannia* Balogh, 1938
    Type. *Willmannia sejiformis* Balogh, 1938
5. *Zuluacarus* Trägårdh, 1906
    Type. *Zuluacarus termitophilus* Trägårdh, 1906

Discussion: Liroaspids have been found mostly in tropical countries, but species of *Liroaspis* have been collected in northern Europe and in the northern half of North America. The structure of their stout chelicerae indicates that they are predaceous. Specimens have been collected from plants, and Fox 1947 collected two specimens from two rats in Puerto Rico. The presence of *Liroaspis armatus* on rats does not necessarily mean that they are ectoparasitic on these hosts. They may have been on the rats purely by accident, or they may prey upon the large fauna of ectoparasites that infests rats. Except for their occurrence on rats liroaspids are of no known economic or medical importance.

References:

Balogh, J. 1938. Systematische Studien über eine neue Milbengattung: Willmannia gen. nov. Zool. Anz. 123:259–265.

Fox, I. 1947. Seven new mites from rats in Puerto Rico. Ann. Ent. Soc. America. 40:598–603.

Trägårdh, I. 1943. Further contributions towards the comparative morphology of the Mesostigmata (Acarina), the Antennophoridae, and the Megisthanidae. Arkiv. för Zoologi. 34A. N:o 20:1–10.

———. 1946. Outlines of a new classification of the Mesostigmata (Acarina) based on comparative morphological data. Lunds Universitets Arsskrift. N.F. Avd. 2. 42: No. 4:1–37.

———. 1946. Contributions towards the comparative morphology of the Mesostigmata (Acarina) VII. The praesternal hairs and the male genital aperture. Särtryk ur Entomologsk Tidskrift. Arg. 67. Häft. 3:88–108.

Epicriidae Berlese, 1885

Figure 37

Diagnosis: Epicriids can be readily recognized by the pattern of small elevations on the dorsal surface that gives the appearance of a fine geometrical network. The sternal plates of the females are divided so that sternal plate I is separated from plates II, III, and IV. The male genital aperture is situated in the sternal plate and is closed by a divided circular disk that bears a pair of setae. Epicriids are usually small (0.5 mm.) and golden brown in color.

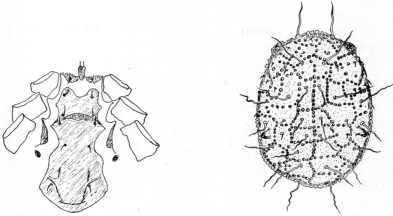

Figure 37   *Epicrius mollis* (Kramer), 1876. Right, dorsal view of female; left, ventral plates of female. (After Trägårdh 1942)

Genera and subgenera:

1. *Epicrius* G. Canestrini and Fanzago, 1877
   a. *Epicrius* s. str.
      Type. *Gamasus mollis* Kramer, 1876 (= *Epicrius geometricus* G. Canestrini and Fanzago, 1877)
   b. *Diepicrius* Berlese, 1916
      Type. *Epicrius* (*Diepicrius*) *parisiensis* Berlese, 1916
2. *Cornubia* Turk, 1943
   Type. *Cornubia ornata* Turk, 1943

Discussion: Epicriids are usually found in moss or accumulations of plant roots or rhizomes. On Guam *Epicrius sp.* was found among the rhizomes of epiphytic ferns that live in the tops of the trees of the rain forest. Epicriids are not known to be of any economic or medical importance.

References:

Trägårdh, I. 1942. Zur Kenntnis der Gattung Epicrius Berlese (Acarina). Arkiv. för Zoologi. 34A. N:o 4:1–10.
——. 1943. Further contributions towards the comparative morphology of the Mesostigmata (Acarina) the Antennophoridae and the Megisthanidae. Arkiv. för Zoologi. 34A. N:o 20:1–10.

——. 1946. Outline of a new classification of the Mesostigmata (Acarina) based on comparative morphological data. Lunds Universitets Arsskrift. N.F. Avd. 2. 42: No. 4:1–37.

——. 1946. Contributions towards the comparative morphology of the Mesostigmata (Acarina) VII. The praesternal hairs and the male genital aperture. Särtryk ur Entomologsk Tidskrift. Arg. 67. Häft. 3:88–108.

MICROGYNIINA TRÄGÅRDH, 1942

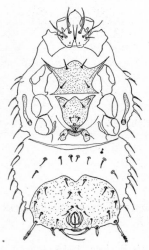

This group was recognized as a cohort by Trägårdh and was erected to contain two new species found by Forsslund in Sweden. Each species was recognized by Trägårdh as representing a new genus and family. The sub-order is characterized by Trägårdh as follows: the male genital aperture is located in the sternal shield and is not ring-shaped; the plate is not segmented and is directed forwards. The female genital aperture is a small transverse fissure placed far back without any connection with either the sternal or ventral plates. Three or four dorsal shields are present. The peritreme is short and tarsus I lacks a peduncle.

Figure 38 Microgynium rectangulatum Trägårdh, 1942. Ventral view of female. (After Trägårdh 1942)

Key to the Microgyniina

1. Dorsal side with three plates; ventral plate of female divided
   longitudinally   Microgyniidae

   Dorsal side with four plates; ventral plate of female entire
                                                          Microsejidae

Microgyniidae Trägårdh, 1942

Figure 38

Diagnosis: Microgyniids are small (0.3–0.4 mm.), colorless to light yellowish brown mites with three dorsal plates and a divided ventral plate in the female.

Genus:

Microgynium Trägårdh, 1942
Type. *Microgynium rectangulatum* Trägårdh, 1942

Discussion: M. *rectangulatum* was found under the loose bark of old tree stumps. Larvae, nymphs, males, and females were collected. Only one nymphal stadium was described. These mites are of no known economic or medical importance.

References:

Trägårdh, I. 1942. Microgyniina, a new group of Mesostigmata. Entomologisk Tidskrift Arg. 63. Häft. 3–4:120–133.
——. 1943. Further contributions towards the comparative morphology of the Mesostigmata (Acarina) the Antennophoridae and the Megisthanidae. Arkiv. för Zoologi. 34A. N:o 20:1–10.
——. 1946. Outlines of a new classification of the Mesostigmata (Acarina) based on comparative morphological data. Lunds Universitets Arsskrift. N.F. Avd. 2. 42: No. 4:1–37.
——. 1946. Contributions towards the comparative morphology of the Mesostigmata (Acarina) VII. The praesternal hairs and the male genital aperture. Särtryk ur Entomologsk Tidskrift. Arg. 67. Häft. 3:88–108.

Microsejidae Trägårdh, 1942

Figure 39

Diagnosis: The microsejids are similar to the previous family but differ in that there are four dorsal plates and an undivided ventral plate in the female.

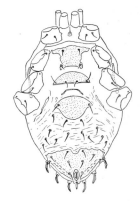

Figure 39 *Microsejus truncicola* Trägårdh, 1942. Ventral view of female. (After Trägårdh 1942)

Genus:

> *Microsejus* Trägårdh, 1942
> Type. *Microsejus truncicola* Trägårdh, 1942

Discussion: These mites are found under the loose bark of tree stumps. Only nymphs and adults are known. They are of no known economic or medical importance.

References:

Trägårdh, I. 1942. Microgyniina, a new group of Mesostigmata. Entomologisk Tidskrift Arg. 63. Häft. 3–4:120–133.

——. 1943. Further contributions towards the comparative morphology of the Mesostigmata (Acarina) the Antennophoridae and the Megisthanidae. Arkiv. för Zoologi. 34A. N:o 20:1–10.

——. 1946. Outlines of a new classification of the Mesostigmata (Acarina) based on comparative Morphological data. Lunds Universitets Arsskrift. N.F. Avd. 2. 42: No. 4:1–37.

——. 1946. Contributions towards the comparative morphology of the Mesostigmata (Acarina) VII. The praesternal hairs and the male genital aperture. Särtryk ur Entomologsk Tidskrift. Arg. 67. Häft. 3:88–108.

GAMASIDES LEACH, 1815

Gamasid mites are among the commonest type found in most collections, whether from debris or as ectoparasites of vertebrates or invertebrates. Since the monumental works of Berlese, no author has achieved a really clear understanding of this vast assemblage of species. The classification of the group that follows is largely taken from Vitzthum 1941.

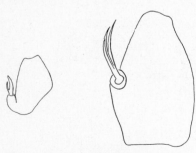

Figure 40 The specialized setae on the palpal tarsus of a laelaptid (left) and non-laelaptid (right) mite. The other setae on the palpal tarsus have been omitted.

Of special value in the classification of these mites is a forked seta at the base of the palpal tarsus (Figure 40). Those species that have more than two tines on the seta can readily be placed into their respective families, but those with only two tines are more difficult.

Gamasids can be recognized readily in the males because the chelicerae are more or less modified to function in the transfer of spermatophores to the females and the male opening is anterior to the sternal plate. The females are recognized by the characteristic arrangement of the ventral plates as described by Trägårdh 1946. The lateral plates are absent, and the metasternal plates are either free and fused with the corresponding endopodal plates, or small, or fused with the sternal plate. The epigynial plate bears a pair of setae and it may or may not be fused with the ventral plate.

Key to the Gamasides

1. Lacking large bell- or bucket-shaped suckers at sides of anal opening   2

   With large bell- or bucket-shaped suckers at sides of anal opening   Discozerconidae

2. Male genital opening at anterior margin of sternal plate; no dark transverse bands on sternal plate of nymph   3

   Male genital opening in special presternal plate; sternal plate usually with dark transverse band in nymph   Poecilochiridae

3. Females without jugular plates; copulatory suckers absent in male   4

   Females with jugular plates; copulatory suckers on raised cone of ventroanal plate   Aceosejidae

4. Podosoma and opisthosoma insensibly fused; no constriction between the two regions   5

   Body elongated; opisthosoma separated from podosoma by deep furrow   Rhodacaridae

5. Lateral, ventral, anterior projections of pedipalpal coxae not harpoon-shaped; chelicerae chelate or stylettiform   6

   Females with lateral, ventral, anterior projections of pedipalpal coxae harpoon-shaped; chelicerae without fixed digit; movable digit with large, recurved teeth   Ixodorhynchidae

6. Base of gnathosoma forms narrow sheath for chelicerae   7

   Base of gnathosoma forms broad cavity or camerostome that encloses chelicerae but not palps   Spelaeorhynchidae

7. Coxae movable   8

Coxae immovable, arranged radially; legs stout; parasitic on bats
Spinturnicidae

8. Forked seta on palpal tarsus with more than two tines   10
Forked seta on palpal tarsus with two tines   9

9. Dorsal plate entire or divided into large anterior and small posterior plate   16
Dorsal plate divided into two subequal plates that cover most of dorsum   Ascaidae

10. Forked seta on palpal tarsus with three tines   11
Forked seta on palpal tarsus with four tines   Veigaiaidae

11. Epigynial plate without pointed apex thrust between pair of metasternal plates   12
Epigynial plate with pointed apex thrust between pair of metasternal plates   Parasitidae

12. Leg ı similar to other legs   13
Leg ı reduced, thin, without typical pretarsus, caruncle, or claws
Macrochelidae

13. Females with parapodal, peritremal, and metapodal plates not fused and not extending posteriorly lateral to ventral plate or all lateral plates fused with ventral plate   14
Parapodal, peritremal, and metapodal plates fused and extend behind coxae ıv lateral to ventral plate   Pachylaelaptidae

14. Dorsal plate entire   15
Dorsal plate divided into two   Gamasolaelaptidae

15. Pretarsus and caruncle of leg ı similar to those of other legs
Neoparasitidae
Pretarsus and caruncle of leg ı reduced, not like other legs
Pseudoparasitidae

16. Tritosternum present with lacinae in females   20
Tritosternum absent or reduced without lacinae in females   17

17. Chelicerae reduced or non-chelate except for few parasites of nasal cavities of birds; males without apophyses on leg ıı   18
Chelicerae chelate; parasites in the external auditory meatus of cattle and antelopes; basal portion of tritosternum reduced or lacking in females, males with apophyses on leg ıı   Raillietidae

18. Body shape oval; genital plate of female may be fairly well developed; parasites in respiratory passages of birds and snakes   19

    Body shape elongated oval to wormlike; genital plate of female rudimentary or lacking; parasites in lungs of mammals
              Halarachnidae

19. Dorsal plate undivided and covering more than podosoma, or if podosomal in position truncate posteriorly with a pair of long setae at its posterior border; parasitic in lungs of snakes
              Entonyssidae

    Dorsal plate usually divided or restricted to podosoma; parasitic in nasopharynx of birds   Rhinonyssidae

20. Setae over body sparse; tectum not shaped like tongue, not provided with long lateral teeth   21

    Setae numerous over body resembling a pelage; tectum shaped like tongue with long lateral anteriorly directed teeth   Haemogamasidae

21. Chelae reduced   Dermanyssidae

    Chelae not reduced   22

22. Epigynial plate drop-shaped, may be excavated posteriorly to accommodate anal plate   23

    Epigynial plate truncate or concave posteriorly   Phytoseiidae

23. Peritreme extremely short, less than five times diameter of stigma in length   Iphiopsidae

    Peritreme long, more than five times diameter of stigma in length
              Laelaptidae

Discozerconidae Berlese, 1910

Figures 41a, b

Diagnosis: The key character—the presence of large bell-shaped suckers flanking the anus—at once distinguishes members of this family from all others. Even in the absence of the suckers, however, these mites are readily separable from other gamasids in that the sternal plates are divided into a pair of anterior laterals and a pair of posterior laterals fused with the endopodal plates. All tarsi have pretarsi, caruncles, and small to vestigial claws. Body setae are extremely short and stout.

Genera:

1. *Discozercon* Berlese, 1910
   Type. *Discozercon mirabilis* Berlese, 1910
2. *Allozercon* Vitzthum, 1926
   Type. *Allozercon fecundissimus* Vitzthum, 1926
3. *Atacoseius* Berlese, 1905
   Type. *Atacoseius pellucens* Berlese, 1905
4. *Discomegistus* Trägårdh, 1911
   Type. *Discomegistus pectinatus* Trägårdh, 1911
5. *Heterozercon* Berlese, 1888
   Type. *Heterozercon degeneratus* Berlese, 1888

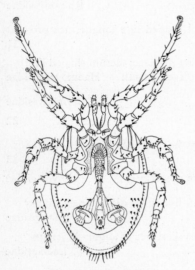 

Figure 41 a *Heterozercon oudemansi* Finnegan, 1931. Ventral view of female. (After Finnegan 1931)

Figure 41 b *Discozercon mirabilis* Berlese, 1910. Ventral view of female. (After Berlese 1914)

Discussion: The placement of *Atacoseius* in the family is somewhat doubtful since the type species is known only from immature specimens that do not exhibit all of the characteristics of the family. Vitzthum reports that Berlese proposed the family Heterozerconidae for the group in 1892, but a search to verify his report was unsuccessful.

The discozerconids are ectoparasites of large millipedes, centipedes, termites, snakes, and some are free-living or at least have been found unassociated with a host. All of the species are tropical or subtropical in distribution. None is known to be of medical or economic importance.

References:

Berlese, A. 1910. Brevi diagnosi di generi e specie nuovi di Acari. Redia 6 (2): 346–388.

Finnegan, Susan. 1931. On a new species of mite of the family Heterozerconidae parasitic on a snake. Proc. Zool. Soc. London 1931: 1349–1357.

Vitzthum, H. G. 1926. Malayische Acari. Treubia 8: 106.

Poecilochiridae Willmann, 1940

Figure 42

Diagnosis: The family is characterized by Willmann on the basis of the males and deutonymphs as follows: the male genital opening is in a special presternal plate; in other respects it is similar to *Parasitus,* (leg II of the males has well-developed apophyses). Deutonymphs are strongly heteromorphic, with very long legs and exceptionally long, stiff setae. Cheliceral chelae are present with an anterior, projecting, leaflike process. The sternal plate usually has a dark, transverse band. Neumann reports that the females are similar to the Parasitidae.

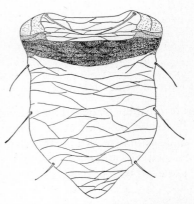

Figure 42 *Poecilochirus necrophori* Vitzthum, 1930. Sternal plate of deutonymph. (After Cooreman 1943)

Genus:

Poecilochirus G. and R. Canestrini, 1882
Type. *Poecilochirus carabi* G. and R. Canestrini, 1882

Discussion: Poecilochirids are found associated with beetles and in caves or burrows inhabited by beetles. Species have been reported from Europe and Asia. They are not known to be of any medical or economic importance.

References:

Neumann, K. W. 1943. Die Lebengeschicte der Käfermilbe *Poecilochirus necrophi* Vitzthum, nebst Beschreiberung aller Entwicklungstufen. Zool. Anz. 142:1–21.

Vitzthum, H. G. 1930. Milben als Pestträger? Zool. Jahrb. Syst. 60:381–428.

Willmann, C. 1940. Neue Milben aus Höhlen der Balkanhablinsel, gesammelt von Prof. Dr. K. Absolon, Brünn. Zool. Anz. 130:209–218.

Aceosejidae N.F.

Figure 43

Figure 43 *Aceoseius muricatus* (Koch), 1839. Lateral view of male. (After Sellnick 1941)

Diagnosis: The females can be recognized because they possess jugular plates. In other words the anterior sternal plate I is separated from the other sternal plates and is further split into two so that one half lies on either side of the tritosternum. Sternal setae I are on these plates. The epigynial plate bears a single pair of setae. Posterior to the epigynial plate there is a large ventroanal plate. The male is unique in that the ventroanal plate is provided with a cone-shaped elevation that bears a pair of genital suckers. All legs are provided with pretarsi, caruncles, and claws.

Genus:

> *Aceosejus* Sellnick, 1941
> Type. *Sejus muricatus* Koch, 1839

Discussion: Only the type species is recognized as belonging to this family. The splitting of the sternal plate in the female and the presence of suckers on a cone of the ventroanal plate of the male are such peculiar features that a new family had to be erected to accommodate this genus. These mites live in rotting wood and are of no known economic or medical importance.

Reference:

Sellnick, M. 1941. Einige Milbenarten C. L. Kochs. Zool. Anz. 133:146–155.

Rhodacaridae Oudemans, 1902

Figure 44

Diagnosis: The following diagnosis is taken from Vitzthum 1941. The rhodacarids are colorless, golden, or rose-red mites that are from 0.3 to 0.5 mm. in length. They are elongated, and the length is usually three times as great as the width. The opisthosoma is separated by a deep furrow from the podosoma and some movement between the opisthosoma and podosoma is possible. A dividing line may also separate the propodosoma from the metapodosoma. The sternal plate projects anteriorly so that it covers the male genital opening. Tarsi ii, iii, and iv have pretarsus, caruncle, and claws. Tarsus i either lacks an ambulacral apparatus or the pretarsus and claws are vestigial. The anterior margin of the tectum is attenuated into three-toothed points. The middle element is usually much longer than the lateral ones.

Figure 44
Rhodacarus roseus Oudemans, 1910. Ventral view of male. (After Banks 1915)

Genera:

1. *Rhodacarus* Oudemans, 1902
    Type. *Rhodacarus roseus* Oudemans, 1902
2. *Rhodacaropsis* Willmann, 1935
    Type. *Rhodacaropsis inexpectatus* Willmann, 1935
3. *Rhodacarellus* Willmann, 1935
    Type. *Rhodacarellus subterraneus* Willmann, 1935

Discussion: Rhodacarids are frequently found in material collected from litter. The family has not been well studied and many species await description. They are of no known medical or economic importance.

Reference:

Willmann, C. 1935. III. Ueber eine eigenartige Milbenfauna im Küstengrundwasser der Kielen Bucht. Schr. naturw. Ver. Schl.-Holst. 20: 422–434.

Ixodorhynchidae Ewing, 1923

Figure 45

Diagnosis: Ixodorhynchids are readily recognized by their harpoon-shaped anterior lateral extensions of the pedipalpal coxae in the females, protonymphs, and deutonymphs. These stages also have a peculiar chelicera that lacks a fixed digit and has large, recurved teeth on the movable digit. Larvae and tritonymphs have not been observed and in fact may not exist. The males lack both of the features so characteristic of the other stages. They can be recognized, however, because even though the harpoon blade is lacking on the anterior, lateral processes of the pedipalps the basal portion of these processes are similar to those of the other stages. Chelicerae of males are chelate and modified for transferring spermatophores.

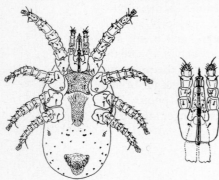

Figure 45 *Ixodorhynchus butantanensis* (Fonseca), 1934. Ventral view of female and gnathosoma. (After Fonseca 1934)

Genus:

Ixodorhynchus Ewing, 1923 (= *Ixobioides* Fonseca, 1934)
Type. *Ixodorhynchus liponyssoides* Ewing, 1923

Discussion: These peculiar mites have been found only as parasites of snakes. The type species was collected from the eye of a snake at Madrid, Iowa. The only other species, *I. butantanensis* (Fonseca), 1934 was collected from a snake *Optis merremi* Wagler, 1824, from Brazil. These mites are of no known economic or medical importance.

References:

Ewing, H. E. 1923. The dermanyssid mites of North America. Proc. U. S. Nat. Mus. 62 Art. 13:1–26.

Fonseca, F. da. 1934. Der Schlangenparasit *Ixobioides* novi generis n. sp. (Acarina, Ixodorhynchidae nov. fam.) Zeit. Parasitenk. 6:508–527.

Spelaeorhynchidae Oudemans, 1902

Figure 46

Diagnosis: Spelaeorhynchids can be readily recognized by the peculiar arrangement of the tectum and the attachment of the chelicerae and palps. The tectum surrounds a broad opening (camerostome) in the idiosoma, into which the chelicerae may be withdrawn. The stigmata are small and are situated lateral to the space between coxae III and IV. The median hypostome is stylet-shaped. Chelicerae are large and terminate in two large hooks. The dorsal plate covers only the podosoma and the posterior dorsal surface of the body is not sclerotized. Dorsally the tectum has a broad connection with the dorsal plate.

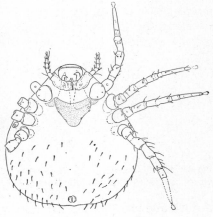

Figure 46 Ventral view of *Spelaeorhynchus* sp.

Genus:

Spelaeorhynchus Neumann, 1902
Type. *Spelaeorhynchus praecursor* Neumann, 1902

Discussion: Spelaeorhynchids are parasitic on Central and South American bats. They are aberrant in that they do not conform to or show very close affinities with any of the mites. That they properly belong to the Mesostigmata is beyond question, although Banks and Neumann held that they were closely related to the ticks. They are placed in the Gamasides following the lead of Vitzthum 1941. These mites are not known to be of any medical or economic importance.

Reference:

Neumann, G. 1902. *Spelaeorhynchus praecursor* n. g. n. sp., nouvel acarien parasite. Arch. de Parasitol. 5:31–37.

Spinturnicidae Oudemans, 1901

Figures 47, 48

Diagnosis: Spinturnicids are brown, medium-sized mites from 0.5 to 1 mm. long. They are usually flat, and in *Periglischrus* (Figure 48) the opisthosoma has lateral expansions. The dorsal plate is entire or

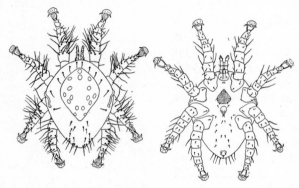

Figure 47 *Spinturnix carloshoffmanni* Hoffmann, 1944. Dorsal and ventral views of female. (After Hoffmann 1944)

divided into two. The legs are relatively long but very stout. All of the coxae are immovable and arranged radially. The tarsi are provided with short pretarsi, large caruncles, and strong claws. The tritosternum is reduced to a delicate plate or is replaced by a relatively large

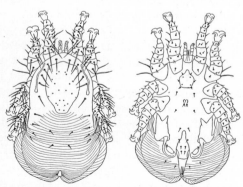

Figure 48 *Periglischrus vargasi* Hoffmann, 1944. Dorsal and ventral views of female. (After Hoffmann 1944)

praeendopodal plate. The anal opening is subterminal or terminal on a small projection. The peritremes and stigmata are frequently dorsal rather than ventral.

Genera:

1. *Spinturnix* v. Heyden, 1826 (= *Pteroptus* Dufour, 1832 and *Diplostaspis* Kolenati, 1857)
   Type. *Spinturnix myoti* Kolenati, 1856 (see Opinion 128 of the International Commission on Zoological Nomenclature)
2. *Ancystropus* Kolenati 1856 (= *Leiostaspis* Kolenati, 1857)
   Type. *Ancystropus zeleborii* Kolenati, 1856
3. *Meristaspis* Kolenati, 1857
   Type. *Meristaspis lateralis* Kolenati, 1857
4. *Periglischrus* Kolenati, 1857
   Type. *Periglischrus caligus* Kolenati, 1857
5. *Tympanospinctus* Berlese, 1918
   Type. *Tympanospinctus paradoxus* Berlese, 1918

Discussion: Spinturnicids have been found almost exclusively on bats. The one exception, *Tympanospinctus paradoxus,* was found on *Crassarchus fasciatus.* It is impossible to tell from Berlese's description whether or not *T. paradoxus* is in reality a spinturnicid, but since he assigned it to this family it probably is. Species of the family have been found on bats all over the world. The genus *Spinturnix* gives birth to living young. The family is not known to be of any medical or economic importance.

References:

Hirst, S. 1927. Note on Acari, mainly belonging to the genus *Spinturnix* von Heyden. Proc. Zool. Soc. London. Pt. II:323–338.

Vitzthum, H. G. 1931. Neue parasitische Fledermaus-milben aus Venezuela Ziet. f. Parasitenk. 4:1–47.

Ascaidae Oudemans, 1905

Figure 49

Diagnosis: Ascaids are distinguished by the presence of a bifurcate seta at the base of the palpal tarsus and a dorsal plate that is divided into an anterior and posterior section of approximately equal dimensions. The tarsi of all legs have pretarsi, caruncles, and claws. The female genital plate is truncated or rounded anteriorly and is sepa-

rated by a straight or slightly curved line from the ventroanal plate.
(Vitzthum 1941 follows Oudemans 1939 in the use of the familial

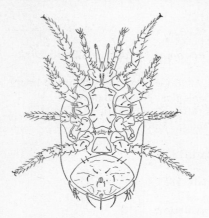

name Allolaelaptidae. Such a
course is contrary to the practice
of forming familial names and is
not followed here.)

Figure 49 *Asca quinquesetosa* Wharton, 1941. Ventral view of female.
(After Wharton 1941)

Genera:

1. *Asca* v. Heyden, 1826
    Type. *Acarus aphidioides* Linnaeus, 1758
2. *Cyrtolaelaps* Berlese 1887 (= *Protolaelaps* Trägårdh, 1912, *non*
    Cyrtolaelaps Berlese, 1892)
    Type. *Gamasus mucronatus* G. and R. Canestrini, 1881
    (= *Gamasellus brevispinosus* Trägårdh, 1910
    = *Asca affinis* Oudemans, 1902)
3. *Dendrolaelaps* Halbert, 1915
    Type. *Dendrolaelaps oudemansi* Halbert, 1915
4. *Gamasellus* Berlese, 1892
    Type. *Gamasus falciger* G. and R. Canestrini, 1882
5. *Laelogamasus* Berlese, 1904
    Type. *Gamasus* (*Laelogamasus*) *simplex* Berlese, 1904
6. *Lobocephalus* Kramer, 1898
    Type. *Lobocephalus acuminatus* Kramer, 1898 (poorly described,
    position uncertain)

Discussion: Ascaids are characteristically found in litter and other
accumulations of organic debris. They are fairly common, but little
information is available on their life cycle or habits. Wharton 1941
found specimens in debris from a boobie's nest, while Fox 1947 reports a specimen from a rat in Puerto Rico. The record of Fox should
not be taken as demonstrating parasitism in this group. The chelicerae

are large and strongly toothed in the fashion of predaceous species. Ascaids are not known to be of any medical or economic importance.

References:

Oudemans, A. C. 1939. Neue Funde auf dem Gebiete der Systematik und der Nomenclatur der Acari. III. Zool. Anz. 126:20–24.

Wharton, G. W. 1941. Acarina collected on the presidential cruise of 1938. Smithsonian Miscellaneous Collections. 99. No. 12:1–8.

Veigaiaidae Oudemans, 1939

Figure 50

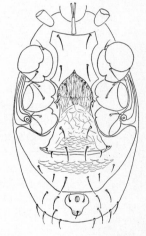

Figure 50 *Veigaia transisalae* (Oudemans), 1901. Ventral view of female. (After Willmann 1936)

Diagnosis: Veigaiaids may be recognized not only by the four tines of the forked seta on the palpal tarsus but also by the peculiar shape of the tectum. The tectum has two small, lateral, toothed processes and a long, thin, median projection that may or may not bear terminal teeth on its slight anterior expansion. The dorsal plate is divided into two either completely or partially. Partial division results when the fissure between the plates does not reach the midline. The epigynial plate of the female is significantly sclerotized only between coxae IV. The plate, however, is extensive and has a thin anterior margin. Sclerotized structures are present in the walls of the vagina. The male has apophyses on leg II and a well-developed extension of the movable digit for use in copulation.

Genera:

1. *Veigaia* Oudemans, 1905 (= *Cyrtolaelaps* Berlese, 1892 non Berlese, 1887)
   Type. *Gamasus nemorensis* Koch, 1836
2. *Cyrthydrolaelaps* Berlese, 1904
   Type. *Cyrthydrolaelaps hirtus* Berlese, 1904

Discussion: Little is known concerning the biology of these mites. Willmann reports them from numerous caves, but others have been found on the surface. They are of no economic or medical importance as far as is now known.

References:

Berlese, A. 1904. Acari nuovi. Redia 2:10–32.
Willmann, C. 1936. Mitteleuropäische Arten der Gattung Veigaia (Parasitidae, Acari). Zool. Anz. 116:249–258.

Parasitidae Oudemans, 1901

Figure 51

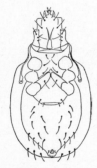

Diagnosis: The females of the family Parasitidae can be easily recognized because they have a pair of large, metasternal plates flanking the epigynial plate. The males usually have exceptionally large apophyses on leg II but other families also have similar males. Tarsi of all legs are provided with a pretarsus, caruncle, and claws. The forked seta on the palpal tarsus has three tines. In the males, the movable digit of the chelicera is greatly modified for copulation. The dorsal plate is entire or, more usually, divided into two. The tectum is basically tridentate. The ventral plates have various arrangements, but the epigynial plate is always triangular with a posterior base and anterior apex. Sclerotized structures are present in the vaginal wall.

Figure 51 *Pergamasus probsti* Oudemans, 1912. Ventral view of female. (After Vitzthum 1940).

Genera:

1. *Parasitus* Latreille, 1795 (= *Carpais* Latreille, 1796
   = *Gamasus* Latreille, 1802)
   Type. *Acarus fucorum* DeGeer, 1778
2. *Amblygamasus* Berlese, 1903
   Type. *Gamasus tiberinus* G. and R. Canestrini, 1882
3. *Eugamasus* Berlese, 1893
   Type. *Gamasus magnus* Kramer, 1876
4. *Holoparasitus* Oudemans, 1936
   Type. *Gamasus calcaratus* Koch, 1839

5. *Nemnichia* Oudemans, 1936
   Type. *Zercon elegantulus* Koch, 1839 (incomplete information, position doubtful)
6. *Oocarpais* Berlese, 1916
   Type. *Oocarpais donisthorpei* Berlese, 1916
7. *Parasitellus* Willmann, 1939
   Type. *Eugamasus ferox* Trägårdh, 1910
8. *Pergamasus* Berlese, 1903
   Type. *Acarus crassipes* Linnaeus, 1758
9. *Trachygamasus* Berlese, 1906
   Type. *Gamasus pusillus* Berlese, 1892

Discussion: Parasitid mites are found typically in accumulations of organic material such as rotting logs and litter. They are of no known economic or medical importance. However, since they are predaceous they probably aid in the destruction of many small insects.

References:

Berlese, A. 1905. Monografia del genere *Gamasus* Latr. Redia 3:66–304 + 18 Pl.
Oudemans, A. C. 1939. Neue Funde auf dem Gebeite der Systematik und der Nomenklatur der Acari. IV. Zool. Anz. 126:195–201.

Macrochelidae Vitzthum, 1930

Figure 52

Diagnosis: The elongated, usually clawless leg I of macrochelids will distinguish them from other gamasids. The ventral plates of the females are also diagnostic. The sternal plate bears three setae and two pores. The metasternal plates are minute and not fused with endopodal plates. Each metapodal plate bears a seta and a pore at its anterior border. The epigynial plate is truncate anteriorly and posteriorly; it bears a single pair of setae. The ventral plate is fused with the anal plate and may be considerably reduced. The tectum consists of a median, narrow, branched or toothed element that may or may not be flanked by smaller lateral elements. The dorsal plate is usually entire.

Genera and subgenera:

1. *Macrocheles* Latreille, 1829
   a. *Machrocheles* s. str.
      Type. *Acarus muscae* Scopoli, 1772 (= *Acarus marginatus* Hermann, 1804)

b. *Coprholaspis* Berlese, 1918
   Type. *Holostaspis glabra* Müller, 1859 (= *Gamasus stercorarius* Kramer, 1876)
c. *Gamasholaspis* Berlese, 1903
   Type. *Gamasholaspis gamasoides* Berlese, 1903
d. *Geholaspis* Berlese, 1918
   Type. *Gamasus longispinosus* Kramer, 1878
e. *Holaspulus* Berlese, 1903
   Type. *Holostaspsis* (*Holaspulus*) *tenuipes* Berlese, 1903
f. *Nothroholaspis* Berlese, 1903
   Type. *Holostaspis tridentinus* G. and R. Canestrini, 1882

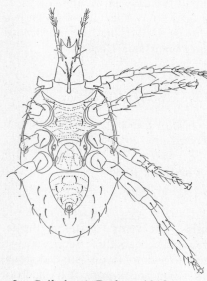

Figure 52 *Macrocheles coprophila* Womersley, 1942. Ventral view of female. (After Womersley 1942)

2. *Calholaspis* Berlese, 1918
   Type. *Calholaspis superbus* Berlese, 1918
3. *Euepicrius* Womersley, 1942
   Type. *Euepicrius filamentosus* Womersley, 1942
4. *Holocelaeno* Berlese, 1910
   a. *Holocelaeno* s. str.
      Type. *Holocelaeno mitis* Berlese, 1910
   b. *Euholocelaeno* Berlese, 1918
      Type. *Holocelaeno bursiformes* Berlese, 1910
5. *Holostaspella* Berlese, 1903
   a. *Holostaspella* s. str.
      Type. *Holostaspis* (*Holostaspella*) *sculpta* Berlese, 1903

b. *Prholaspina* Berlese, 1918
　　Type. *Holostaspella micrarhena* Berlese, 1916
c. *Tricholocelaeno* Berlese, 1918
　　Type. *Holocelaeno longicoma* Berlese, 1910
6. *Macrolaspis* Oudemans, 1931
　　Type. *Gamasus opacus* Koch, 1839
7. *Neopodocinum* Oudemans, 1902
　　Type. *Neopodocinum jaspersi* Oudemans, 1902
8. *Parholaspis* Berlese, 1918
　　Type. *Parholaspis desertus* Berlese, 1918
9. *Trigonholaspis* Vitzthum, 1930
　　Type. *Trigonholaspis salti* Vitzthum, 1930

Discussion: Macrochelids are extremely common and are found in the soil, on invertebrates, and on vertebrates. Although they are regularly associated with various hosts they are probably not parasitic in the usual sense. Pereira and de Castro 1945, however, have found that there is reason for the association in at least one case. *Macrocheles muscae* (Scopoli), 1772 was found to feed in all instars but the first (that does not feed) on the eggs of the housefly. Such a habit indicates that macrochelids may have considerable economic as well as medical importance although as yet the group has not been well investigated from this aspect.

References:

Cooreman, J. 1943. Note sur la faune des Hautes-Fagnes en Belgique. Bull. Mus. Roy. Hist. Natur. Belgique. 19, No. 63:1–28.
Pereira, C. and M. P. de Castro. 1945. Contribuicoo para o conhecimento da especie tipo de *"Macrocheles Latr."* ("Acarina"): *"M. muscae-domesticae* (Scopoli, 1772)" emend. Arquivos Inst. Biol. 16:153–186.
Oudemans, A. C. 1931. Acarologishe Aanteekenigen. CVII. Ent. Ber. 8:272–273.
Vitzthum, H. G. 1926. Malayische Acari. Treubia. 8, Linn. 1–2:1–198.

Pachylaelaptidae Vitzthum, 1931

Figure 53

Diagnosis: The ventral armature of the female will distinguish pachylaelaptids from most other gamasids. The parapodal, peritremal, and metapodal plates are fused into one and extend posterior to coxae IV. They may actually abut the ventral plate and with it cover the major portion of the ventral surface posterior to the coxae. The forked seta on the palpal tarsus has three tines. All tarsi are provided with pretarsi.

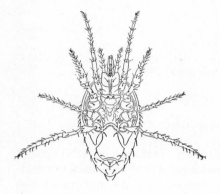

Figure 53   Pachylaelaps roosevelti (Wharton), 1941. Ventral view of female. (After Wharton 1941)

Genera and subgenera:

1. *Pachylaelaps* Berlese, 1886
   a. *Pachylaelaps* s. str.
      Type. *Gamasus pectinifer* G. and R. Canestrini, 1881
   b. *Brachylaelaps* Berlese, 1910
      Type. *Pachylaelaps (Brachylaelaps) rotundus* Berlese, 1910
   c. *Elaphrolaelaps* Berlese, 1910
      Type. *Pachylaelaps (Elaphrolaelaps) fenestratus* Berlese, 1910
   d. *Olopachys* Berlese, 1910
      Type. *Pachylaelaps (Olopachys) scutatus* Berlese, 1910
   e. *Onchodellus* Berlese, 1904
      Type. *Pachylaelaps (Onchodellus) reticulatus* Berlese, 1904
   f. *Paralaelaps* Trägårdh, 1908
      Type. *Paralaelaps kibonotensis* Trägårdh, 1908
   g. *Platylaelaps* Berlese, 1905
      Type. *Pachylaelaps (Platylaelaps) latus* Berlese, 1905
2. *Coprolaelaps* Berlese, 1908
   Type. *Coprolaelaps caputmedusae* Berlese, 1908
3. *Megalolaelaps* Berlese, 1892
   Type. *Pachylaelaps haeros* Berlese, 1888
4. *Pachylaella* Berlese, 1916
   Type. *Pachylaella robustissma* Berlese, 1896
5. *Sphaerolaelaps* Berlese, 1903
   Type. *Laelaps holothyroides* Leonardi, 1896

Discussion: Pachylaelaptids are found in accumulations of organic debris or on insects, especially beetles. They are of no known economic or medical importance.

References:

Berlese, A. 1910. Lista di nuove specie e nuovi generi di Acari. Redia 6:242–271.

Vitzthum, H. G. 1931. Resultats scientifiques du voyage aux Indes Orientales Neerlandaises de LL. AA. Belgique. Acarinen. Mem. Mus. Hist. Nat. Belgique. (Hors. Serie) 3, Fasc. 5:1–55.

Gamasolaelaptidae Oudemans, 1939

Figure 54

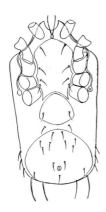

Diagnosis: Gamasolaelaptids are recognized by their divided dorsal plates and the rounded anterior margin of the heavily sclerotized portion of the epigynial plate. All legs are provided with caruncles and claws. The forked seta on the palpal tarsus has three tines. The tectum has a single, long, median, anterior projection in at least some species.

Figure 54 *Digamasellus frenzeli* Willmann, 1936. Ventral view of female. (After Willmann 1936)

Genera:

1. *Gamasolaelaps* Berlese, 1903 (= *Metaparasitus* Oudemans and Voigts, 1904)
   Type. *Cyrtolaelaps aurantiacus* Berlese, 1903
       (= *Metaparasitus soholes* Oudemans and Voigts, 1904)
2. *Digamasellus* Berlese, 1905
   Type. *Gamasellus* (*Digamasellus*) *perpusillus* Berlese, 1905
3. *Euryparasitus* Oudemans, 1901
   Type. *Gamasus emarginata* Koch, 1839
4. *Halolaelaps* Berlese and Trouessart, 1889
   Type. *Gamasus marinus* Brady, 1875 (= *Halolaelaps glubrinsculus* Berlese and Trouessart, 1889

5. *Gamasodes* Oudemans, 1939
    Type. *Gamasodes spiniger* Oudemans, 1936 (= *Gamasus spinipes* Koch, 1841, *non Gamasus spinipes* Say, 1821)
6. *Saintdidieria* Oudemans, 1939
    Type. *Parasitus sexclavatus* Oudemans, 1902

Discussion: Gamasolaelaptids live in damp soil or moss where they probably prey on other small arthropods or their eggs. *Saintdidieria sexclavatus* was associated with psoroptid mites of horses. They are of no known medical or economic importance.

References:

Oudemans, A. C. 1939. Neue Funde auf dem Gebiete der Systematik und der Nomenklatur der Acari. IV. Zool. Anz. 126:195–201.
Womersley, H. 1942. Additions to the Acarina—*Parasitoidea* of Australia. Trans. Roy. Soc. South Australia. 66:142–171.

Neoparasitidae Oudemans, 1939

Figure 55

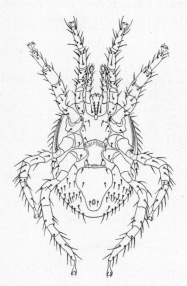

Diagnosis: Neoparasitids are similar to the gamasolaelaptids but are readily separated from them because they have an entire dorsal plate rather than one divided into anterior and posterior sections. The epigynial plate is not triangular and possesses a membranous anterior margin that may be thrown into folds. All legs are provided with caruncles and claws. The specialized seta on the palpal tarsus has three tines.

Figure 55 Neoparasitus oudemansi (Oudemans), 1901. Ventral view of female. (After Vitzthum 1926)

Genera and subgenera:

1. *Neoparasitus* Oudemans, 1901 (= *Pachyseius* Berlese 1910)
   Type. *Neoparasitus oudemansi* Oudemans, 1901
   (= *Pachyseius quartus* Vitzthum, 1926)
2. *Austrogamasus* Womersley, 1942
   Type. *Cyrtolaelaps gracilipes* Banks, 1916
3. *Beaurieina* Oudemans, 1929
   Type. *Neopodocinum nederveeni* Oudemans, 1903 (= *Megalolaelaps spinirostris* Berlese, 1910)
4. *Donia* Oudemans, 1939
   Type. *Hypoaspis gehennalis* Oudemans, 1916
5. *Epicriopsis* Berlese, 1916
   a. *Epicriopsis* s. str.
      Type. *Gamasus horridus* Kramer, 1876
   b. *Actinoseius* Berlese, 1916
      Type. *Actinoseius terrificus* Berlese, 1916
6. *Epiphis* Berlese, 1916
   Type. *Gamasiphis* (*Epiphis*) *rarior* Berlese, 1916
7. *Gamasiphis* Berlese, 1903
   Type. *Gamasus pulchellus* Berlese, 1887
8. *Hydrogamasus* Berlese, 1892
   Type. *Gamasus salinus* Laboulbene, 1851 (= *Gamasus littoralis* G. and R. Canestrini, 1881)
9. *Megaliphis* Willmann, 1938
   Type. *Gamasiphis* (*Megaliphis*) *giganteus* Willmann, 1938
10. *Ologamasus* Berlese, 1888 (= *Ologamasellus* Berlese, 1914)
    a. *Ologamasus* s. str.
       Type. *Gamasus aberrans* Berlese, 1888
    b. *Micriphis* Berlese, 1914
       Type. *Gamasiphis gamasellus* Berlese, 1913
11. *Periphis* Berlese, 1914
    Type. *Eumaeus hemisphaericus* Koch, 1842
12. *Sphaeroseius* Berlese, 1904
    Type. *Laelaps ecitonis* Wasmann, 1901

Discussion: Neoparasitids are found in soil, moss, and decaying organic material. They are of no known economic or medical importance.

References:

Vitzthum, H. G. 1926. Malayische Acari. Treubia. 8:1–198.
Womersley, H. 1942. Additions to the Acarina—*Parasitoidea* of Australia. Trans. Roy. Soc. South Australia. 66:142–171.

Pseudoparasitidae Vitzthum, 1941

Figure 56

Diagnosis: Pseudoparasitids have much in common with the preceding two families but they may be recognized by the reduction of the pretarsus and caruncle of leg I and the modification of the claws of this appendage. The epigynial plate is not triangular. It may or may

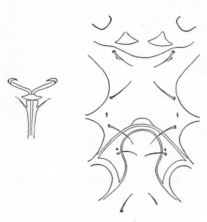

not be fused with the ventral plate.The dorsal plate is entire although there may be a suggestion of a horizontal suture present. The specialized seta on the palpal tarsus has three tines.

Figure 56 Leptogamasus suecicus Trägårdh, 1936. Tarsus I of female showing modified claws and caruncle and ventral plates of female. The claws of leg I of the male are not modified. (After Trägårdh 1936)

Genera and subgenera:

1. *Pseudoparasitus* Oudemans, 1902 (= *Hoplolaelaps* Berlese, 1903 but not 1910)
   a. *Pseudoparasitus* s. str.
      Type. *Laelaps meridionalis* G. and R. Canestrini, 1882
   b. *Alloparasitus* Berlese, 1920
      Type. *Pseudoparasitus angulatus* Berlese, 1916
   c. *Praeparasitus* Berlese, 1920
      Type. *Pseudoparasitus* (*Praeparasitus*) *collaris* Berlese, 1920
   d. *Pseudopachys* Berlese, 1916
      Type. Pseudoparasitus (*Pseudopachys*) *parasitizans* Berlese, 1916
2. *Leptogamasus* Trägårdh, 1936
   Type. *Leptogamasus suecicus* Trägårdh, 1936
3. *Sessiluncus* G. Canestrini, 1898
   Type. *Gamasus heterotarsus* G. Canestrini, 1897

Discussion: The Gamasolaelaptidae, Neoparasitidae, and Pseudoparasitidae are poorly known and the number of undescribed species in these families is extremely large. Most of the gamasid mites found in soil, moss, or organic debris belong to one of these three families. It is probable that additional knowledge will reveal that a realignment of the genera will be desirable. Pseudoparasitids are not known to be of any economic or medical importance.

References:

Trägårdh, I. 1936. *Leptogamasus,* a new genus of Acari from Sweden. Ent. Tidsk. 1936:228–234.

Vitzthum, H. G. 1926. Malayische Acari. Treubia. 8:1–198.

Raillietidae Vitzthum, 1941

Figure 57

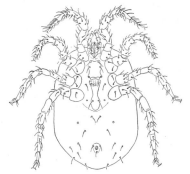

Diagnosis: Females can be recognized by the reduction or absence of the basal portion of the tritosternum, a fairly well sclerotized epigynial plate, and an oval shape. Males have apophyses on leg II and thus differ from other males that have a two-tined, specialized seta on the palpal tarsus. The dorsal plate in both sexes is undivided. All legs possess pretarsi, caruncles, and claws. They are parasites in the external auditory meatus of cattle and antelopes.

Figure 57 *Raillietia auris* (Leidy), 1872. Ventral view of female. (After Hirst 1922)

Genus:

Raillietia Trouessart, 1902
Type. *Gamasus auris* Leidy, 1872

Discussion: Only two species have been described in this family: *Raillietia auris* Leidy, 1872; and *Raillietia hopkinsi* Radford, 1938. According to Hirst 1922, *R. auris* is present in North America and Europe and in some places is rather common. *R. auris* is reported to gain its nourishment from the wax and sloughed epidermal cells. It probably does not suck blood. *R. hopkinsi* was found in the ears of the antelope *Kobus defassa ugandae* Neumann where it probably lives a life similar to *R. auris* from cattle. No pathology is associated with infestation by raillietids. *R. auris* passes the larval stage within the egg and nymphs or eggs containing nymphs are liberated by the females.

References:

Hirst, S. 1922. Mites injurious to domestic animals. Brit. Mus. (Nat. Hist.) Econ. Ser. 13:1–107.
Radford, C. D. 1938. Notes on some new species of parasitic mites. Parasitol. 30:427–440.

Halarachnidae Oudemans, 1906

Figure 58

Diagnosis: Halarachnids are endoparasites in the respiratory passages of mammals. They appear to represent an extreme modification of the laelaptid mites. Their body shape varies from oval (*Pneumonyssus*) to wormlike (*Orthohalarachne attenuata*). The dorsal plate is reduced

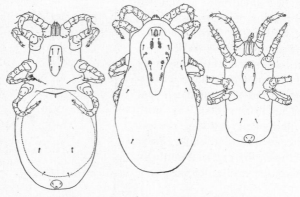

Figure 58 *Pneumonyssus simicola* Banks, 1901. Ventral view of male (right), female (left), and dorsal view of female (center). (After Vitzthum 1931)

and undivided, the tritosternum is absent, and the sternal plate is reduced. Only three pairs of sternal setae are present. The genital plate of female is rudimentary, while the male genital opening is in the anterior margin of the sternal plate. The anal opening is posterior on an anal plate that bears three or four setae. Stigmata with small peritremes lateral to the region of coxae IV are present. The tectum is simple and triangular, while the hypostome is triangular and pilose. Chelicerae with the movable digit more strongly developed than the fixed digit are present. The palps have four segments. Forked hair which has two tines is present on the palpal tarsus. All legs are provided with pretarsi, caruncles, and claws.

Genera:

1. *Halarachne* Allman, 1847
   Type. *Halarachne halichoeri* Allman, 1847 (= *Rhinixodes* Nehring, 1884 and *Rhinacarus* Nehring, 1884)
2. *Pneumonyssus* Banks, 1901 (= *Pneumotuber* Landois and Hoepke, 1914)
   Type. *Pneumonyssus simicola* Banks, 1901
3. *Orthohalarachne* Newell, 1947
   Type. *Halarachne attenuata* Banks, 1910

Discussion: Newell 1947 has given an excellent account of the morphology and systematics of this family. His paper forms the basis for most of the following discussion, although other authors have been consulted.

Halarachnids live in the air passages of mammals. Their life cycles are unknown but a few pertinent facts concerning their biology have been observed. Doetschman 1944 and others have found the six-legged larvae associated with the adult males and females. No nymphs belonging to this family have been seen. It should, however, be kept in mind that the life history has not yet been observed in its entirety and the methods by which new hosts are invaded have not yet been determined. The genus *Halarachne* is found exclusively in the respiratory passages of seals of the family Phocidae, the *Orthohalarachne* parasitize the other families of the Pinnipedia, and *Pneumonyssus* is found in apes, dogs, and other mammals.

Although infection with species of *Pneumonyssus* is fairly common in some primates, no human infections have been discovered. Human pulmonary acariasis is a common ailment in some areas such as parts of India, and during World War II the syndrome produced by infection of human respiratory passages with mites was known as Tropical Eosinophilia. The mites that were recovered were not halarachnids, but common, free-living species.

References:

Carter, Henry F. and V. St. E. D'Abrera. 1946. Mites (Acarina)—a probable factor in the aetiology of spasmodic bronchitis and asthma associated with high eosinophilia. Trans. Roy. Soc. Trop. Med. & Hyg. 39:373–395.

Chandler, W. L. and D. S. Ruhe. 1940. *Pneumonyssus caninum* n. sp., a mite from the frontal sinus of the dog. J. Parasitol. 26(1):59–70.

Doetschman, Willis H. 1944. A new species of endoparasitic mite of the family Halarachnidae (Acarina). Trans. Amer. Micro. Soc. 63:68–72.

Newell, Irwin M. 1947. Studies on the morphology and systematics of the family Halarachnidae Oudemans 1906 (Acari, Parasitoidea). Bull. Bingham. Oceanogr. Coll. 10(4):235–266.

Vitzthum, H. G. 1931. *Pneumonyssus simicola* Banks. Z. Parasitenk. 4: 48–74.

Entonyssidae Ewing, 1923

Figure 59

Diagnosis: Entonyssids are parasitic in the lungs of snakes. They are oval in shape and may reach 1 mm. in length. The tritosternum is rudimentary in the female and according to Radford 1937 is absent in both males and females of *E. bedfordi* Radford, 1937. The dorsal plate is

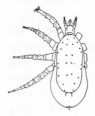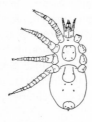

Figure 59 *Entonyssus glasmacheri* Vitzthum, 1935. Dorsal and ventral views of female. (After Vitzthum 1935)

undivided and usually reaches the posterior margin. If the plate is restricted to the propodosoma there will be two strong setae on its posterior margin. All legs are provided with pretarsi, caruncles, and claws. The chelicerae lack well-developed teeth. The forked seta on the palpal tarsus bears two tines.

The following key to the subfamilies is taken from Turk 1947, who considers them to be of familial rank.

Key to the Entonyssidae

1. Chelae with movable digit falciform and fixed digit harpoon-like with retrograde tooth or with both digits falciform generally without setae   Entonyssinae

   Chelae of female with weakly sclerotized, long movable digit that is strongly recurved laterally and lacks teeth and setae; fixed digit reduced   Pneumophionyssinae

Genera:

1. *Entonyssus* Ewing, 1923
   Type. *Entonyssus halli* Ewing, 1923
2. *Hammertonia* Turk, 1947
   Type. *Entonyssus bedfordi* Radford, 1937
3. *Ophiopneumicola* Hubbard, 1938
   Type. *Ophiopneumicola colubri* Hubbard, 1938

Pneumophionyssinae Turk, 1947

Genus:

Pneumophionyssus Fonseca, 1940
Type. *Pneumophionyssus aristoterisi* Fonseca, 1940

Discussion: Entonyssids have been found only in the respiratory passages of snakes. Their life history has not yet been completely elucidated, but it is probably considerably foreshortened. Fully developed larvae have been seen in the females so the assumption that they are ovoviviparous is well founded. Radford 1937 is the only author who reports finding nymphs of this family. Turk 1947 suggests that Radford's observations may have been inaccurate and that the larvae molt directly into the adult males and females. Since no one has followed the complete cycle of any species the question must remain open. Entonyssids have been found in America and Africa. There is no reason to suppose that they will not eventually be found in other localities. As far as is known these mites cause their hosts little discomfort. They are not known to be of any economic or medical importance.

References:

Radford, C. D. 1937. A new species of mite of the genus *Entonyssus* Ewing. The North Western Naturalist. Mar. 1937:38–42.

Turk, F. A. 1947. Studies of Acari IV. A review of the lung mites of snakes. Parasitol. 38:17–26.

Vitzthum, H. G. 1935. Uber die Gattung *Entonyssus* Ewing (Acari). Zeit. Parasitenk. 7:709–716.

Rhinonyssidae Trouessart, 1895

Figure 60

Diagnosis: Rhinonyssids are fairly large (from 0.5 to 1.6 mm. in length). They are oval in shape and have weakly sclerotized plates.

The legs are well developed, and all tarsi have pretarsi, caruncles, and claws. The dorsal plate is restricted to the propodosoma or has two or three plates or is absent. The setae are short on the body and appendages. Stigmata are present with or without short dorsal peritremes. Chelicerae generally have small to rudimentary shears. The tritosternum is absent.

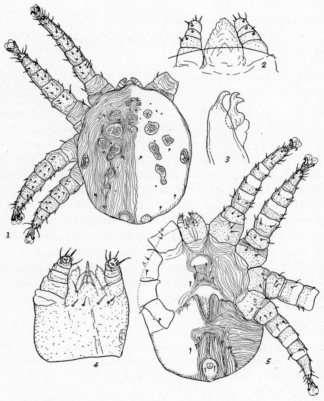

Figure 60 *Larinyssus orbicularis* Strandtmann, 1948. Female. 1. Dorsal view. 2. Dorsal view of palps and tectum. 3. Chela. 4. Ventral view of gnathosoma. 5. Ventral view. (After Strandtmann 1948)

Genera and subgenera:

1. *Rhinonyssus* Trouessart, 1894
   a. *Rhinonyssus* s. str.
      Type. *Rhinonyssus coniventris* Trouessart, 1894

b. *Cas* (New name for *Rhinacarus* Castro, 1948, Arq. Inst. S. Paulo
18: 257. Not *Rhinacarus* Nehring, 1884.)
Type. *Rhinonyssus* (*Rhinacarus*) *angrensis* Castro, 1948
2. *Larinyssus* Strandtmann, 1948
Type. *Larinyssus orbicularis* Strandtmann, 1948
3. *Neonyssus* Hirst, 1921 (= *Neonyssoides* Hirst, 1924)
a. *Neonyssus* s. str.
Type. *Neonyssus intermedius* Hirst, 1921
b. *Paraneonyssus* Castro, 1948
Type. *Neonyssus* (*Paraneonyssus*) *enriettii* Castro, 1948
c. *Rochanyssus* Castro, 1948
Type. *Neonyssus* (*Rochanyssus*) *werneri* Castro, 1948
d. *Travanyssus* Castro, 1948
Type. *Neonyssus* (*Travanyssus*) *paranensis* Castro, 1948
e. *Vitznyssus* Castro, 1948
Type. *Dermanyssus nitzchi* Giebel, 1871
4. *Ptylonyssoides* Vitzthum, 1935
Type. *Ptylonyssoides triscutatus* Vitzthum, 1935
5. *Ptilonyssus* Berlese and Trouessart, 1889
a. *Ptilonyssus* s. str.
Type. *Ptilonyssus echinatus* Berlese and Trouessart, 1889
b. *Flavionyssus* Castro, 1948
Type. *Ptilonyssus* (*Flavionyssus*) *rabelloi* Castro, 1948
c. *Rhinonyssoides* Hirst, 1921
Type. *Rhinonyssoides trouessarti* Hirst, 1921
6. *Rallinyssus* Strandtmann, 1948
Type. *Rallinyssus caudistigmus* Strandtmann, 1948
7. *Rhinoecius* Cooreman, 1946
Type. *Rhinoecius oti* Cooreman, 1946
8. *Sommatricola* Trägårdh, 1904
Type. *Sommatricola levinseni* Trägårdh, 1904
9. *Sternostoma* Berlese and Trouessart, 1889
Type. *Sternostoma cryptorhyneum* Berlese and Trouessart, 1889
10. *Sternostomum* Trouessart, 1895
Type. *Sternostomum rhinoletrum* Trouessart, 1895

Discussion: Rhinonyssids are viviparous and produce larvae in which
the nymphs are already developed. They are parasitic in the nasal
passages of birds all over the world, and probably only a fraction of
the species has been found since few birds have been examined for
them. Trouessart reported that they can do damage to chicks. Strandtmann 1948 suggests that it might be interesting to investigate the possible role that these mites may play in ornithosis.

82 *Acarology*

References:

Bregetova, N. C. 1950. New species of endoparasitic mites of the family Rhinonyssidae (Gamasoidea, Acarina). Akad. Nauk. SSSR Dok. 71 (5): 1005–1008.

Castro, M. P. de. 1948. Reestruturação genérica da familia "Rhinonyssidae Vitzthum, 1935" (Acari Mesostigmata: Gamasides) e descrição de algumas espécies novas. Arq. Inst. Biol. Sao Paulo Brasil 18:253–284.

Strandtmann, R. W. 1948. The mesostigmatic nasal mites of birds. I. Two new genera from shore and marsh birds. J. Parasitol. 34:505–514.

———. 1950. The mesostigmatic nasal mites of birds. II. New and poorly known species of Rhinonyssidae. J. Parasitol. 37 (2): 129–140.

Vitzthum, H. G. 1935. Milben aus der Nasenhöle von Vögeln. J. Ornith. 83:563–587.

Haemogamasidae Oudemans, 1926

Figure 61

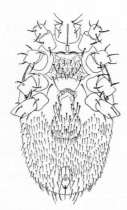

Figure 61 *Haemogamasus mandschuricus* Vitzthum, 1930. Ventral view of female. (After Vitzthum 1930)

Diagnosis: These are medium-sized, oval mites. The body is heavily clothed with setae that give a furlike appearance on both the dorsal and ventral surfaces. The dorsal plate is entire in the larvae, nymphs, and adults. Ventral plates of males and females that in other families have only a few setae may be covered by setae in this family. All tarsi are provided with pretarsi, caruncles, and claws. The tritosternum is present. The metapodal plates are small and the stigmata with long, anteriorly directed peritremes are present. The tectum is tongue-like and has numerous irregular projections.

Genera:

1. *Haemogamasus* Berlese, 1889
   Type. *Haemogamasus hirsutus* Berlese, 1889
2. *Acanthochela* Ewing, 1933
   Type. *Acanthochela chiliensis* Ewing, 1933

3. *Euhaemogamasus* Ewing, 1933
   Type. *Euhaemogamasus onychomydis* Ewing, 1933
4. *Ischyropoda* Keegan, 1951
   Type. *Ischyropoda spiniger* Keegan, 1951

Discussion: Keegan 1950 removed *Acanthochela* from the family because he could not determine the nature of the chelicerae or tectum on the type material in the United States National Museum. Examination of the material with a phase-contrast microscope reveals that the tectum and chelicerae are typical of the Haemogamasidae.

Haemogamasids are parasitic on small mammals all over the world. They frequently spend most of their time in nests and only get on the host to feed. They have a typical life cycle and pass through a larval and two nymphal stages before becoming adults. The fact that these mites are common on small mammals suggests that they may be important in the transmission of plague, typhus, tularemia, and perhaps other diseases. Investigation of their disease-carrying potentialities is yet to be undertaken.

References:

Ewing, H. E. 1933. New genera and species of parasitic mites of the super-family Parasitoidea. Proc. U.S. Nat. Mus. 82: Art. 30:1–14.

Keegan, H. L. 1951. The mites of the subfamily Haemogamasinae (Acari: Laelaptidae). Proc. U.S. Nat. Mus. 101(3275):203–268.

Vitzthum, H. 1930. Milben als Pestträger? Zool. Jahrb. 60:381–428.

Dermanyssidae Kolenati, 1859

Figures 62—64

Diagnosis: Dermanyssids are medium-sized mites. The dorsal plate is either undivided in the female or is divided so that the anterior plate is large and the posterior one extremely small. The ventral plates of the female are typical of the suborder except that they are somewhat reduced. The sternal plate has three pairs of setae, while the metasternal plates are reduced and lateral to the genital plate. The genito-ventral plate is drop-shaped posteriorly. The anal plate has three characteristic setae. In the Dermanyssidae the chelicerae may be extremely elongated and terminate in a minute shear so that they appear to be a pair of needle-like structures, or they may be more normal with merely reduced chelae. Tritosternum is present. All legs have pretarsi, caruncles, and claws.

Genera:

1. *Dermanyssus* Dugès, 1834
   Type. *Acarus gallinae* DeGeer, 1778
2. *Allodermanyssus* Ewing, 1923
   Type. *Dermanyssus sanguineus* Hirst, 1914

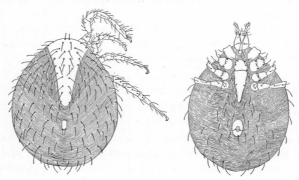

Figure 62 *Allodermanyssus sanguineus* (Hirst), 1914. Dorsal and ventral views of female.

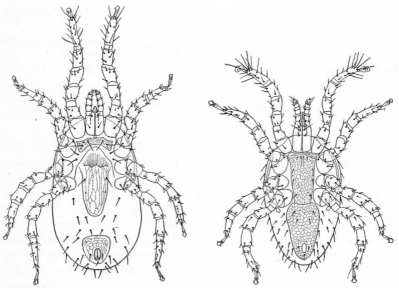

Figure 63 *Dermanyssus gallinae* (De-Geer). Ventral view of female. (After Hirst 1922)

Figure 64 *Dermanyssus gallinae* (De-Geer). Ventral view of male. (After Hirst 1922)

3. *Bdellonyssus* Fonseca, 1941 (= *Leiognathus* Canestrini, 1885 homonym = *Liponyssus* of authors = *Fonsecaonyssus* Radford, 1950)
   Type. *Leiognathus bacoti* Hirst, 1913
4. *Brevisterna* Keegan, 1949
   Type. *Euhaemogamasus utahensis* Ewing, 1933
5. *Echinonyssus* Hirst, 1925
   Type. *Echinonyssus nasutus* Hirst, 1925
6. *Ellsworthia* Turk, 1945 (= *Hemilaelaps* Ewing, 1923 homonym)
   Type. *Hemilaelaps americanus* Ewing, 1923
7. *Hirstesia* Fonseca, 1948
   Type. *Liponyssus sternalis* Hirst, 1921
8. *Hirstonyssus* Fonseca, 1948
   Type. *Dermanyssus arcuatus* Koch, 1839
9. *Ichoronyssus* Kolenati, 1858 (= *Chiroptonyssus* Auguston, 1945 = *Lepronyssus* Kolenati, 1858 = *Spinolaelaps* Radford, 1940)
   Type. *Dermanissus scutatus* Kolenati, 1856
10. *Kolenationyssus* Fonseca, 1948
    Type. *Kolenationyssus athleticus* Fonseca, 1947
11. *Lepronyssoides* Fonseca, 1943
    Type. *Liponissus pereirai* Fonseca, 1935
12. *Liponysella* Hirst, 1925 (= *Geneiadolaelaps* Ewing, 1929)
    Type. *Liponyssus madagascarensis* Hirst, 1921
13. *Liponyssoides* Hirst, 1913
    Type. *Dermanyssus (Liponyssoides) muris* Hirst, 1913
14. *Macronyssus* Kolenati, 1858
    Type. *Caris longimana* Kolenati, 1856
15. *Manisicola* Lawrence, 1939
    Type. *Manisicola africana* Lawrence, 1939
16. *Manitherionyssus* Vitzthum, 1925
    Type. *Liponyssus heterotarsus* Vitzthum, 1925
17. *Myonyssoides* Hirst, 1925
    Type. *Myonyssoides capensis* Hirst, 1925
18. *Myonyssus* Tiraboschi, 1904 (= *Tetragonyssus* Ewing, 1923)
    Type. *Myonyssus decumani* Tiraboschi, 1904
19. *Neoichoronyssus* Fonseca, 1943
    Type. *Liponissus wernecki* Fonseca, 1935
20. *Neoliponyssus* Ewing, 1929 (= *Oudemansiella* Fonseca, 1948)
    Type. *Liponyssus gordonensis* Hirst, 1923
21. *Ophionyssus* Mégnin, 1884 (= *Serpenticola* Ewing, 1923)
    Type. *Ophionyssus natricis* Mégnin, 1884
22. *Tur* (New name for *Protonyssus* Turk, 1947, Ann. Mag. Nat. Hist. 11 14: 348. Not *Protonyssus* Trouessart, 1915.)
    Type. *Protonyssus uniscutatus* Turk, 1946

23. *Radfordiella* Fonseca, 1948
     Type. *Radfordiella oudemansi* Fonseca, 1948
24. *Steatonyssus* Kolenati, 1858
     Type. *Acarus musculi* Schrank, 1803

Discussion: Dermanyssids typically have a larval and two nymphal
stages before becoming adult males and females. They are parasitic on
vertebrates and are of considerable economic and medical importance.
The family is frequently subdivided into two subfamilies, the Dermanyssinae with needle-like chelicerae, and the Liponissinae with more
normal chelicerae. Only three genera—*Dermanyssus, Liponyssoides,*
and *Allodermanyssus*—are included in the Dermanyssinae. Some authors have given familial standing to the two groups. Fonseca 1948
has written a monograph of those genera that are sometimes included
in the Liponissinae or Liponissidae. He, however, refers to the group
as the Macronyssidae. The arrangement of the genera presented here
is based largely on Fonseca's 1948 monograph, Vitzthum 1941, and
the advice of R. W. Strandtmann *in litt.* The Dermanyssidae are as yet
poorly known so that the present picture must still be considered as
tentative.

   Dermanyssus gallinae (DeGeer, 1778) is an important pest of
domestic birds, especially chickens and pigeons, in all parts of the
world. Heavy infestation with these mites can cause the death of their
hosts, while light infestations result in reduced egg production and
poor growth. The mites normally feed at night and infest the host only
at this time. During the day they are found in the cracks of roosts,
coops, and nests. At times they may be so numerous in nests that
brooding hens will leave their eggs. *D. gallinae* will also attack man,
especially children. A family in Durham, North Carolina, complained
of a severe dermatitis on their baby. The mother and father were not
affected. Examination of the house revealed numerous specimens of
D. gallinae on an electric clock in the living room. The clock was
slightly warmer than the rest of the room and it is probable that the
mites were attracted to it for this reason. The gutter on the roof of the
house was used extensively by pigeons and their droppings had collected in a great pile on the roof of the porch. After removal of
the droppings and elimination of the pigeons the mites disappeared
and the child was no longer bothered. Recently the virus of St. Louis
encephalitis has been recovered from chicken mites and it is suggested
that *D. gallinae* serves as a reservoir for the disease (M. G. Smith *et
al.* 1948). As more and more work is done on the epidemiology of

human diseases it is probable that many mites will be found to play an essential role.

Allodermanyssus sanguineus (Hirst) is normally a parasite of small rodents. It also has the habit of occasionally biting man and has been reported from large eastern cities such as Boston, New York, and Baltimore as a human parasite. Recently a new disease, rickettsialpox, was found to be carried by this mite in New York City. The disease was originally confused with chickenpox but intensive work demonstrated that it was new (Huebner 1947).

Bdellonyssus sylviarum (Canestrini and Fanzago), a typical fowl mite, is known to harbor neurotropic viruses (Reeves *et al.* 1949). During World War II it was found that *Bdellonyssus bacoti* Hirst acted as the intermediate host of *Litomosoides carinii,* a filarial worm that lives in cotton rats. Since the mites, rats, and worms could be readily cultured they were used extensively in investigations on filariasis (Williams and Brown 1945).

References:

Anderson, C. R. 1944. Rat mite dermatitis. Acariasis caused by the tropical rat mite, *Liponyssus bacoti* Hirst, 1914. Arch. Dermatol. and Syphilol. 50(2):90–95.

Bishopp, F. C. and H. P. Wood. 1939. Mites and lice on poultry. U. S. Dept. Agr. Farmers' Bull. 801:1–25.

Fonseca, F. da. 1948. A monograph of the genera and species of Macronyssidae Oudemans, 1936 (synom. Liponissidae Vitzthum, 1931) (Acari). Proc. Zool. Soc. London. 118:249–334.

Huebner, R. J. 1947. Rickettsialpox a new disease. Amer. J. Clin. Path. 17:970–971.

Roueché, B. 1950. The alerting of Mr. Pomerantz. MD. 5(3):73–82.

Smith, Margaret G. *et al.* 1948. Experiments on the role of the chicken mite *Dermanyssus gallinae* and the mosquito in the epidemiology of St. Louis encephalitis. J. Exp. Med. 87:119–138.

Williams, R. W. and H. W. Brown. 1945. The development of *Litomosoides carinii* filariid parasite of the cotton rat in the tropical rat mite. Science. 102:482–483.

Phytoseiidae Berlese, 1916

Figure 65

Diagnosis: This family includes a rather heterogeneous group of genera that is characterized by the shape of the epigynial plate. The plate is truncated or concave posteriorly. The specialized seta on the palpal tarsus has two tines.

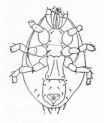 

Figure 65 *Seiulus bakeri* Garman, 1948. Dorsal and ventral views of female. (After Garman 1948)

The family can be subdivided into two subfamilies, the Phytoseiinae, recently studied and defined by Garman 1948, and the Podocininae, a poorly defined group of genera. These subfamilies can be separated as follows:

Key to the Phytoseiidae

1. With few setae on dorsal plate; pretarsi, caruncles, and claws on all legs; dorsal plate undivided   Phytoseiinae

   Without this combination of characters   ·   Podocininae

Phytoseiinae Berlese, 1916

Genera and subgenera:

1. *Phytoseius* Ribaga, 1902
   Type. *Gamasus plumifer* Canestrini and Fanzago, 1876
2. *Amblyseius* Berlese, 1904 (= *Borinquolaelaps* Fox, 1946)
   Type. *Seius obtusus* Berlese, 1889
3. *Amblysiopsis* Garman, 1948
   Type. *Amblyseius (Amblysiopsis) americanus* Garman, 1948
4. *Ameroseius* Berlese, 1903
   Type. *Acarus corbicula* Sowerby, 1806 (= *Seius echinatus* Koch, 1839 = *Seius muricatus* Koch, 1839 = *Seius hirsutus* Berlese, 1887, *sed non Seius muricatus* Berlese, 1887)
5. *Iphidulus* Ribaga, 1902
   Type. *Iphidulus communis* Ribaga, 1902
6. *Lasioseius* Berlese, 1916
   a. *Lasioseius* s. str.
      Type. *Lasioseius aba,* new name for *Seius muricatus* Berlese, 1887
   b. *Cheiroseius* Berlese, 1916
      Type. *Seius unguiculatus* Berlese, 1916
   c. *Leioseius* Berlese, 1916
      Type. *Ameroseius minusculus* Berlese, 1905

d. *Zercoseius* Berlese, 1916
    Type. *Seius spathuliger* Leonardi, 1899
e. *Zygoseius* Berlese, 1916
    Type. *Zygoseius furciger* Berlese, 1916
7. *Melichares* Hering, 1838
    Type. *Melichares agilis* Hering, 1838
8. *Seiopsis* Berlese, 1923
    Type. *Amblyseius (Seiopsis) brevipilis* Berlese, 1923
9. *Seiulus* Berlese, 1887 (= *Echinoseius* Ribaga, 1902)
    Type. *Seiulus hirsutigenus* Berlese, 1887
10. *Seius* Koch, 1836
    Type. *Seius togatus* Koch, 1836
11. *Tristomus* Hughes, 1948
    Type. *Tristomus butleri* Hughes, 1948
12. *Typhlodromus* Scheuten, 1857
    Type. *Gamasus vepallidus* Koch, 1839 (= *Typhlodromus pyri* Scheuten, 1857)

Podocininae Berlese, 1916

Genera:

1. *Podocinum* Berlese, 1882
    Type. *Laelaps sagax* Berlese, 1882
2. *Antennoseius* Berlese, 1916
    Type. *Antennoseius delicatus* Berlese, 1916
3. *Asternolaelaps* Berlese, 1923
    Type. *Asternolaelaps fecundus* Berlese, 1923
4. *Asternoseius* Berlese, 1910
    Type. *Asternoseius ciliatus* Berlese, 1910
5. *Blattisocius* Keegan, 1944
    Type. *Typhlodromus tineivorus* Oudemans, 1929 (= *Blattisocius triodons* Keegan, 1944)
6. *Episeiella* Willmann, 1938
    Type. *Episeiella heteropoda* Willmann, 1938
7. *Hoploseius* Berlese, 1914
    Type. *Zercon cometa* Berlese, 1910
8. *Platyseius* Berlese, 1916 (=*Episeius* Hull, 1918)
    Type. *Platyseius capillatus* Berlese, 1916
9. *Thinoseius* Halbert, 1920
    Type. *Thinoseius berlesei* Halbert, 1920
10. *Zerconopsis* Hull, 1918
    Type. *Gamasus remiger* Kramer, 1876
11. *Iphiseius* Berlese, 1916 (This genus was listed by Vitzthum 1941, but no type is designated. The original reference has not been located.)

Discussion: Members of the Phytoseiidae are frequently found on plants where they are extremely beneficial because they are predaceous and help to keep the species that feed on plants in check. Garman 1948 points out that pesticides that affect this group of mites may be harmful if applied to plants because they will allow the plant feeders to go unchecked. Garman also discusses the classification of these mites, but many of his conclusions are not followed here.

References:

Garman, P. 1948. Mite species from apple trees in Connecticut. Conn. Agr. Expt. Sta. Bull. 520:1–27.

Hughes, A. M. 1948. The mites associated with stored food products. Ministry of Agriculture and Fisheries, London, pp. 1–168.

Keegan, H. L. 1944. On a new genus and species of parasitid mite. J. Parasitol. 30:181–183.

Lord, F. T. 1949. The influence of spray programs on the fauna of apple orchards in Nova Scotia. III. Mites and their predators. Canad. Ent. 81 (8):202–214.

Iphiopsidae Kramer, 1886

Figure 66

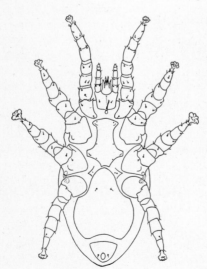

Diagnosis: The most useful characteristic in identifying iphiopsids is the minute peritreme. All legs have pretarsi and caruncles. The specialized seta on the palpal tarsus has two tines. The epigynial plate may be drop-shaped or excavated posteriorly.

Figure 66 *Jacobsonia tertia* Vitzthum, 1931. Ventral view of female. (After Vitzthum 1931)

Genera:

1. *Iphiopsis* Berlese, 1882
   Type. *Iphis mirabilis* Berlese, 1882
2. *Berlesia* Canestrini, 1884
   Type. *Berlesia rapax* Canestrini, 1884
3. *Jacobsonia* Berlese, 1910
   Type. *Iphiopsis (Greeniella) submollis* Berlese, 1910
      (*Iphis* homonym of *Iphis* Meigen, 1800 and
      Greeniella homonym of *Greeniella* Cockerell, 1897)

Discussion: Iphiopsids are parasites or commensals of insects and myriopods. They are of no known economic or medical importance.

Reference:

Vitzthum, H. G. 1931. Eine afrikanische Jacobsonia (Acari). Zool. Anz. 96:153–159.

Laelaptidae Berlese, 1892

Figures 67, 68

Diagnosis: Laelaptids have two tines on the specialized seta on the palpal tarsus. The epigynial plate is drop-shaped or excavated posteriorly and the peritreme is elongated. Most species have pretarsi, caruncles, and claws on all legs. The dorsal plate is undivided. Coxa II has a toothlike projection from the anterior border.

The family Laelaptidae as here restricted still includes a large number of fairly diverse genera. Vitzthum 1941 includes in the Laelaptidae thirteen subfamilies. He was justified in this treatment because of the confusion that existed concerning the limits of the subfamilies. While this confusion still exists, some recent papers have added light to the subject and nine of the subfamilies (Railliettidae—Laelaptidae) have been raised to familial rank and the subfamily Podocininae is included in the Phytoseiidae. The separations between the families in many cases is still not completely clear. There remain in the Laelaptidae three subfamilies. The group of genera here included in the Laelaptidae requires a thorough revision and the following grouping follows Vitzthum 1941 in most cases and is admittedly unsatisfactory. Much study over a long period of time by many investigators must be undertaken before a satisfactory classification of this group of mites is achieved. The following key will separate most of the species into their proper subfamilies.

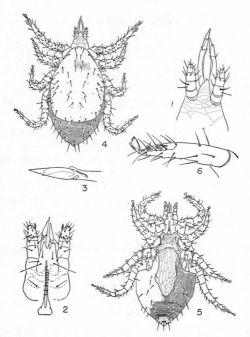

Figure 67 *Myrmonyssus chapmani* Baker and Strandtmann, 1948. Female.
1. Dorsal view of gnathosoma. 2. Ventral view of gnathosoma. 3. Chela. 4. Dorsal view of female. 5. Ventral view of female. 6. Tarsus I. (After Baker and Strandtmann 1948)

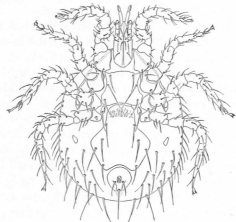

Figure 68 *Echinolaelaps echidninus* (Berlese), 1887. Ventral view of female. (After Hirst 1922)

Key to the Laelaptidae

1. Anterior border of tectum convex with continuous or serrate margin   2

   Anterior margin of tectum with lance-shaped projection
   Hyletastinae

2. Associated with insects; ventral setae usually weak   Hypoaspidinae

   Associated with mammals; ventral setae usually spinelike
   Laelaptinae

Hyletastinae Vitzthum, 1941

Genera and subgenera:

1. *Hyletastea* Gistel, 1884 (= *Iphis* Koch, 1836)
   Type. *Iphis globulus* Koch, 1839
2. *Copriphis* Berlese, 1910
   a. *Copriphis* s. str.
      Type. *Iphis pterophilus* Berlese, 1882
   b. *Peletiphis* Berlese, 1911
      Type. *Copriphis* (*Peletiphis*) *insignis* Berlese, 1911
   c. *Alliphis* Halbert, 1923
      Type. *Gamasus halleri* G. and R. Canestrini, 1881
3. *Cosmiphis* Vitzthum, 1926
   Type. *Emaeus bosschai* Oudemans, 1901
4. *Eviphis* Berlese, 1903
   a. *Eviphis* s. str.
      Type. *Eumaeus pyrobolus* Koch, 1839
   b. *Oloiphis* Berlese, 1916
      Type. *Eviphis magnificus* Berlese, 1916
5. *Iphidozercon* Berlese, 1903
   Type. *Eviphis gibbus* Berlese, 1903
6. *Melittiphis* Berlese, 1918
   Type. *Laelaps* (*Iphis*) *alvearius* Berlese, 1895
7. *Uroiphis* Berlese, 1903
   Type. *Uroiphis scabratus* Berlese, 1903

Hypoaspidinae Vitzthum, 1941

Genera and subgenera:

1. *Hypoaspis* G. Canestrini, 1885
   a. *Hypoaspis* s. str.
      Type. *Laelaps kramerii* G. and R. Canestrini, 1881

  b. *Androlaelaps* Berlese, 1903
    Type. *Laelaps hermaphrodita* Berlese, 1903
  c. *Cosmolaelaps* Berlese, 1903
    Type. *Laelaps claviger* Berlese, 1883
  d. *Gymnolaelaps* Berlese, 1920
    Type. *Laelaps myrmecophilus* Berlese, 1892
  e. *Holostaspis* Kolenati, 1858
    Type. *Holostaspis isotricha* Kolenati, 1858
  f. *Laelaspis* Berlese, 1903
    Type. *Iphis astronomicus* Berlese, 1889
  g. *Leptolaelaps* Berlese, 1918
    Type. *Hypoaspis* (*Leptolaelaps*) *elegans* Berlese, 1918
  h. *Pneumolaelaps* Berlese, 1920
    Type. *Iphis bombicolens* G. Canestrini, 1885
  i. *Stratiolaelaps* Berlese, 1916
    Type. *Laelaps* (*Iphis*) *miles* Berlese, 1882
2. *Anystipalpus* Berlese, 1911
  Type. *Anystipalpus percicola* Berlese, 1911
3. *Arctoseius* Thor, 1930
  Type. *Arctoseius lateroincisus* Thor, 1930
4. *Coleolaelaps* Berlese, 1914
  Type. *Laelaps* (*Iphis*) *agrestis* Berlese, 1887
5. *Dinogamasus* Kramer, 1898 (= *Greenia* Oudemans, 1901
  = *Greeniella* Banks, 1904 = *Dolaea* Oudemans, 1912)
  Type. *Dinogamasus crassipes* Kramer, 1898
6. *Iphidosoma* Berlese, 1892 (*Parasitidae?*)
  Type. *Holostaspis fimetaria* Müller, 1859
7. *Jördensia* Oudemans, 1937
  Type. *Gamasus cossi* Dugès, 1834
8. *Julolaelaps* Berlese, 1916
  Type. *Julolaelaps dispar* Berlese, 1916
9. *Laelantennus* Berlese, 1916
  Type. *Laelantennus lagena* Berlese, 1916
10. *Ljunghia* Oudemans, 1932
  Type. *Ljunghia selenocosmiae* Oudemans, 1932
11. *Meliponaspis* Vitzthum, 1930
  Type. *Meliponaspis debilipes* Vitzthum, 1930
12. *Myrmeciphis* Hull, 1923
  Type. *Myrmeciphis crawleianus* Hull, 1923
13. *Myrmolaelaps* Trägårdh, 1906
  Type. *Myrmolaelaps equitans* Trägårdh, 1906
14. *Myrmoleichus* Berlese, 1903
  Type. *Myrmoleichus coronatus* Berlese, 1903

15. *Myrmonyssus* Berlese, 1903
    a. *Myrmonyssus* s. str.
      Type. *Myrmonyssus diplogenius* Berlese, 1903
    b. *Laelaspulus* Berlese, 1903
      Type. *Myrmonyssus acuminatus* Berlese, 1903
16. *Myrmozercon* Berlese, 1902
    Type. *Myrmozercon brevipes* Berlese, 1902
17. *Neoberlesia* Berlese, 1892
    Type. *Neoberlesia equitans* Berlese, 1892
18. *Neocypholaelaps* Vitzthum, 1941 (= *Cypholaelaps* Berlese, a homonym)
    Type. *Laelaps ampullula* Berlese, 1892
19. *Ololaelaps* Berlese, 1903
    a. *Ololaelaps* s. str.
      Type. *Laelaps venetus* Berlese, 1903
    b. *Cypholaelaps* Berlese, 1916 (*non* = *Cypholaelaps* Berlese, 1918)
      Type. *Ololaelaps* (*Cypholaelaps*) *haemisphaericus* Berlese, 1916
20. *Paradoxiphis* Berlese, 1910
    Type. *Paradoxiphis tennibrachiatus* Berlese, 1910
21. *Phytojacobsonia* Vitzthum, 1925
    Type. *Phytojacobsonia irregularis* Vitzthum, 1925
22. *Podolaelaps* Berlese, 1888
    Type. *Podolaelaps ambulacralis* Berlese, 1888
23. *Proctolaelaps* Berlese, 1914
    Type. *Proctolaelaps productus* Berlese, 1923
24. *Stamfordia* Trägårdh, 1906
    Type. *Stamfordia carabicola* Trägårdh, 1906
25. *Stylochirus* G. and R. Canestrini, 1882
    Type. *Stylochirus rovennensis* G. and R. Canestrini, 1882
26. *Urozercon* Berlese, 1901 (= *Termitacarus* Trägårdh, 1906)
    Type. *Urozercon paradoxus* Berlese, 1901
27. *Varroa* Oudemans, 1904
    Type. *Varroa jacobsoni* Oudemans, 1904

Laelaptinae Berlese, 1892

Genera and subgenera:

1. *Laelaps* Koch, 1839
    a. *Laelaps* s. str.
      Type. *Acarus muris* Ljungh, 1799 (= *Laelaps agilis* Koch, 1839)
    b. *Eugynolaelaps* Berlese, 1918
      Type. *Laelaps* (*Eugynolaelaps*) *coriaceus* Berlese, 1918
    c. *Heterolaelaps* Hirst, 1926
      Type. *Heterolaelaps antipodianus* Hirst, 1926

    d. *Macrolaelaps* Ewing, 1929
      Type. *Laelaps sanguisugus* Vitzthum, 1924
    e. *Mesolaelaps* Hirst, 1926
      Type. *Mesolaelaps anomalus* Hirst, 1926
    f. *Tricholaelaps* Vitzthum, 1926
      Type. *Laelaps (Tricholaelaps) comatus* Vitzthum, 1926
2. *Cavilaelaps* Fonseca, 1935
    Type. *Cavilaelaps bresslaui* Fonseca, 1935
3. *Echinolaelaps* Ewing, 1929
    Type. *Laelaps echidninus* Berlese, 1887
4. *Eubrachylaelaps* Ewing, 1929 (= *Cyclolaelaps* Ewing, 1931)
    Type. *Laelaps hollisteri* Ewing, 1925
5. *Eulaelaps* Berlese, 1903 (= *Hemilaelaps* Hull, 1918)
    a. *Eulaelaps* s. str.
      Type. *Laelaps stabularis* Koch, 1839
    b. *Pseudolaelaps* Berlese, 1916
      Type. *Laelaps (Hoplolaelaps) doderoi* Berlese, 1910
6. *Gigantolaelaps* Fonseca, 1939
    Type. *Gigantolaelaps vitzthumi* Fonseca, 1939
7. *Haemolaelaps* Berlese, 1910 (= *Atricholaelaps* Ewing, 1929
    = *Ischnolaelaps* Fonseca, 1935)
    Type. *Laelaps (Haemolaelaps) marsupialis* Berlese, 1910
8. *Longolaelaps* Vitzthum, 1926
    Type. *Longolaelaps longulus* Vitzthum, 1926
9. *Mysolaelaps* Fonseca, 1935
    Type. *Mysolaelaps parvispinosus* Fonseca, 1935
10. *Neolaelaps* Hirst, 1926
    Type. *Liponyssus magnistigmatus* Vitzthum, 1918
11. *Neoparalaelaps* Fonseca, 1935
    Type. *Neoparalaelaps bispinosus* Fonseca, 1935
12. *Ophidilaelaps* Radford, 1947
    Type. *Ophidilaelaps imphalensis* Radford, 1947
13. *Scissuralaelaps* Womersley, 1945
    Type. *Scissuralaelaps nova-guinea* Womersley, 1945
14. *Ugandolaelaps* Radford, 1942
    Type. *Ugandolaelaps protoxera* Radford, 1942

Unassigned genera: Three genera are based on nymphs and males. These cannot properly be included under any subfamily because the classification is based primarily on the females. Radford 1942 reports that *Ligilaelaps* and *Mungosicola* are represented in part by females. However, his drawing stated to be a female of *Mungosicola ugandae* is definitely not a female but a nymph.

Genera:

1. *Rad* (New name for *Banksia* Radford, 1942. Parasitol, 34:299.
   Not *Banksia* Voigts and Oudemans, 1905.)
   Type. *Laelaps longiseta* Banks, 1909
2. *Ligilaelaps* Radford, 1942
   Type. *Eulaelaps ewingi* Pearse, 1930
3. *Mungosicola* Radford, 1942
   Type. *Mungosicola ugandae* Radford, 1942

Discussion: Laelaptid mites are world-wide in distribution. They are usually parasitic. They parasitize invertebrates as well as vertebrates and are the most common ectoparasites of mammals. Their life histories vary in that larval and nymphal stages can be reduced. No laelaptids have yet been implicated in the transmission of diseases from animal to man, but there are so many species and their opportunities for acting as vectors are so numerous that they will probably be incriminated when they are investigated.

Echinolaelaps echidninus (Berlese) transmits *Hepatozoan muris* (Balfour) from rat to rat. This protozoan uses the mites as a definitive host. It gets into the rat (many species of the genus *Rattus* serve as hosts) when infected mites are ingested. *Haemolaelaps arcuatus* (Koch) transmits *Hepatozoan criceti* (Danilewsky), a similar protozoan, to the hamster (*Cricetus frumentarius* Nöller).

As already mentioned, the taxonomy of the laelaptids is extremely difficult because of the large number of species included and the lack of careful study. The following references will serve as an introduction to the large mass of literature.

References:

Berlese, A. 1904. Acari mirmecofili Redia 1:300–474 + Pls. VII-XX.
Ewing, H. E. 1925. New parasitic mites of the genus Laelaps. Proc. Ent. Soc. Wash. 27:1–7.
Fonseca, F. da. 1939. Notas de acareologia XXV. Os Laelaptidae gigantes, parasitas de roedores sul-americanos; genero e especies novas (Acari). Mem. Inst. Butantan. 12:7–101.
Radford, C. D. 1943. Genera and species of parasitic mites (Acarina). Parasitol. 35:58–81.
Vitzthum, H. G. 1930. Milben als Pestträger Zool. Jahrb. Syst. 60:381–428.
Womersley, H. 1937. Studies on Australian Acarina. Laelaptidae. Parasitol. 29:530–538.

THINOZERCONINA TRÄGÅRDH, 1946

The dorsal plate is divided into a large propodosomal plate and a smaller posterior plate. The peritreme is dorsal in both sexes, while the sternal plates are absent or weakly sclerotized in the female except for well-developed jugular plates in the Thinozerconidae. The epigynial plate is narrow, has one pair of setae, and is not articulated to a ventral plate. The male genital opening is in the sternal plate.

Key to the Thinozerconina

1. Jugular plates of female well-developed; male genital opening
    between coxae III   Thinozerconidae

    Female lacking sclerotized jugular plates; male genital opening
    between coxae II   .   Dasyponyssidae

Thinozerconidae Halbert, 1915

Figure 69

Diagnosis: The thinozerconids are medium-sized mites that have an elongated oval shape and are somewhat pointed posteriorly. Their dorsal plate is divided into two and is partially flanked by the dorsal

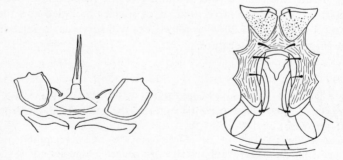

Figure 69   *Thinozercon michaeli* Halbert, 1915. Ventral plates (right) and tritosternum (left) of female. (After Trägårdh 1946)

peritremal plates. The epigynial plate is narrow and tongue-like with one pair of setae posteriorly. The male genital opening is small and is closed by a pair of minute semicircular plates, the first of which carries a pair of stout setae.

Genera:

1. *Thinozercon* Halbert, 1915
   Type. *Thinozercon michaeli* Halbert, 1915
2. *Dithinozercon* Berlese, 1916
   Type. *Thinozercon (Dithinozercon) halberti* Berlese, 1916

Discussion: This family is very poorly known. Both included genera are monotypic. *Thinozercon* is from the Old World, and *Dithinozercon* from the New. Probably many new forms in this group await discovery.

References:

Berlese, A. 1916. Centuria terza di acari nuovi Redia 12:295.
Halbert, J. N. 1915. Clare Island Survey, part 39:11. Proc. Roy. Irish Acad. 31:82.

Dasyponyssidae Fonseca, 1940

Figures 70–73

Diagnosis: Both sexes have a divided dorsal plate. The peritreme of the female extends dorsally and transversely between the anterior and posterior sections of the dorsal plates, while that of male flanks the anterior dorsal plate for a short distance. Leg I of both sexes is remarkably enlarged so that it is more than twice as stout as legs II-IV. Body setae show some sexual dimorphism, those of the female being expanded, while those of the male are normal. Ventral plates of the male are divided. Sternal plates I and II are fused to a single plate in which the male genital opening is situated. Sternal plates III and IV are fused on each side but are separated at the midline. The ventral plate is reduced and has a single pair of setae. The anal plate has seven pairs of setae and one median posterior seta.

Genus:

Dasyponyssus Fonseca, 1940
Type. *Dasyponyssus neivai* Fonseca, 1940

Discussion: Dasyponyssus neivai was discovered in Brazil on an armadillo. It is here placed in the Thinozerconina because of its obvious morphological affinities with *Thinozercon*. It does, however, show some relationship to the Gamasides and may even represent a distinct

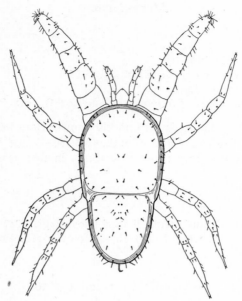

Figure 70 *Dasyponyssus neivai* Fonseca, 1940. Dorsal view of male. (After Fonseca 1940)

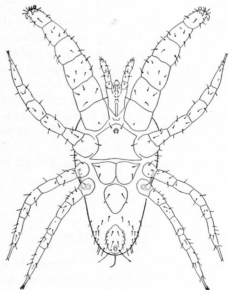

Figure 71 *Dasyponyssus neivai* Fonseca, 1940. Ventral view of male. (After Fonseca 1940)

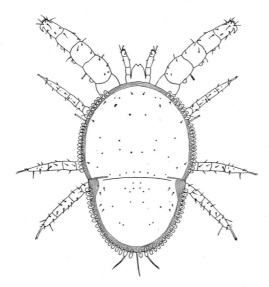

Figure 72 *Dasyponyssus neivai* Fonseca, 1940. Dorsal view of female. (After Fonseca 1940)

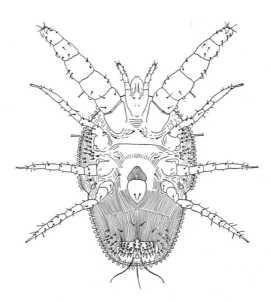

Figure 73 *Dasyponyssus neivai* Fonseca, 1940. Ventral view of female. (After Fonseca 1940)

group. Additional data are required before this family can be included with certainty in any group.

Reference:

Fonseca, F. da. 1940. Notas de Acareologia. XXIV. *Dasyponyssus neivai* gen. n., sp. n., acariano parasita de *Euphractus sexcinctus* (L.) Acari, Dasyponyssidae fam. n.). Rev. Ent. Rio de Janeiro 11:104–119, 5 figs.

DIARTHROPHALLINA TRÄGÅRDH, 1946

The penis is biarticulated, directed posteriorly, and situated in a groove between coxae III. Presternal setae are present. The epigynial plate is enclosed in the fused sternal and ventral plates but is not separated from the ventral plate by a suture. Only one family is known.

Diarthrophallidae Trägårdh, 1946

Figures 74, 75

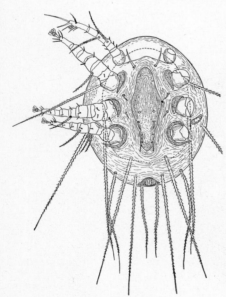

Diagnosis: Diarthrophallids are characterized in addition to the fundamental structures mentioned in the subordinal diagnosis by many other features. Leg I is modified as a tactile organ and lacks a caroncle and claws. Legs II-IV have a well-developed ambulacral apparatus. The setae on the dorsal side are long and stiff and in the living mite project dorsally. The dorsal plate is entire.

Figure 74 *Diarthrophallus quercus* (Pearse and Wharton), 1936. Ventral view of nymph. (After Trägårdh 1946)

Genera:

1. *Diarthrophallus* Trägårdh, 1946
   Type. *Urosejus quercus* Pearse and Wharton, 1936
2. *Brachytremella* Trägårdh, 1946
   Type. *Brachytremella spinosa* Trägårdh, 1946
3. *Passalobia* Lombardini, 1926
   Type. *Passalobia quadricaudata* Lombardini, 1926

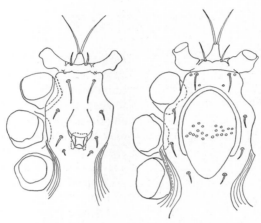

Figure 75 *Diarthrophallus quercus* (Pearse and Wharton), 1936. Ventral plates of male (left) and female (right). (After Trägårdh 1946)

Discussion: Diarthrophallids are similar to the uropodids in general appearance. However, as Trägårdh 1946 points out they are amply distinct. All members of the family are found on beetles of the family Passalidae. They have been found in South America, North America, Central America, and New Guinea.

D. *quercus* Pearse and Wharton, 1936, is common on passalid beetles in the vicinity of Durham, North Carolina.

Reference:

Trägårdh, I. 1946. Diarthrophallina, a new group of Mesostigmata, found on passalid beetles. Entom. Medd. 24:370–394.

Acarology

ZERCONINA TRÄGÅRDH, 1944

This suborder is directly related to the Gamasides, and if it were not for the position of the male genital opening in the center of the sternal plate it would most certainly be included with the Gamasides. Only one family is recognized in this group and thus its morphology can be discussed at the familial level.

Zerconidae Berlese, 1892

Figure 76

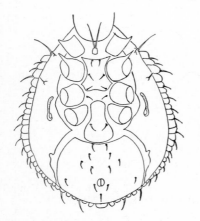

Figure 76 *Prozercon kochi* Willmann, 1943. Ventral view of female. (After Willmann 1943)

Diagnosis: Zerconids are small mites with flat bodies that are broadest in the posterior region so that they have a somewhat triangular shape. Their dorsal plate may or may not be divided. Tarsus I lacks caruncles and frequently has a reduced pretarsus, while tarsi II, III, and IV are all provided with pretarsi, caruncles, and claws. The ventroanal plate is large and broad. The male genital opening is located in the middle of the sternal plate and is closed by a double plate attached at its anterior margin. The epigynial plate has only one pair of setae and is not fused to the endopodal plates. The metasternal plates are so weakly sclerotized that their position can be detected only by the presence of the metasternal setae. The sternal plate has the usual three pairs of sternal setae.

Genera:

1. *Zercon* Koch, 1836
   Type. *Zercon dimidatus* Koch, 1841
2. *Parazercon* Trägårdh, 1931
   Type. *Zercon sarakensis* Willmann, 1939
   (= *Zercon ornatus* Trägårdh, 1910, *non Zercon ornatus* Berlese, 1904)

3. *Prozercon* Willmann, 1943
   Type. *Zercon fimbriatus* Koch, 1839
4. *Seiodes* Berlese, 1887
   Type. *Seioides ursinus* Berlese, 1887
5. *Triangulazercon* Jacot, 1938
   Type. *Zercon peltatus* Koch, 1836
      (= *Zercon triangularis* Koch, 1836)
6. *Trizerconoides* Jacot, 1938
   Type. *Zercon radiatus* Berlese, 1910

Discussion: Zerconids belong to the large fauna that inhabits the upper layers of the soil, litter, and beds of moss. They are of no known economic or medical importance.

References:

Jacot, A. P. 1938. The Geenton mites of Florida. Florida Ent. 21:49–57.
Trägårdh, I. 1946. Outlines of a new classification of the Mesostigmata (Acarina) based on comparative morphological data. Lunds Univ. K. Fysiogr. Sällsk. Handl. N. F. Bd. 57 Nr. 4:1–37.

TRACHYTINA TRÄGÅRDH, 1937

Trägårdh 1941 gives a good account of this group (cohort of Trägårdh) and he divides it into three families that are obviously closely related. Therefore, a diagnosis of the group will be given along with Trägårdh's key to the families, and a separate diagnosis for each family will be omitted. The same plan will be followed for the discussion and reference in order to avoid repetition.

Diagnosis: They are intermediate between the Gamasides and Uropodina. The articulations of coxae I are similar to the Gamasides in that the coxae do not cover the broad-based tritosternum. The genital openings are similar to but not identical with those of the Uropodina. The metasternal plate in the female is not fused with the sternal and ventral plates and is situated lateral to the epigynial plate. In adults the dorsal surface is covered by nymphal skins. The habit of the retention of the cast nymphal skins is unusual in the Mesostigmata and is restricted to the Trachytina. However, several of the Oribatei exhibit this peculiar phenomenon.

Key to the Trachytina
(after Trägårdh, 1941)

1. Epigynial plate hinged to ventral plate   2

   Epigynial plate fused with ventral plate   Polyaspidae

2. Metasternal plates narrow, elongated, flanking sides of epigynial
   plate   Trachytidae

   Metasternal plates almost obliterated, only traces being left in
   posterior angles of genital orifice   Polyaspinidae

Trachytidae Trägårdh, 1938

Figure 77

Genera:

1. *Trachytes* Michael, 1894
   Type. *Celaeno aegrota* Koch, 1841
2. *Neoseius* Oudemans, 1903 (? deutonymph only known stage)
   Type. *Uroseius novus* Oudemans, 1902
3. *Uroseius* Berlese, 1888
   Type. *Uropoda acuminata* Koch, 1847

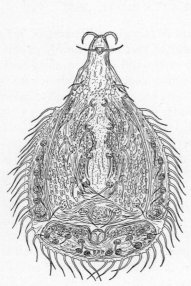

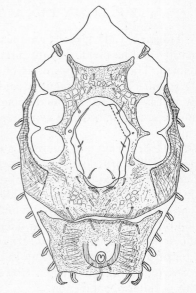

Figure 77 *Trachytes aegrota* (Koch), 1841. Dorsal view of female. (After Trägårdh 1941)

Figure 78 *Dipolyaspis sansonei* Berlese, 1916. Ventral view of female. (After Trägårdh 1941)

Polyaspidae Berlese, 1917

Figure 78

Genera:

1. *Polyaspis* Berlese, 1881
   Type. *Polyaspis patavinus* Berlese, 1881
2. *Calotrachytes* Berlese, 1916
   Type. *Trachynotus fimbriatus* Michael, 1908
3. *Dipolyaspis* Berlese, 1916
   Type. *Polyaspis (Dipolyaspis) sansonei* Berlese, 1916

Polyaspinidae Trägårdh, 1941

Figure 79

Genus:

Polyaspinus Berlese, 1916
Type. *Polyaspinus cylindricus* Berlese, 1916

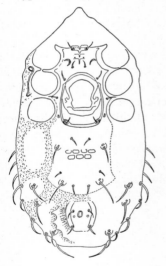

Discussion: Little is known about the life of this interesting group of mites. Trägårdh finds them under the bark of decayed stumps so that they are probably found in concentrations of rotting organic matter high in cellulose. This group is of no known medical or economic importance.

Figure 79 *Polyaspinus cylindricus* Berlese, 1916. Ventral view of female. (After Trägårdh 1941)

Reference:

Trägårdh, I. 1941. Further contributions towards the comparative morphology of the Mesostigmata III. On the Polyaspididae. Berl. Zool. Bidrag. F. Uppsala 20:345–357.

UROPODINA KRAMER, 1881

The Uropodina are characterized (except for the intermediate group of genera in the family Discourellidae) by the arrangement of the gnathosoma. The anterior ventral portion of the body is excavated so that the gnathosoma and tritosternum are enclosed in a cavity, the dorsal wall of which is formed by the body wall while coxae I can close it ventrally. This cavity is frequently called a camerostome. The metasternal plates of this group are also either greatly reduced (*Urodiaspis* and *Uroplitella*) or completely absent. The male genital opening is in the center of the sternal plate, as is the epigynial plate. The tritosternum is frequently divided into three lacinae anteriorly. The dorsal plate is usually entire in the adults. Depressions for the legs are found on the ventral surface so that the short legs may be folded compactly against the body. The stigmata are opposite leg II or III. The peritremes are usually convoluted to conform to the ridges that limit the depressions into which the legs can be folded. The chelicerae usually extend for some distance into the idiosoma and in some cases may almost reach the posterior end.

Twelve families are placed in this group with assurance. Two other families that are questionable are included here. The Trematuridae Berlese, 1917 was supposedly characterized by the presence of four stigmata. Trägårdh 1942 has shown Berlese to be in error as regards the number of stigmata, but Trägårdh was unable to clarify the systematic position of *Trematura patavina* (Canestrini), 1885 with the aid of Berlese's specimens. The family Discourellidae lacks the camerostome and is thus intermediate between the Uropodina and the Trachytina. A key to the families modified from Trägårdh 1944 follows.

Figure 80 The arrangement of the dorsal plates of representative genera of the Uropodina. Top row, from left to right, *Phaulodiaspis, Urodiaspis, Oodinychus;* middle row, *Phaulodinychus, Trematurella, Phyllodinychus;* and bottom row, *Eutrachytes, Cilliba, Urodinychus.* (After Trägårdh 1944 and Vitzthum 1935)

Key to the Uropodina

1. Camerostome present   2

   Camerostome absent   Discourellidae

2. Dorsal plate restricted to dorsal surface   3

   Dorsal plate extends laterally and ventrally so that only central portion of ventral surface not covered by dorsal plate

     Coxequesomidae

3. Ventral, posterior, marginal plates absent   4

   A pair of ventral, posterior, marginal plates present   Planodiscidae

4. Dorsal marginal plate present   5

   Dorsal marginal plates absent   Circocyllibanidae

5. Stigmata opposite coxae II or between II and III   7

   Stigmata opposite coxae III   6

6. Tritosternum covered by coxae I   Trematuridae

   Tritosternum not covered by coxae I   Cillibidae

7. Anterior ends of marginal plate fused with dorsal plate anteriorly   8

   Anterior ends of marginal plate not fused with dorsal plate

     Trematurellidae

8. Depressions to accommodate legs present   10

   Depressions to accommodate legs absent   9

9. Distinct posterior dorsal plate present   Eutrachytidae

   Posterior dorsal plate not distinct   Prodinychidae

10. Posterior dorsal plate absent   11

    Posterior dorsal plate present   Urodiaspidae

11. Marginal plates fused with dorsal plate   12

    Marginal plates fused with ventral plate   Trachyuropodidae

12. Marginal plate completely surrounds dorsal plate   13

    Marginal plate reduced posteriorly   Phaulodinychidae

13. Marginal plate scalloped on its inner border   Urodinychidae

    Marginal plate not scalloped   Uropodidae

In order to make the above key more readily understandable sketches of the arrangement of the dorsal plates in representative genera are shown in Figure 80.

Discourellidae

(New name for Protouropodidae Trägårdh, 1941)

Figure 81

Diagnosis: To the Discourellidae belong those genera that lack a camerostome that is protected by the first pair of coxae but that have an epigynial plate characteristic of the suborder Uropodina. The tritosternum in this family is unusual in that it is broad at the base.

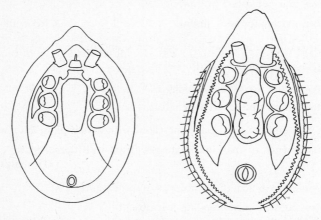

Figure 81 *Discourella modesta* Leonardi, 1900. Left, ventral view of female and *Apionoseius lagenaeformis* (Berlese), 1904; right, ventral view of female. (After Trägårdh 1941)

Genera:

1. *Discourella* Berlese, 1910
   Type. *Discopoma venusta* Berlese, 1884
        (= *Discourella discopomoides* Berlese, 1910)
2. *Apionoseius* Berlese, 1904
   Type. *Trachytes lagenaeformis* Berlese, 1904
3. *Polyaspidella* Berlese, 1910
   Type. *Polyaspidella berenicea* Berlese, 1910

Discussion: Trägårdh 1941 proposed the familial name Protouropodidae for the family. The name Discourellidae is here suggested for the group and the genus *Discourella* Berlese, 1910 is considered the type of the family. The family is clearly intermediate between the Uropodina and Trachytina. Specimens of the family have been found in Canada, Austria, and Java. The family is probably universally distributed. Its habits are similar to other members of the Uropodina. Discourellids are of no known economic or medical importance.

Reference:

Trägårdh, I. 1941. Further contributions towards the comparative morphology of the Mesostigmata, III. On the Polyaspididae. Berl. Zool. Bidrag. Uppsala 20:345–357.

Coxequesomidae Sellnick, 1926

Figure 82

Diagnosis: The tritosternum is covered by the first pair of coxae. Grooves for the legs are flat. The genital and anal openings are each surrounded by a discrete plate. The dorsal plate extends laterally and ventrally so that it covers all but the central portion of the ventral surface.

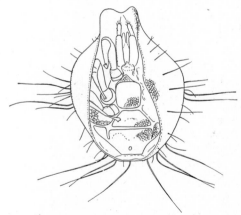

Figure 82 *Coxequesoma collegianorum* Sellnick, 1926. Ventral view of female. (After Sellnick 1926)

Genera:

1. *Coxequesoma* Sellnick, 1926
   Type. *Coxequesoma collegianorum* Sellnick, 1926
2. *Antennequesoma* Sellnick, 1926
   Type. *Antennequesoma reichenspergeri* Sellnick, 1926

Discussion: Coxequesomids are myrmecophiles. They are of no known economic or medical importance.

Reference:

Sellnick, Max. 1926. Alguns novos Acaros (Uropodidae) myrmecophilos e termitophilus. Arch. Mus. Rio de Janeiro 26:29–56, 27 figs.

Planodiscidae Sellnick, 1926

Figure 83

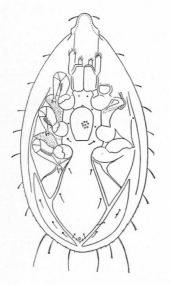

Diagnosis: The tritosternum is covered by coxae ɪ. The grooves for the legs are well developed. The anal and genital openings are in a single ventral plate. There is a ventral marginal plate on either side at the posterior end of the body. The dorsal plate is not surrounded by a dorsal marginal plate.

Figure 83 *Planodiscus squamatum* Sellnick, 1926. Ventral view of female. (After Sellnick 1926)

Genus:

Planodiscus Sellnick, 1926
Type. *Planodiscus squamatum* Sellnick, 1926

Discussion: Planodiscids are of no known economic or medical importance. The only representative of the family was found associated with ants.

Reference:

Sellnick, Max. 1926. Alguns novos Acaros (Uropodidae) myrmecophilos e termitophilus. Arch. Mus. Rio de Janeiro 26:29–56, 27 figs.

Circocyllibanidae Sellnick, 1926

Figure 84

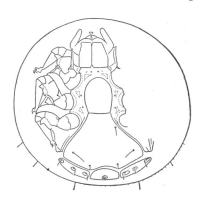

Diagnosis: The tritosternum is covered by coxae I. The grooves for the legs are well developed. The genital and anal openings are located in separate plates. The dorsal plate is not surrounded by a dorsal marginal plate.

Figure 84 *Circocylliba camerata* Sellnick, 1926. Ventral view of female. (After Sellnick 1926)

Genus:

Circocylliba Sellnick, 1926
Type. *Circocylliba camerata* Sellnick, 1926

Discussion: *C. camerata* is a myrmecophile and is of no known economic or medical importance.

Reference:

Sellnick, Max. 1926. Alguns novos Acaros (Uropodidae) myrmecophilos e termitophilus. Arch. Mus. Rio de Janeiro 26:29–56, 27 figs.

Trematuridae Berlese, 1917

Figure 85

Diagnosis: The tritosternum is covered by coxae I. The grooves for the legs are strongly developed. The dorsal plate is surrounded by a marginal plate that has smooth, inner borders. Stigmata are in the grooves for leg III. The plates are strongly sculptured.

Genus:

Trematura Berlese, 1917
Type. *Uropoda patavina* G. Canestrini, 1885

Discussion: Trägårdh 1942 studied specimens of *T. patavina* from the Berlese collection. He was unable to work out its morphology satisfactorily, and therefore he does not include the family in his 1944 account of the Uropodina. The Trematuridae are included in this account, as are the three previous families proposed by Sellnick 1926, as they are in Vitzthum's key work of 1941. *T. patavina* is of no known economic or medical importance.

Figure 85   *Trematura patavina* (Canestrini), 1885. Portion of venter to show stigma and peritreme. (After Trägårdh 1942)

Reference:

Trägårdh, I. 1942. Über die Trematurini Berlese (Acarina). Zool. Anz. 139:109–112.

Trematurellidae Trägårdh, 1944

Figure 80

Diagnosis: The dorsal and ventral plates are deeply sculptured. The marginal plates are completely separated from the ventral plate and dorsal plate by a thin membrane. The dorsal plate is undivided and the marginal plate is cleft by a suture anteriorly.

Genus:

    Trematurella Trägårdh, 1942
    Type. *Trematurella stylifera* Trägårdh, 1942

Discussion: *T. stylifera* is of no known economic or medical importance.

Reference:

Trägårdh, I. 1942. Über die Trematurini Berlese (Acarina). Zool. Anz. 139:109–112.

Cillibidae Trägårdh, 1944

Figure 86

Diagnosis: The tritosternum is not covered by coxae I. The marginal plate is continuous anteriorly but is distinct from the dorsal plate. The posterior region of the dorsal plate is indistinctly separated from the rest of the dorsal plate by a suture. The stigmata are located opposite coxae III. Grooves for the legs are well developed.

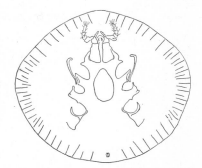

Figure 86   *Thrichocylliba comata* (Leonardi), 1895. Ventral view of female. (After Berlese 1904)

Genera:

1. *Cilliba* v. Heyden, 1827 (= *Discopoma* G. and R. Canestrini, 1882)
   Type. *Notaspis cassideus* Hermann, 1804
2. *Thrichocylliba* Berlese, 1904
   Type. *Discopoma comata* Leonardi, 1895

Discussion: Cillibids are of no known economic or medical importance.

Reference:

Trägårdh, I. 1944. Zur Systematik der Uropodiden. Ent. Tidsk. 65:173–186.

Eutrachytidae Trägårdh, 1944

Figure 80

Diagnosis: In this family the marginal plate is fused anteriorly with the dorsal plate. A distinct posterior, dorsal plate is present, but grooves for the legs are absent.

Genus:

    Eutrachytes Berlese, 1914
    Type. *Celaeno truncata* Berlese, 1888

Discussion: This family is of no known economic or medical importance.

Reference:

Trägårdh, I. 1944. Zur Systematik der Uropodiden. Ent. Tidsk. 65: 173–186.

Prodinychidae Berlese, 1916

Figure 87

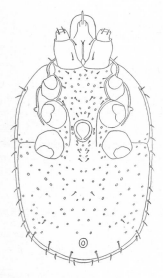

Diagnosis: The tritosternum is covered by coxae I. Grooves for the legs are either absent or poorly developed. The marginal plate is continuous posteriorly and fused with the dorsal plate anteriorly. When the plates are separated the marginal plate clings to the ventral plate.

Figure 87 *Prodinychus formicarius* Vitzthum, 1925. Ventral view of male. (After Vitzthum 1940)

Genera:

1. *Prodinychus* Berlese, 1913
   Type. *Dinychus fimicolus* Berlese, 1903
2. *Clausiadinychus* Sellnick, 1930
   Type. *Clausiadinychus cristatus* Sellnick, 1930
3. *Dentidinychus* Sellnick, 1926
   Type. *Dentidinychus zikani* Sellnick, 1926
4. *Dinychus* Kramer, 1882
   Type. *Dinychus perforatus* Kramer, 1882
5. *Discotrachytes* Berlese, 1916
   Type. *Discotrachytes splendidiformis* Berlese, 1916
6. *Metadinychus* Berlese, 1916
   Type. *Metadinychus argasiformes* Berlese, 1916

7. *Trichodinychus* Berlese, 1916
   Type. *Uropoda vulpina* Berlese, 1888
8. *Urolaelaps* Berlese, 1916
   Type. *Urolaelaps macropi* Berlese, 1916

Discussion: Vitzthum proposed the name Dinychidae for this family in 1931. The family is of no known economic or medical importance.

Reference:

Trägårdh, I. 1944. Zur Systematik der Uropodiden. Ent. Tidsk. 65:173–186.

Urodiaspidae Trägårdh, 1944

Figure 88

Diagnosis: The marginal plate is fused to the dorsal plate anteriorly. When dissected the dorsal plate clings to the marginal plate. A large, distinct, posterior dorsal plate is present. Metasternal plates are also present but they are very small at the posterior corners of the epigynial plate.

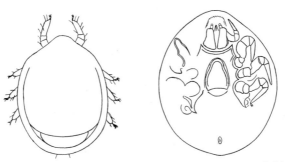

Figure 88 *Urodiaspis tecta* (Kramer), 1876. Female dorsum (left) and venter (right). (After Berlese 1887)

Genera:

1. *Urodiaspis* Berlese, 1916
   Type. *Uropoda tecta* Kramer, 1876
2. *Diurodinychus* Berlese, 1916
   Type. *Urodiaspis* (*Diurodinychus*) *rectangulovatus* Berlese, 1916

Discussion: This family is of no known economic or medical importance.

Reference:

Trägårdh, I. 1944. Zur Systematik der Uropodiden. Ent. Tidsk. 65:173–186.

Trachyuropodidae Berlese, 1917

Figure 89

Diagnosis: In the trachyuropodids the tritosternum is hidden by coxae I. Grooves for the legs are well developed. All the plates are sculptured. The marginal plate is fused to the ventral plates, and no posterior dorsal plate is present.

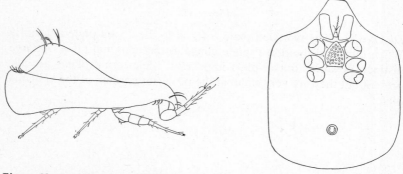

Figure 89   *Trachyuropoda crustosa* Vitzthum, 1926. Lateral (left) and ventral (right) views of female. (After Vitzthum 1926)

Genera and subgenera:

1. *Trachyuropoda* Berlese, 1888 (= *Michaeliella* Berlese, 1904)
     a. *Trachyuropoda* s. str.
        Type. *Trachyuropoda festiva* Berlese, 1888
     b. *Dinychura* Berlese, 1913
        Type. *Trachyuropoda* (*Urojanetia*) *rectangula* Berlese, 1913
     c. *Urojanetia* Berlese, 1913 (= *Janetiella* Berlese, 1904 *nom. praeocc.*)
        Type. *Uropoda coccinea* Michael, 1891
2. *Cephalouropoda* Berlese, 1903
     Type. *Uropoda berlesiana* Berlese, 1887

3. *Comydinychus* Berlese, 1917
   Type. *Uropoda caputmedusae* Berlese, 1901
4. *Deraiophorus* G. Canestrini, 1897
   Type. *Deraiophorus chyzeri* Canestrini, 1897
5. *Dinychopsis* Berlese, 1916
   Type. *Dinychopsis fractus* Berlese, 1916 (*non Dinychus appendiculatus* Berlese, 1910)
6. *Leonardiella* Berlese, 1904
   Type. *Uropoda canestriniana* Berlese, 1891
7. *Neodiscopoma* Vitzthum, 1941 (= *Discopoma* G. and R. Canestrini in the sense of Berlese, 1904)
   a. *Neodiscopoma* s. str.
      Type. *Uropoda splendida* Kramer, 1882
   b. *Capitodiscus* Vitzthum, 1931 (= *Cephalodiscus* Berlese, 1916 *nom. praeocc.*)
      Type. *Discopoma venusta* Berlese, 1884
   c. *Crinitodiscus* Sellnick, 1931
      Type. *Discopoma* (*Crinitodiscus*) *beieri* Sellnick, 1931
   d. *Olodiscus* Berlese, 1917
      Type. *Discopoma integra* Berlese, 1910
   e. *Phymatodiscus* Berlese, 1917
      Type. *Discopoma miranda* Berlese, 1904
8. *Uropolyaspis* Berlese, 1903
   Type. *Uropoda hamulifera* Michael, 1894
9. *Urospina* Sellnick, 1931
   Type. *Uropoda plana* Sellnick, 1931

Discussion: Like many other families of the Uropodina the trachyuropodids are frequently found associated with ants. They are of no known economic or medical importance.

Reference:

Trägårdh, I. 1944. Zur Systematik der Uropodiden. Ent. Tidsk. 65:173–186.

Phaulodinychidae Berlese, 1917

Figure 90

Diagnosis: The tritosternum is covered by coxae I. Grooves for the legs are well developed. The single ventral plate is not fused to the marginal or dorsal plates. The marginal plate is reduced posteriorly.

Genera:

1. *Phaulodinychus* Berlese, 1903 (= *Halouropoda* Halbert, 1915)
   Type. *Phaulodinychus repletus* Berlese, 1903
2. *Diphaulocylliba* Vitzthum, 1925
   Type. *Phaulocylliba amplior* Berlese, 1923
3. *Phaulocylliba* Berlese, 1903
   Type. *Phaulocylliba ventricosa* Berlese, 1903
4. *Phaulodiaspis* Vitzthum, 1925
   Type. *Urodiscella advena* Trägårdh, 1912

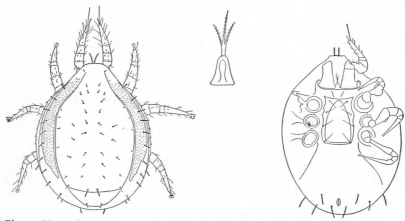

Figure 90 *Phaulodiaspis advena* (Trägårdh), 1912. Dorsal view of female (left); tritosternum (center); ventral view of female (right). (After Trägårdh 1912)

Discussion: This family is of no known economic or medical importance.

Reference:

Trägårdh, I. 1944. Zur Systematik der Uropodiden. Ent. Tidsk. 65:173–186.

Urodinychidae Berlese, 1917

Figure 91

Diagnosis: The tritosternum is covered by coxae I. Well-developed grooves are present for the legs. The marginal plate is continuous posteriorly and its inner margin is scalloped.

Genera and subgenera:

1. *Urodinychus* Berlese, 1903
   a. *Urodinychus* s. str.
      Type. *Uropoda carinata* Berlese, 1888
   b. *Leiodinychus* Berlese, 1917
      Type. *Uropoda krameri* G. and R. Canestrini, 1882
   c. *Macrodinychus* Berlese, 1917
      Type. *Urodinychus parallelepipedus* Berlese, 1916
2. *Calurodiscus* Radford, 1950 (= *Urodiscus* Berlese, 1916, *nom. prae-occ.*)
   Type. *Urodiscus obesus* Berlese, 1916

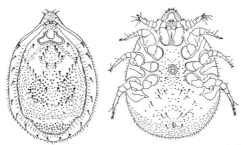

Figure 91 *Urodinychus polyphemus* Vitzthum, 1935. Dorsal (left) and ventral (right) views of male. (After Vitzthum 1935)

Discussion: This family is of no known economic or medical importance.

Reference:

Trägårdh, I. 1944. Zur Systematik der Uropodiden. Ent. Tidsk. 65:173–186.

Uropodidae Berlese, 1917

Figure 92

Diagnosis: The tritosternum is covered by coxae I. Grooves for the legs are well developed. The marginal plate is fused anteriorly to the dorsal plate, but the inner surface of the marginal plate is not scalloped. The plates appear to be mirror-smooth even when they are more or less finely punctated.

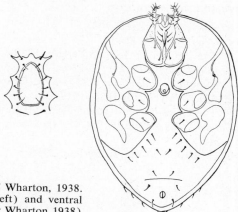

Figure 92 *Uropoda pearsei* Wharton, 1938.
Ventral plates of female (left) and ventral
view of male (right). (After Wharton 1938)

Genera and subgenera:

1. *Uropoda* Latreille, 1806 (= *Nummulus* Berlese, 1884)
   Type. *Acarus orbicularis* Müller, 1776 (= *Acarus vegetans* Latreille,
   1806 = *Discopoma romana* G. and R. Canestrini, 1882 in the
   sense of Berlese, 1884, *sed non* = *Acarus vegetans* DeGeer,
   1768)
2. *Centrouropoda* Berlese, 1916
   Type. *Uropoda rhombogyna* Berlese, 1910
3. *Cyclacarus* Ewing, 1933
   Type. *Cyclacarus aberrans* Ewing, 1933
4. *Cyllibula* Berlese, 1916
   Type. *Cillibano* (*Cyllibula*) *infumata* Berlese, 1916
5. *Encylliba* Berlese, 1917
   Type. *Cilliba bordagei* Oudemans, 1912
6. *Fuscuropoda* Vitzthum, 1924
   Type. *Notaspis marginatus* C. L. Koch, 1839
7. *Marginura* Sellnick, 1926
   Type. *Marginura adhaerens* Sellnick, 1926
8. *Metagynella* Berlese, 1919
   Type. *Metagynella paradoxa* Berlese, 1919
9. *Olouropoda* Berlese, 1916
   Type. *Uropoda* (*Olouropoda*) *nitidissima* Berlese, 1916
10. *Oplitis* Berlese, 1884 (= *Uroplitella* Berlese, 1904)
    Type. *Uropoda paradoxa* G. Canestrini and Berlese, 1884
11. *Pseudouropoda* Oudemans, 1936 (= *Notaspis* C. L. Koch, 1836, *sed
    non Notaspis* Hermann, 1804; = *Uropoda* Berlese, 1917)

a. *Pseudouropoda* s. str.
   Type. *Acarus vegetans* DeGeer, 1768
b. *Calouropoda* Berlese, 1916
   Type. *Uropoda pergitta* Berlese, 1904
c. *Trichouropoda* Berlese, 1916
   Type. *Uropoda longiseta* Berlese, 1888
12. *Urodiscella* Berlese, 1903
    Type. *Uropoda ricasoliana* Berlese, 1889
13. *Uroobovella* Berlese, 1903
    a. *Uroobovella* s. str.
       Type. *Uropoda obovata* G. Canestrini and Berlese, 1884
    b. *Urocyclella* Berlese, 1913
       Type. *Uroobovella* (*Urocyclella*) *parvula* Berlese, 1913
14. *Uroplitana* Sellnick, 1926
    Type. *Uroplitana acinaca* Sellnick, 1926
15. *Urosternella* Berlese, 1903
    Type. *Uropoda* (*Urosternella*) *foraminifera* Berlese, 1903

Uncertain genera:

1. *Liponissus* Kolenati, 1858 (*non Liponyssus* of authors)
   Type. *Dermanissus setosus* Kolenati, 1856
2. *Neuteria* Oudemans, 1905
   Type. *Uropoda tropica* Oudemans, 1905
3. *Paulitzia* Oudemans, 1915
   Type. *Uropoda africana* Oudemans, 1905

Discussion: Like the other families, uropodids are of no known economic or medical importance. They are world-wide in distribution and frequently attach themselves to insects, especially in the nymphal stages. They probably do no harm to their hosts.

Reference:

Trägårdh, I. 1944. Zur Systematik der Uropodiden. Ent. Tidsk. 65:173–186.

CELAENOPSINA TRÄGÅRDH, 1938

The Celaenopsina are characterized by a pair of lateral plates that developed on the ventral surface as anterior elongations of the ventral plate. These lateral plates have taken over the function of the epigynial plate and the latter is reduced or completely obliterated. With the reduction of the epigynial plate there has been no development of a median plate. The metasternal plates are no longer attached to the sternal plates I-III but are separate and in some cases drastically reduced in size. The metasternal plates vary considerably within the group from the Celaenopsidae where they are large, uncovered, free, and possess both the typical seta and pore, to the condition found in *Lobogynoides* and other genera where they are small, covered, and lack the seta but possess two pores, and to the condition found in *Lobogynium* and other genera where they are fused with the sternal plate.

Key to the Celaenopsina

1. Metasternal plates partially or completely covered by lateral plates   2

   Metasternal plates not covered   Celaenopsidae

2. Anterior lateral lobes of ventral plate, lateral plates, not separated from ventral plate   3

   Lateral plates separated by suture from ventral plate; epigynial plate reduced and visible only at posterior junction of lateral plates   Diplogyniidae

3. Anal plate separate from ventral plate   Euzerconidae

   Anal plate fused with ventral plate   Schizogyniidae

Diplogyniidae Trägårdh, 1941

Figure 93

Diagnosis: Diplogyniids can be recognized by the presence of a pair of lateral plates that are triangular and hinged to the ventral plate laterally. These lateral plates meet in the midline anteriorly and are separated posteriorly by a small remnant of the epigynial plate. The metasternal plates are reduced and partially covered by the anterior margins of the lateral plates. Posterior to the lateral plates the ventral plate extends to the posterior end of the body and includes the anal plate. Lateral to the ventral plate there is a pair of metapodal plates that reach the posterior end. The male genital aperture is in front of the sternal plate and is flanked by a pair of presternal setae. Trägårdh 1950 has described fourteen new genera and split the family into five subfamilies. Four of the subfamilies are monotypic while the Diplogyniinae contains all of the other genera. A key to the subfamilies taken from Trägårdh 1950 follows.

Key to the Diplogyniidae

1. Anal shield separated from ventral shield   Neodiplogyniinae

    Anal shield not separated from ventral shield   2

2. Narrow band with minute spinules around margin

       Heterodiplogyniinae

    No such band   3

3. Dorsal side densely clothed with minute setae   Trichdiplogyniinae

    Dorsal side not clothed with such setae   4

4. Dorsal shield with row of hook-shaped bristles   Meinertulinae

    Dorsal shield without such bristles   Diplogyniinae

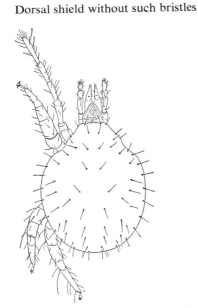 

Figure 93 *Diplogynium tropica* (Oudemans), 1927. Dorsal view of female (left) and ventral view of female (right). (After Oudemans 1928)

Genera:

1. *Diplogynium* Canestrini, 1889 (= *Anoplocelaeno* Berlese, 1910)
    Type. *Diplogynium acuminatum* Canestrini, 1889
2. *Antennocelaeno* Berlese, 1903
    Type. *Antennophorus braunsi* Wasmann, 1902

3. *Brachysternum* Trägårdh, 1950
   Type. *Brachysternum acuminatum* Trägårdh, 1950
4. *Cryptometasternum* Trägårdh, 1950
   Type. *Cryptometasternum natalense* Trägårdh, 1950
5. *Diplogyniella* Trägårdh, 1950
   Type. *Diplogyniella levinseni* Trägårdh, 1950
6. *Diplogyniopsis* Trägårdh, 1950
   Type. *Diplogyniopsis multidentata* Trägårdh, 1950
7. *Heterodiplogynium* Trägårdh, 1950
   Type. *Heterodiplogynium vestitum* Trägårdh, 1950
8. *Lobogynioides* Trägårdh, 1950
   Type. *Lobogynioides obtusum* Trägårdh, 1950
9. *Lobogynium* Trägårdh, 1950
   Type. *Lobogynium rotundatum* Trägårdh, 1950
10. *Megachaetochela* Trägårdh, 1950
    Type. *Megachaetochela warreni* Trägårdh, 1950
11. *Meinertula* Trägårdh, 1950
    Type. *Meinertula hamifera* Trägårdh, 1950
12. *Microdiplogynium* Trägårdh, 1950
    Type. *Microdiplogynium reticulatum* Trägårdh, 1950
13. *Neodiplogynium* Trägårdh, 1950
    Type. *Neodiplogynium schubarti* Trägårdh, 1950
14. *Passalacarus* Pearse and Wharton, 1936
    Type. *Passalacarus sylvestris* Pearse and Wharton, 1936
15. *Schizodiplogynium* Trägårdh, 1950
    Type. *Schizodiplogynium capillatum* Trägårdh, 1950
16. *Trichodiplogynium* Trägårdh, 1950
    Type. *Trichodiplogynium hirsutum* Trägårdh, 1950
17. *Tridiplogynium* Trägårdh, 1950
    Type. *Tridiplogynium inexpectatum* Trägårdh, 1950

Discussion: These large, handsome mites live as ectoparasites or commensals of large beetles and possibly other insects. They are of no known medical or economic importance.

References:

Pearse, A. S., *et al.* 1936. The ecology of *Passalus cornutus* Fabricius, a beetle that lives in rotting logs. Ecol. Monogr. 6:455–490.

Trägårdh, I. 1946. Outline of a new classification of the Mesostigmata (Acarina), based on comparative morphological data. K. Fysiogr. Sällsk. Handl. N. F. 57, Nr. 4:1–37.

Trägårdh, I. 1950. Studies on the Celaenopsidae, Diplogyniidae and Schizogyniidae. Arkiv. för Zoologi. Ser. 2, bd. 1, nr. 25:361–451.

Euzerconidae Trägårdh, 1938

Figure 94

Diagnosis: Euzerconids are similar to the Diplogyniidae but differ in that the lateral plates in the female are not separated by sutures from the ventral plate. The genital opening is therefore T-shaped. The anal plate is separate from the ventral plate.

Figure 94 *Euzercon latus* (Banks), 1909. Ventral view of female.

Genus:

Euzercon Berlese, 1888
Type. *Euzercon balzani* Berlese, 1888

Discussion: Members of this family live associated with beetles. They are world-wide in distribution but are of no known economic or medical importance.

Reference:

Trägårdh, I. 1946. Outline of a new classification of the Mesostigmata (Acarina), based on comparative morphological data. K. Fysiogr. Sällsk. Handl. N. F. 57, nr. 4:1-37.

Celaenopsidae Berlese, 1892

Figure 95

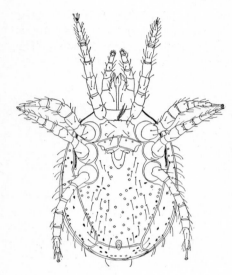

Diagnosis: Celaenopsids are similar to the preceding families but their epigynial plate is obliterated by the lateral plates which are fused medially as well as to the ventral plate posteriorly. The metasternal plates are free, large, and rectangular in shape so that they appear to be genital valves. The genital opening, however, is posterior to the metasternal plates.

Figure 95 *Celaenopsis cuspidata* (Kramer), 1876. Ventral view of female. (After Vitzthum 1940)

Genera:

1. *Celaenopsis* Berlese, 1886 (= *Antennocelaeno* Berlese, 1903)
   Type. *Gamasus cuspidatus* Kramer, 1876
2. *Ceratocelaenopsis* Trägårdh, 1950
   Type. *Ceratocelaenopsis womersleyi* Trägårdh, 1950
3. *Dinocelaeno* Oudemans, 1936
   Type. *Gamasus gigas* Dugès, 1834
4. *Neocelaeno* Berlese, 1910
   Type. *Celaenopsis cryptodonata* Berlese, 1901
5. *Pleuronectocelaeno* Vitzthum, 1926
   Type. *Celaenopsis (Pleuronectocelaeno) austriaca* Vitzthum, 1926

Discussion: As with other members of the suborder these mites are of no known economic or medical importance.

References:

Trägårdh, I. 1946. Outline of a new classification of the Megostigmata (Acarina), based on comparative morphological data. K. Fysiogr. Sällsk. Handl. N. F. 57, nr. 4:1–37.

Trägårdh, I. 1950. Studies on the Celaenopsidae, Diplogyniidae and Schizogyniidae. Arkiv. för Zoologi. Ser. 2, bd. 1, nr. 25:361–451.

Schizogyniidae Trägårdh, 1950

Figure 96

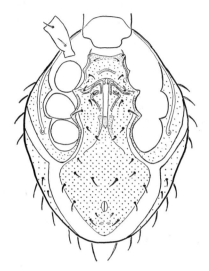

Diagnosis: This family is similar to the Diplogyniidae but differs in that both lateral and anal plates are fused with the ventral plates. The lateral plates are not fused in the midline as in the Celaenopsidae, however, and the sternal plate has a medial, crescentic ridge. Males are not known.

Figure 96 *Schizogynium intermedium* Trägårdh, 1950. Ventral view of female. (After Trägårdh 1950)

Genus:

Schizogynium Trägårdh, 1950
Type. *Schizogynium intermedium* Trägårdh, 1950

Discussion: Trägårdh 1950 considers the family to be intermediate between the Euzerconidae and the Diplogyniidae. Like the other members of the Celaenopsina species of this family are parasitic on beetles. The two known species are from Africa.

Reference:

Trägårdh, I. 1950. Studies on the Celaenopsidae, Diplogyniidae and Schizogyniidae. Arkiv. för Zoologi. Ser. 2, bd. 1, nr. 25:361–451.

FEDRIZZIINA TRÄGÅRDH, 1937

The females in this group are easily recognized because they have a median plate in addition to or in place of an epigynial plate. The median plate is in reality a sclerotized portion of the vaginal wall. The metasternal plates are fused with the sternal plate if these plates are present. Lateral shields are present or if absent they are secondarily reduced. The male genital opening is in the center of the sternal plate that is closed by a plate attached at its anterior margins.

The Fedrizziina can be conveniently separated into seven families as indicated by the following key that is a modification of one published by Trägårdh 1946.

Key to the Fedrizziina

1. Sternal and metasternal plates sclerotized   2

   Sternal and metasternal plates not sclerotized in female; their positions indicated only by locations of sternal and metasternal setae
        Parantennulidae

2. Lateral plates separate   3

   Lateral plates fused along midline; median plate reduced
        Syngynaspidae

3. Median plate not fused to sternal plate   4

   Median plate fused to sternal plate   Cercomegistidae

4. Lateral plates completely sclerotized   5

   Lateral plates sclerotized only along median margin
        Antennophoridae

5. Lateral plates triangular   Paramegistidae

   Lateral plates linear   Fedrizziidae

Parantennulidae Willmann, 1940

Figure 97

Diagnosis: The dorsal plate is undivided, and the sternal and metasternal plates of the females are lacking. Tarsus I has no ambulacral apparatus, while tarsi II, III, and IV have large caruncles and tiny claws. Chelicerae are chelate.

Genera:

1. *Parantennulus* Berlese, 1904
   Type. *Antennophorus scolopendrarum* Berlese, 1886
2. *Diplopodophilus* Willmann, 1940
   Type. *Diplopodophilus antennophoroides* Willmann, 1940

Discussion: These mites are found on myriapods and carabid beetles. They are of no known economic or medical importance.

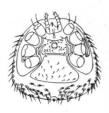 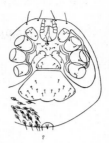

Figure 97   *Diplopodophilus antennophoroides* Willmann, 1940. Ventral view of male (left) and female (right). (After Willmann 1941)

Reference:

Willmann, C. 1940. Neue Milben aus Höhlen der Balkanhalbinsel, ge-sammelt von Prof. Dr. K. Absolom, Brünn. Zool. Anz. 130:209–218.

———. 1941. Die Acari der Höhlen der Balkanhalbinsel. Studien aus dem Gebiete der Allgemeinen Karstforschung, der Wissenschaftlichen Hohlenkunde, der Eiszeitforschung und den Nachbargebieten. Biological serie nr. 8, pp. 1–80.

Syngynaspidae Trägårdh, 1938

Figure 98

Diagnosis: The lateral plates of the female are fused along the midline. The median plate is reduced.

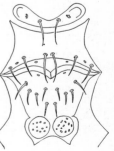

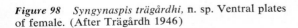

Figure 98   *Syngynaspis trägårdhi*, n. sp. Ventral plates of female. (After Trägårdh 1946)

Genus:

Syngynaspis
Type. *Syngynaspis trägårdhi* n. sp.

Discussion: In 1937 Trägårdh described a new genus *Syngynaspis* but failed to assign a specific name to the unique species on which the genus was based. This species described by Trägårdh 1937 (Ark. Zool. 29 No. 11:6, Figure 9) is here named *Syngynaspis trägårdhi.* Trägårdh erected the family Syngynaspidae for this form in 1938.

Reference:

Trägårdh, I. 1937. Zur Systematik der Mesostigmata. Ark. Zool. 29 No. 11:1–8.

Cercomegistidae Trägårdh, 1938

Figure 99

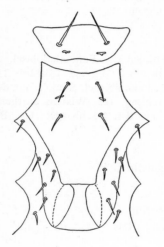

Diagnosis: The median plate is fused with the sternal plates. The lateral plates are long and narrow and overlap the epigynial plate posteriorly.

Figure 99 *Cercomegistus* sp. Ventral plates of female. (After Trägårdh 1937)

Genera:

1. *Cercomegistus* Berlese, 1914
   Type. *Cercomegistus bruckianus* Berlese, 1914
2. *Neo-Oudemansia*
   Type. *Neo-Oudemansia trägårdhi* n. sp.

Discussion: The genus *Neo-Oudemansia* was described by Trägårdh in 1938 for a form that he failed to name. *N. trägårdhi* is here proposed for the species (Trägårdh, I. 1938. Ent. Tidsk. 3–4:137, Figure 19).

Reference:

Trägårdh, I. 1938. Further contributions towards the comparative morphology and classification of the Mesostigmata. Ent. Tidsk. 3–4:123–158.

Antennophoridae Berlese, 1892

Figure 100

Diagnosis: Antennophorids are broadly oval in shape and have an undivided dorsal plate. Tarsus I lacks an ambulacral apparatus, while tarsi II, III, and IV have pretarsi and caruncles and at times weak claws. The median plate is a transverse, strongly sclerotized bar. The lateral plates are sclerotized medially, and the epigynial plate is fused with the ventral plate.

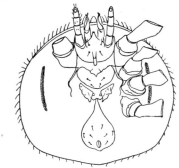

Figure 100 *Antennophorus foreli* Berlese, 1904. Ventral view of female. (After Berlese 1904)

Genera and subgenera:

1. *Antennophorus* Haller, 1877
   Type. *Antennophorus uhlmanni* Haller, 1877 (not Jannet, 1897)
2. *Antennurella* Berlese, 1904 (= *Eufedrizzia* Sellnick, 1938)
   Type. *Antennurella trouessarti* Berlese, 1904
3. *Celaenopsoides* Gunther, 1942 (doubtful)
   Type. *Celaenopsoides buloloensis* Gunther, 1942
4. *Celaenosthanus* Vitzthum, 1930
   Type. *Celaenosthanus trigonophilus* Vitzthum, 1930
5. *Messoracarus* Silvestri, 1912
   a. *Messoracarus* s. str.
      Type. *Messoracarus mirandus* Silvestri, 1912
   b. *Leptantennus* Berlese, 1916
      Type. *Messoracarus (Leptantennus) pendulipes* Berlese, 1916
6. *Ophiomegistus* Banks, 1914
   Type. *Ophiomegistus luzonensis* Banks, 1914
7. *Physalozercon* Berlese, 1903
   Type. *Antennophorus raffray* Wasmann, 1902
8. *Ptochares* Silvestri, 1910
   Type. *Ptochares daveyii* Silvestri, 1910

Discussion: These mites are associated with insects and large myriapods. They are of no known economic or medical importance.

Reference:

Trägårdh, I. 1943. Further contributions towards the comparative morphology of the Mesostigmata (Acarina) the Antennophoridae and the Megisthanidae. Arkiv. för Zoologi. 34A. N:o 20:1–10.

Paramegistidae Trägårdh, 1946

Figure 101

Diagnosis: The lateral plates are well developed, and are hinged to or fused with the ventral plate. The median plate is separated into two lateral elements in the female. The male genital opening is posterior to the sternal plate.

Figure 101 *Micromegistus bakeri* Trägårdh, 1948. Ventral view of female (left) and male (right). (After Trägårdh 1948)

Genera and subgenera:

1. *Paramegistus* Trägårdh, 1906
   Type. *Paramegistus confrater* Trägårdh, 1906
2. *Echinomegistus* Berlese, 1903
   a. *Echinomegistus* s. str.
      Type. *Antennophorus wheeleri* Wasmann (in Berlese, 1903)
   b. *Antennomegistus* Berlese, 1904
      Type. *Antennophorus caputcarabi* Berlese, 1903
3. *Micromegistus* Trägårdh, 1948
   Type. *Micromegistus bakeri* Trägårdh, 1948
4. *Neomegistus* Trägårdh, 1906
   Type. *Neomegistus iulidicola* Trägårdh, 1906

Discussion: Mites of this family are found associated with insects and myriapods. They are of no known economic or medical importance.

Reference:

Trägårdh, I. 1948. Description of *Micromegistus,* a new genus of the Paramegistidae, with notes on *Neomegistus, Paramegistus* and *Echinomegistus* (Acarina). Ent. Tidsk. 69:127–131.

Fedrizziidae Trägårdh, 1937

Figure 102

Diagnosis: Fedrizziids are flat, broadly oval, and have an undivided dorsal plate. Their legs are short, leg I being thinner than the others. Tarsi I without, tarsi II, III, and IV with pretarsi, caruncles, and claws. Chelicerae are chelate with ornate extensions. The tectum is triangular with a median-pointed projection. In the females the median plate is very large, the lateral plates are linear, and the epigynial plate is absent. The genital opening of the males is in the posterior sternal plate.

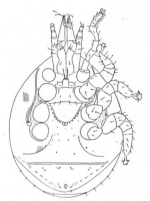

Figure 102 *Fedrizzia strandi* (Oudemans), 1927. Ventral view of female. (After Oudemans 1928)

Genera:

1. *Fedrizzia* Canestrini, 1884 (= *Toxopeusia* Oudemans, 1927)
   Type. *Fedrizzia grossipes* Canestrini, 1884 (= *Toxopeusia strandi* Oudemans, 1927)
2. *Klinckowstroemia*
   Type. *Klinckowstroemia trägårdhi* n. sp.

Discussion: In 1938 Trägårdh proposed the genus *Klinckowstroemia* for a form that he failed to assign a specific name. This form is the type of *Klinckowstroemia* and is here named *K. trägårdhi* (Trägårdh, I. 1938. Ent. Tidsk. 59:133–134, Figure 14). Mites of this family live associated with insects and myriapods and are of no known economic importance.

Reference:

Trägårdh, I. 1946. Outlines of a new classification of the Mesostigmata (Acarina). K. Fysiogr. Sällsk. Handl. N. F. 57 No. 4:1–37.

CHAPTER IV

The Suborder Ixodides Leach, 1815

THE Ixodides or ticks are all parasitic. Ticks as well as being similar in habits also have many morphological features in common, such as a piercing hypostome with recurved teeth, chelicerae with lateral teeth on the movable digits, a pitlike sensory organ on tarsus I (Haller's organ), large size, and lateral stigmata without sinuous peritremes. Although ticks are similar to mesostigmatid mites there is no group of species intermediate between the two. It therefore seems desirable to consider the ticks as a separate suborder.

Vitzthum 1941 divides the Ixodides into three subgroups each of which is represented by a single family. Rather than introduce group names, these will be ignored.

No special discussion of the morphology of ticks will be needed for the understanding of the key to families.

Key to the Ixodides

1. Scutum present in all stages 2

    Scutum absent in all stages .... Argasidae

2. Palpal tarsus terminal in position; scutum similar in texture to unmodified integument in females   Nuttalliellidae

    Palpal tarsus imbedded in ventral apex of tibia; scutum of different texture than unmodified integument   Ixodidae

Argasidae G. Canestrini, 1890

Figure 103

Diagnosis (from Cooley and Kohls 1944): The argasids are non-scutate Ixodides with slight sexual dimorphism. Both adults and

137

nymphs have a leathery, wrinkled, granulated integument, which is either mammilated or has tubercles. The capitulum in the adults and nymphs is either subterminal or distant from the anterior margin; in larvae it is subterminal or terminal. In depleted adults and nymphs especially, the capitulum is in a more or less marked depression (camerostome). Articulations of the palpi of all stages are free (never

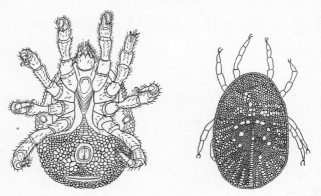

Figure 103   *Antricola coprophilus* (McIntosh), 1935. Ventral view of female (left) and *Argas persicus* (Oken), 1818. Dorsal view of female (right). (After Cooley and Kohls 1944)

fused). Porose areas are absent in both sexes. When present the eyes are placed on the supracoxal folds. Spiracles in adults and nymphs are usually placed anterior to coxae IV. Pulvilli are usually rudimentary or absent in adults and nymphs but sometimes well developed (functional) in larvae. Nymphal stages are plural and the number variable.

Genera:

1. *Argas* Latreille, 1795
   Type. *Acarus reflexus* Fabricius, 1794
2. *Antricola* Cooley and Kohls, 1942
   Type. *Ornithodoros coprophilus* McIntosh, 1935
3. *Ornithodoros* Koch, 1844
   Type. *Argas savignyi* Audouin, 1826
4. *Otobius* Banks, 1912
   Type. *Argas megnini* Dugès, 1884

Discussion: The Argasidae are world-wide in distribution and occur on a wide variety of hosts. Snakes, turtles, many birds, and at least eight orders of mammals are known to be attacked. Typically the ticks feed intermittently after the habit of bed bugs. Eggs are laid a few at a time. The larvae hatch and feed on the host for an extended period. They then detach and molt into nymphs. Nymphs usually require only an hour or two for feeding. After they have fed they leave the host and molt again into the second nymphal stage. Following another short meal the nymph is again ready to transform and eventually males and females are produced. Males can be distinguished from females in many cases only by slight differences in the genital openings. The male opening is usually slightly smaller and more arcuate. *Ornithodoros moubata* and *O. savignyi* have larvae that do not feed and the first nymphs are the primary active stage in the life cycle. *Otobius megnini,* on the other hand, does not feed in the adult stage, and these adults do not have recurved teeth on the hypostome.

Many argasid ticks frequent the burrows, nests, or homes of their hosts, where they feed intermittently. *Ornithodoros talaje,* for example, lives in the crevices of houses in southern Mexico, while *O. moubata* and *Argas persicus* are domestic pests in Africa and Persia respectively. Recently several new species of argasids have been described from bats in North and Central Americas. Cooley and Kohls 1944 state: "There are likely still others that infest bats in the United States and probably in Mexico and Central America." It is not surprising to find argasids on bats since they are notorious for their homing instincts.

Argasid ticks are of considerable economic and medical importance. *Argas persicus* is not only a bothersome domestic pest in parts of its range, but it also infests poultry all over the world, causing much damage by its bites. Not only are the bites injurious but also *A. persicus* transmits a spirochaetal disease to fowls. Cattle are susceptible to the spinose ear tick and deaths of cattle have been ascribed to this tick. Many species bite man and their bites can be extremely painful. Cooley and Kohls 1944 report the following species as attacking man in North America: *A. persicus, Otobius megnini, Ornithodoros coriaceus, O. hermsi, O. nicollei, O. parkeri, O. rudis, O. stageri, O. talaje,* and *O. turicata.* The spirochaets of relapsing fever *Borrelia spp.* are carried to man by at least eleven different species of *Ornithodoros. O. parkeri* has been demonstrated to carry tularemia experimentally. Rocky Mountain spotted fever, and American Q fever have been transmitted experimentally by argasids.

References:

Cooley, R. A. and Glen M. Kohls. 1944. The Argasidae of North America, Central America and Cuba. Am. Midland Naturalist. Mongr. vi + 152.

Nuttal, G. H. F., C. Warburton, W. F. Cooper, and L. E. Robinson. 1908. Ticks. A monograph of the Ixodidae, Part I, The Argasidae, 1–104, Cambridge Univ. Press.

Nuttalliellidae Schulze, 1935

Figure 104

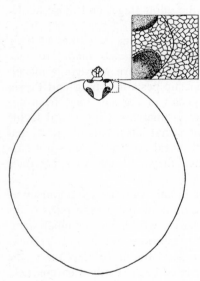

Diagnosis: This family is intermediate between the Argasidae and Ixodidae. The scutum is not heavily sclerotized and is similar in appearance to the leathery integument that covers the entire body. The integument has papillae similar to those found in the Argasidae. The palpi have freely movable segments, but there is a groove on the inner side of the second segment. The gnathosoma is anterior and visible from above as in the Ixodidae.

Figure 104 *Nuttalliella namaqua* Bedford, 1931. Dorsal view of female. (After Bedford 1931)

Genus:

Nuttalliella Bedford, 1931
Type. *Nuttalliella namaqua* Bedford, 1931

Discussion: The type specimen was found under a stone in Little Namaqualand, Africa. It is not known to be of any economic or medical importance.

Reference:

Bedford, G. A. H. 1931. *Nuttalliella namaqua,* a new genus and species of tick. Parasitol. 23:230–232 + Pl. X.

Ixodidae Murray, 1877

Figure 105

Diagnosis: The bodies of this family are oval and the gnathosoma is anterior and visible from above. The scutum of the males extends to the posterior margin, while that of the females is restricted to the propodosoma. Both the larvae and the nymphs have scuta similar to

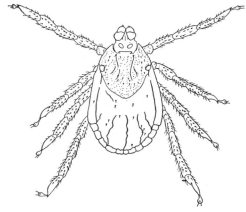

Figure 105 *Dermacentor variabilis* (Say), 1821. Dorsal view of female. (After Cooley 1938)

the females. Eyes may be present or absent. The larvae have two pairs of ventral stigmata lateral to the legs. The nymphs and adults have a single pair of spiracular plates. The terminal segment of the palps is reduced and inserted ventrally on the penultimate segment. Segments of palps are not freely movable. Porose areas are present on the base of the gnathosoma in the females.

The Ixodidae can be divided into three subfamilies by use of the following key:

Key to the Ixodidae

1. Anal grooves do not surround anus anteriorly; ventral surface of males not almost completely covered by series of plates   2

Anal grooves surround anus anteriorly; ventral surface of males almost completely covered by series of plates   Ixodinae

2. Ventral surface of male without plates; scutum usually ornamented   Amblyomminae

Ventral surface of male with four posterior plates, usually plain   Rhipicephalinae

Ixodinae Vitzthum, 1941

Genera and subgenera:

1. *Ixodes* Latreille, 1795
   a. *Ixodes* s. str.
      Type. *Acarus ricinus* Linnaeus, 1758
   b. *Ceratixodes* Neumann, 1902
      Type. *Hyalomma puta* Picard—Cambridge, 1876
   c. *Endopalpiger* Schulze, 1935
      Type. *Endopalpiger luxuriosus* Schulze, 1935
   d. *Eschatocephalus* v. Frauenfeld, 1853
      Type. *Ixodes vespertilionis* Koch, 1844 (= *Eschatocephalus gracilipes* v. Frauenfeld, 1853)
   e. *Exopalpiger* Schulze, 1935
      Type. *Ixodes priscicollaris* Schulze, 1932
   f. *Lepidixodes* Schulze, 1935
      Type. *Eschatocephalus kopsteini* Oudemans, 1925
   g. *Sternalixodes* Schulze, 1935
      Type. *Ixodes cordifer* Neumann, 1908

Amblyomminae Neumann, 1911

Genera and subgenera:

1. *Amblyomma* Koch, 1844 (= *Haemalastor* Koch, 1844)
   Type. *Acarus cajennensis* Fabricius, 1787
2. *Alloceraea* Schulze, 1918
   Type. *Haemaphysalis inermis* Birula, 1895
3. *Amblycentor* Schulze, 1932
   a. *Amblycentor* s. str.
      Type. *Ixodes rhinocerinus* Denny, 1843
   b. *Puncticentor* Schulze, 1933
      Type. *Dermacentor cricumguttatus* Neumann, 1897
4. *Anocentor* Schulze, 1937 (= *Otocentor* Cooley, 1938)
   Type. *Dermacentor nitens* Neumann, 1897 (= *Anocentor columbianus* Schulze, 1937)

5. *Aponomma* Neumann, 1899
   Type. *Ixodes gervaisi* Lucas, 1847
6. *Dermacentor* Koch, 1844
   a. *Dermacentor* s. str.
      Type. *Acarus reticulatus* Fabricius, 1794
   b. *Dermacentorites* Olenev, 1931
      Type. *Cynorhaestes pictus* Hermann, 1804
7. *Haemaphysalis* Koch, 1844
   Type. *Haemaphysalis concinna* Koch, 1844
8. *Indocentor* Schulze, 1933
   Type. *Dermacentor auratus* Supino, 1897

Rhipicephalinae Vitzthum, 1941

Genera and subgenera:

1. *Rhipicephalus* Koch, 1844
   a. *Rhipicephalus* s. str.
      Type. *Ixodes sanguineus* Latreille, 1806
   b. *Pterygodes* Neumann, 1913
      Type. *Rhipicephalus (Pterygodes) fulvus* Neumann, 1913
2. *Boophilus* Curtice, 1891
   a. *Boophilus* s. str.
      Type. *Ixodes annulatus* Say, 1821 (= *Ixodes bovis* Riley, 1867)
   b. *Palpoboophilus* Minning, 1934
      Type. *Rhipicephalus decoloratus* Koch, 1844
   c. *Uroboophilus* Minning, 1934
      Type. *Uroboophilus sharifi* Minning, 1934
3. *Cosmiomma* Schulze, 1919
   Type. *Ixodes hippopotamensis* Denny, 1843
4. *Hyalomma* Koch, 1844
   a. *Hyalomma* s. str.
      Type. *Acarus aegyptius* Linnaeus, 1758
   b. *Hyalommasta* Schulze, 1930
      Type. *Hyalomma syriacum* Koch, 1844
   c. *Hyalommina* Schulze, 1919
      Type. *Hyalomma rhipicephaloides* Neumann, 1901
5. *Margaropus* Karsch, 1879
   Type. *Margaropus winthemi* Karsch, 1879
6. *Nosomma* Schulze, 1919
   Type. *Hyalomma monstrosum* Nuttall and Warburton, 1908
7. *Rhipicentor* Nuttall and Warburton, 1908
   Type. *Rhipicentor bicornis* Nuttall and Warburton, 1908

Discussion: Ticks in general, and ixodids in particular, are perhaps the best known of any of the Acarina. That this is so is not surprising since they are also the largest of the Acarina, parasites of man and his domestic animals as well as wild animals, and the vectors of many serious diseases. Despite the broad knowledge of ticks there is considerable disagreement among specialists on the generic names to be applied to them. The arrangement of the genera listed here is taken largely from Vitzthum 1941, who in turn has followed Schulze. Other specialists prefer to reduce many of Schulze's names to synonymy.

The life cycle of ixodids is fairly simple. The female deposits a large egg-mass on the ground. Six-legged larvae hatch from the eggs. The larvae then feed on a suitable host. After the larvae become engorged with blood they molt and become nymphs. The nymphs have eight legs and are similar in appearance to the adult female. However, they are smaller and lack a genital opening. Nymphs engorge and molt to produce adult males and females. Both males and females feed. The male is encased in a fairly nonelastic integument and so does not increase greatly in size after feeding. The female, on the other hand, swells greatly during engorgement. After copulation and engorgement the female is ready for oviposition.

This general life cycle exhibits many modifications in different details. The majority of ixodids usually parasitize different hosts in the immature and mature stages. For example, *Dermacentor venustus* Neumann (= *D. andersoni* Stiles) has been reported in the larval and nymphal stages from small mammals, while as an adult it has been taken from sheep, goats, man, etc. *D. venustus* drops to the ground in order to molt or lay eggs, so that each tick must find at least three individual hosts if it is to complete its life cycle. *Boophilus annulatus* (Say) on the other hand attaches itself to cattle in the larval stage and does not leave its host until it is ready to lay its eggs. Nuttall 1911 indicates that *Ixodes rincinus* (Linnaeus) can complete its life cycle in as little as one hundred and seventy days, but that under unfavorable conditions it may take two or three years.

Ixodids are of great economic and medical importance. Heavy infestation with ixodid ticks can cause anemia in domestic animals. Several noxious diseases are carried to animals by ticks such as Texas cattle fever to bovines by *Boophilus annulatus* (Say). Ixodids may cause paralysis in man by their bites and they also have been incriminated in transmitting the following diseases to man: Rocky Mountain and other spotted fevers of the Americas, fièvre boutonneuse, Kenya typhus, South African tick-bite fever, the Q fevers, tularemia, and possibly others (Mackie, Hunter, and Worth 1945). Detailed accounts of the role of ixodids as vectors of disease are to be found in most books on parasitology and tropical medicine.

References:

Cooley, R. A. 1938. The genera Dermacentor and Otocentor (Ixodidae) in the United States, with studies in variation. Nat. Inst. Health Bull. No. 171:1–85 + Pls.

———. 1946. The genera Boophilus, Rhipicephalus, and Haemaphysalis (Ioxodidae) of the New World. Nat. Inst. Health Bull. 187: 54 + iii.

Cooley, R. A. and G. M. Kohls. 1945. The genus Ixodes in North America. Nat. Inst. Health Bull. 184:246 + iii.

Douglas, J. R. 1943. The internal anatomy of *Dermacentor andersoni* Stiles. Univ. of Calif. Publ. in Ent. 7(10):207–272 + Pls.

Fielding, J. W. 1926. Australasian Ticks. Dept. of Health Commonwealth of Australia Service Publ. (Trop. Div.) No. 9:1–114.

Neumann, L. G. 1911. Ixodidae. Das Tierreich. Acarina. 26 Lieferung 1–169.

Nuttall, G. H. F. and C. Warburton. 1911. Ticks. A monograph of the Ixodidea, Part II, The Ixodidae. 105–348. Cambridge Univ. Press.

——— and ———. 1915. Ticks. A monograph of the Ixodoidea, Part III, The genus Haemaphysalis. 349–550 + Pls. Cambridge Univ. Press.

Robinson, L. E. 1926. Ticks: A monograph of the Ixodoidea, Part IV, The Genus Amblyomma. 1–302 + Pls. Cambridge Univ. Press.

CHAPTER V

The Suborder Trombidiformes Reuter, 1909

THESE mites possess a pair of stigmata on or near the gnathosoma, although occasionally the stigmata may be absent. The palpi are usually free and highly developed, either as pincer-like clasping organs or sensory organs. The chelicerae are usually modified for piercing, although in the primitive, predaceous families a few have opposed chelae which are apparently for seizing prey. They may or may not possess genital suckers, but anal suckers are never present.

The Trombidiformes are here divided into three groups, the Tetrapodili, the Tarsonemini, and the Prostigmata. The Tetrapodili contains the tiny, wormlike, plant-feeding Eriophyidae which possess only two pairs of legs in all stages and which lack a respiratory system. The Tarsonemini includes the small plant and arthropod parasites with minute mouth parts, small appressed palps, tiny needle-like chelicerae, and with the stigma behind the pedipalps in the female and lacking in the male; many in this group do not possess the full number of legs and appear to be quite degenerate. The Prostigmata is composed of those mites with the stigma opening at the base of the chelicerae; they are usually large mites with large, free-moving mouth parts, in many cases the palps being highly developed as feelers or grasping organs. The chelicerae, although perhaps modified, usually are large and well developed for piercing or grasping. In the Tarsonemini we have a single more or· less homogeneous group, but in the Prostigmata we find many groups, such as those with a thumb-claw complex on the palps (Trombidiidae), those with very simple palps (Rhagidiidae), those with piercing, needle-like chelicerae (Tetranychidae), or those with grasping or crushing mouth parts (Rhagidiidae). These, with their related families, perhaps form the basis for superfamilies, but since this grouping is still in the formative stage no attempt is here made to present categories other than families.

Key to the Trombidiformes

1. Body of normal shape, not wormlike (except in Demodicidae); with normal four pairs of legs (except certain cases in Podapolipodidae and Phytoptipalpidae); with or without well-developed gnathosoma; with respiratory system   2

   Body wormlike, annulate; with only two pairs of anteriorly placed legs; no respiratory system; gnathosoma greatly reduced; palpi minute, lying close to rostrum; chelicerae stylet-like; minute plant-feeding mites   Tetrapodili (Eriophyidae)

2. Chelicerae tiny, stylet-like; palpi minute, lying close to rostrum; gnathosoma as a whole greatly reduced, inconspicuous; tiny mites with or without usual number of legs; stigma of ♀ behind maxillae; ♂ without stigma or tracheae   Tarsonemini

   Chelicerae much larger, easily seen; palpi not minute nor lying close to rostrum (except the wormlike Demodicidae which has four pairs of legs); gnathosoma usually conspicuous; as a whole, large mites with four pairs of legs (except in Phytoptipalpidae where one genus possesses only three pairs of legs); stigma opening at base of chelicerae (*Demodex* without stigma or tracheae)   Prostigmata

TETRAPODILI BREMI, 1872

These are minute, wormlike, plant-feeding mites measuring up to 0.20 mm. in length. They possess two pairs of legs anteriorly which lack tarsal claws but which have a "featherclaw." The body is ringed and the genital opening is located just behind the legs and is covered by a transverse plate. There are no eyes, no heart, no excretory system, and no respiratory system. Only a few setae are present. The Tetrapodili contains only a single family, the Eriophyidae.

Eriophyidae Nalepa, 1898

Figure 106

Diagnosis: The eriophyids are minute, wormlike mites whose propodosoma is shieldlike and has distinctive, specific patterns. The hysterosoma is elongated and annulate. These mites do not possess a respiratory system. Two pairs of anterior legs are present in all stages and all tarsi have rayed claws. The genitalia are situated on the anterior, ventral portion of the body just behind the legs and the genital plate is a transverse rather than a longitudinal slit. Palpi are short and simple. The chelicerae are short and stylet-like for piercing. The anal opening is on the posterior of the body. These mites are either free-living on plants or gall makers. Vitzthum divides this group into the Eriophyidae and Phyllocoptidae, but Keifer's single-family arrangement is followed here.

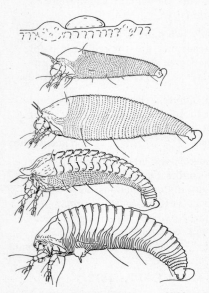

Although the Eriophyidae have been separated from the prostigmatic mites and placed in a separate group, the Tetrapodili, their relationship to the normal eight-legged mites can be demonstrated. In certain of the normal groups some genera begin to lose a pair of legs, as in the Podapolipodidae which are parasitic on insects. This is not surprising since the mode of life in this family would tend towards a parasitic baglike mite. In the Phytoptipalpidae, which are plant feeders and are closely related to the Tetranychidae, one genus, *Phytoptipalpus,* possesses only three pairs of legs. In this same family, *Tenuipalpus eriophyoides* Baker (nymph), although possessing four pairs of legs, is very elongated and annulate, greatly resembling an eriophyid mite. The transverse genital plates also indicate the relationship of the Eriophyidae to the Phytoptipalpidae, since these two families are the only ones which possess this type of organ, other genital openings being longitudinal. The genitalia of the Eriophyidae is located just behind the legs, far anteriorly, while that of the Phytoptipalpidae is at the rear of the body. This difference is not as significant as may be presumed since there probably has been a coalescing of body segments posteriorly in the phytoptipalpid type which gives the appearance of having the genitalia on the extreme end rather than in a more or less normal position. The rayed tarsal appendage of the

Figure 106 Oxypleurites aesculifoliae Keifer. Egg, two nymphal, protogyne, and deutogyne stages. (After Keifer 1942)

eriophyids is somewhat similar to that of the genus *Dolichotetranychus* in the family Phytoptipalpidae. The stylet-like chelicerae and the general biology of the group also indicate a common ancestry with the plant-feeding Tetranychidae and Phytoptipalpidae.

Key to the Eriophyidae
(from Keifer)

1. Three or four setiferous tubercles on shield; rear pair of tubercles always bearing setae that point forward; anterior pair of subdorsal abdominal setae present or absent; foretibia usually with lateral spur; hind patellar seta often laterally placed; female coverflap smooth; female genital glands elliptical or elongate, arising from ducts that project forward and then recurve laterally 2

   One pair of setiferous tubercles on cephalothoracic shield, or these absent; no subdorsal abdominal setae; no lateral spur on foretibia; hind patellar seta always arising from above; female genital coverflap variously sculptured or smooth; female genital glands usually subcircular and on short lateral or diagonally, posteriorly directed ducts originating from rear of genital opening 3

2. Shield with no anterior lobe over rostrum; abdomen wormlike with rings similar dorsoventrally   Phytoptinae

   Shield with anterior lobe over rostrum which is sometimes very short; abdomen divided laterally into broader tergites, and more numerous narrower sternites   Sierraphytoptinae

3. Shield never with lobe overhanging rostrum; abdomen wormlike, with rings similar above and below, at least anteriorly; when rostrum large, not set at right angles to body and with evenly curved chelicerae   Eriophyinae

   Shield usually with anterior lobe over rostrum; abdomen most often divided laterally into broader tergites and narrower sternites; or with large tapering rostrum, set at right angles to body, and with large chelicerae abruptly downcurved in from rostrum base   Phyllocoptinae

Phytoptinae Keifer, 1944

Genera:

1. *Phytoptus* DuJardin, 1851
   Type. *Eriophyes avellanae* Nalepa, 1889
2. *Setoptus* Keifer, 1944
   Type. *"Platyphytoptus" jonesi* Keifer, 1938

Sierraphytoptinae Keifer, 1944
(= Mackiellinae Keifer, 1946)

Genera:

1. *Sierraphytoptus* Keifer, 1939
   Type. *Sierraphytoptus alnivagrans* Keifer, 1939
2. *Austracus* Keifer, 1944
   Type. *Austracus havrylenkonis* Keifer, 1944
3. *Mackiella* Keifer, 1939
   Type. *Mackiella phoenicis* Keifer, 1939
4. *Nalepella* Keifer, 1944
   Type. *Phyllocoptes triceras* Börner, 1906

Eriophyinae Nalepa, 1898

Genera:

1. *Eriophyes* von Siebold, 1850
   Type. *Eriophyes vitis* (Pgst.), 1857
2. *Aceria* Keifer, 1944
   Type. *Eriophyes tulipae* Keifer, 1938
3. *Cecidodectes* Nalepa, 1917
   Type. *Cecidodectes euzonus* Nalepa, 1917
4. *Cecidophyes* Nalepa, 1887
   Type. *Phytoptus galii* Karpelles, 1884
5. *Cymoptus* Keifer, 1946
   Type. *Cymoptus spiniventris* Keifer, 1946
6. *Monochetus* Nalepa, 1898 (= *Monaulax* Nalepa, 1892 *nom. prae-occ.*)
   Type. *Monaulax sulcatus* Nalepa, 1892
7. *Novophytoptus* Roivainen, 1947
   Type. *Novophytoptus rostratae* Roivainen, 1947
8. *Paraphytophus* Nalepa, 1896
   Type. *Paraphytophus paradoxus* Nalepa, 1896
9. *Phytoptochetus* Nalepa, 1917
   Type. *Phytoptochetus tristichus* Nalepa, 1917
10. *Trichostigma* Gerber, 1902
    Type. *Trichostigma crodii* Gerber, 1902

Phyllocoptinae Nalepa, 1898

Genera:

1. *Phyllocoptes* Nalepa, 1889
   Type. *Phyllocoptes carpini* Nalepa, 1887

2. *Abacarus* Keifer, 1944
   Type. *Calepitrimerus acalyptus* Keifer, 1939
3. *Abacoptes* Keifer, 1939
   Type. *Abacoptes platynus* Keifer, 1939
4. *Acamina* Keifer, 1944
   Type. *Calepitrimerus nolinae* Keifer, 1939
5. *Acaphylla* Keifer, 1943
   Type. *Acaphylla steinweideni* Keifer, 1943
6. *Acarelliptus* Keifer, 1940
   Type. *Acarelliptus cocciformis* Keifer, 1940
7. *Acaricalus* Keifer, 1940
   Type. *Acaricalus segundus* Keifer, 1940
8. *Anthocoptes* Nalepa, 1892
   Type. *Phyllocoptes loricatus* Nalepa, 1889
9. *Calacarus* Keifer, 1940
   Type. *Calacarus pulviferus* Keifer, 1940
10. *Calepitrimerus* Keifer, 1938
    Type. *Calepitrimerus cariniferus* Keifer, 1938
11. *Caliphytoptus* Keifer, 1938
    Type. *Caliphytoptus quercilobatae* Keifer, 1938
12. *Callyntrotus* Nalepa, 1894
    Type. *Callyntrotus schlectendali* Nalepa, 1894
13. *Caroloptes* Keifer, 1940
    Type. *Caroloptes fagivagrans* Keifer, 1940
14. *Coptophylla* Keifer, 1944
    Type. *Phyllocoptes lamimani* Keifer, 1939
15. *Cupacarus* Keifer, 1943
    Type. *Cupacarus cuprifestor* Keifer, 1943
16. *Diptilomiopus* Nalepa, 1916
    Type. *Diptilomiopus javanicus* Nalepa, 1916
17. *Epitrimerus* Nalepa, 1898
    Type. *Epitrimerus gemmicola* Nalepa, 1898
18. *Gammaphytoptus* Keifer, 1939
    Type. *Gammaphytoptus camphorae* Keifer, 1939
19. *Oxypleurites* Nalepa, 1891
    Type. *Acanthonotus heptacanthus* Nalepa, 1889, desg. by Keifer, 1938
    (*Tegonotus trouessarti* Nalepa, 1890, desg. by Vitzthum 1943)
20. *Phyllocoptruta* Keifer, 1938
    Type. *Typhlodromus oleivorus* Ashmead, 1879
21. *Phyllocoptyches* Nalepa, 1922
    Type. *Phyllocoptyches gallicolus* Nalepa, 1922
22. *Platyphytoptus* Keifer, 1938
    Type. *Platyphytoptus sabinianae* Keifer, 1938

23. *Quadracus* Keifer, 1944
     Type. *Quadracus urticae* Keifer, 1944
24. *Rhyncaphytoptus* Keifer, 1939
     Type. *Rhyncaphytoptus ficifoliae* Keifer, 1939
25. *Tegonotus* Nalepa, 1890
     Type. *Tegonotus fastigatus* Nalepa, 1890
26. *Tetra* Keifer, 1944
     Type. *"Phyllocoptruta" concava* Keifer, 1939
27. *Thamnacus* Keifer, 1944
     Type. *Phyllocoptes rhamnicola* Keifer, 1938
28. *Tumescoptes* Keifer, 1939
     Type. *Tumescoptes trachycarpi* Keifer, 1939
29. *Vasates* Shimer, 1869
     Type. *Vasates quadripedes* Shimer, 1869

Unassigned genus:

   Flexipalpus Scheuten, 1857
   Type. *Flexipalpus tiliae* Scheuten, 1857

Discussion: Not until Keifer's 1942 work on the alternation of generations in the buckeye rust mite (*Oxypleurites aesculifoliae* Keifer), was the life cycle of certain of the eriophyid mites fully understood. Yothers *et al.* 1930 had studied the citrus rust mite and Baker 1939 the fig mite, but both species belong to those having a simple life cycle without alternation of generations. Keifer's study on the buckeye rust mite has also solved the problem of the pear leaf rust mite, *Epitrimerus pirifoliae* Keifer.

   One female of *Oxypleurites aesculifoliae* resembles the male and is called the *protogyne*. The other female of this species is morphologically different from the primogyne, or primary type, and has no male counterpart. This Keifer calls the *deutogyne*. Originally, owing to differences in striation, the two forms had been described as different species in different genera [*Phyllocoptes aesculifoliae* (protogyne) and *Oxypleurites neocarinatus* (deutogyne)]. The *Oxypleurite* female, or *protogynes,* when reared, produced both forms of females. *Deutogynes* when reared laid eggs which gave birth to egg-laying *protogynes*.

   The following life history of the buckeye rust mite is taken from Keifer 1942.

The deutogynes become active in late winter, leave their hibernating quarters on the twigs and when the buds swell in February, penetrate beneath the outer scales; there they feed on the green tissue of the inner scales.

With the development of the early spring leaves, the deutogynes lay eggs which hatch into nymphs producing primary mites on the leaves. These primaries soon begin active reproduction of additional primary mites. Beginning about the last of April or early May, new deutogynes appear among the primary types and when full fed, these deutogynes travel down the stems 6 inches or more. There they crawl into crevices or other shelters on the previous season's wood. Thus deutogynes are leaving the leaves through May and until leaf drop in the middle of July. The primary mites are confined to the leaves and green tissue and perish with it, although reproduction has largely ceased by early July. The mites prefer the underside of the leaves, but usually there is such a high population that both surfaces are inhabited and considerable leaf "rusting" results. Once the deutogynes attain a suitable crevice they become dormant and partially dry out in late summer. However, winter rains and frost reverse this process and recondition the deutogynes for activity the following spring. There is a high mortality among the deutogynes, principally because of crevice limitation.

While the spring progeny of the buckeye *Oxypleurites* deutogynes were not critically examined, it was noted that the first series of primary types contained egg-laying females, indicating either predormancy fertilization of the deutogynes or a deuterotokous reproductive capacity.

Putman, 1939 (Seventh Ann. Rpt. Ent. Soc. Ont. p. 33), working with *Phyllocoptes fockeui* in Canada, has described what is clearly discerned to be a functional deutogyne, and states that both males and females hatch from eggs laid by overwintering females. He considers that these overwintering females (deutogynes) may have been fertilized before hibernation, since he showed that ordinary unfertilized females (protogyne) produce only males. Putman further noted that the production of "hibernating forms" seemed correlated with foliage hardening, a speculation consistent in the main with observations on the buckeye mite.

The fig mite, *Aceria ficus* (Cotte), which illustrates a simple life cycle, does not directly cause serious injury to the fig in California, as do some eriophyids to their hosts. The mites live in the bud scales, on the leaf surfaces, or inside the green figs. If the population is high enough individual bud scales are scarred and some immature leaves killed within the bud. The scarred or rusted condition is seldom noticed on the mature leaves. However, this rusty condition is quite noticeable within the fig where the usual damage is to the eye scales only. With a large population the scarring may penetrate the interior of the fig. It is thought that the smuts and molds of the figs (*Aspergillus, Hormodendrum, Caldosporium, Rhizopus*) obtain an early foothold on the necrotic areas caused by the feeding of the mites within the fig.

The mites spend the winter within the terminal buds, the population varying from ten to several hundred per bud, with about 10 per cent of the buds infested. Reproduction takes place throughout the winter. In the spring when the leaf buds break open the mites infest both surfaces of the leaves. The population reaches its peak in June and July. Eggs are laid indiscriminately on upper and lower leaf surfaces of young, tender leaves, but the mites are usually found only on the lower surfaces of the mature leaves, probably because the lower surface is more succuient and is shaded from the sun. In cases of extremely heavy infestation the mites may be found on the dorsal leaf surface. First-crop figs are infested within two weeks after the fruit buds have pushed out into figs. About 90 per cent of this crop is infested. Second-crop figs are infested about eight days after being formed and nearly all the second crop is infested by the first of July. However, as the fig ripens and the eye scales loosen, the predaceous mites and thrips take their toll until in a ripe fig only a few mites are to be found. These mites which have found their way into the terminal buds throughout the summer carry over the population during the winter. As high as 50 per cent of the buds examined during the summer have been infested.

The following account of the importance of the eriophyids has been taken from Keifer 1946.

The Eriophyid mites, variously known as gall mites, blister mites, rust mites, and bud mites, are the smallest animals bearing an exterior skeleton with which the agriculturist has to contend. They deform and russet leaves and fruit, blast buds, and if uncontrolled will frequently put their host plant out of production.

Eriophyids exhibit a very intimate mite-host relationship, characterized by considerable host specificity. Gall formation of one kind or another is another aspect of this intimacy, but the majority depend on natural formations on their hosts and cause no discernible injury. They remain in locations where feeding and breeding can take place whenever temperature permits, with few exceptions. The exceptions are specialized aestivating forms which spend their quiescent period in dry bark crevices.

In general there are two types of Eriophyids; the worm-like soft kinds that are gall mites or bud mites, and which do all their feeding and breeding under cover, and the rust mites, which are broader and chunkier, often rather flat, which have heavy back plates to protect them against the action of light and desiccation, and which feed and breed more or less on open-leaf surfaces. This latter type, with few exceptions, constitutes the rust mites, or leaf vagrants.

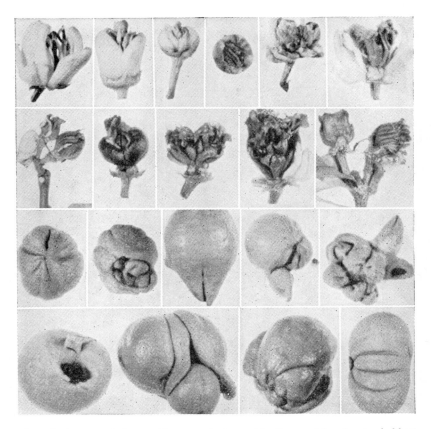

Plate 1 Damage to lemon blossoms, buds, and fruit caused by *Aceria sheldoni* (Ewing). (From A. M. Boyce, Insects and mites and their control, the Citrus Industry, Volume II, 1948. Courtesy of The University of California Press.)

The mite species which are of more or less economic importance in North America number about 50. Of these the pear leaf blister mite is perhaps the most generally known, and one of the most important, since it can put its host out of fruit production.

The Eriophyid mites on grape lack greater importance than they have largely because grapes are so consistently sulfured for mildew. Nevertheless there are two kinds of these mites known in North America, namely, the grape erineum mite, *Eriophyes vitis* (Pgst.), and the grape rust mite, *Calepitrimerus vitis* (Can.). The former species forms erineum patches on the under surface of the leaves and there seems to be a certain amount of varietal resistance to the activities of this mite shown by different kinds of grapes. For example, one kind of grape which is fairly well over-run with erineum patches has been observed to be interlocked with another variety of grape which had few or no erineum patches.

The grape rust mite, which develops deutogynes in the fall, has received little attention in North America.

On citrus, the rust mite, *Phyllocoptruta oleivorus* (Ashm.) is a pest of long standing in the warmest citrus-growing areas of the United States. This mite, which is on an evergreen host, winters on the leaves and produces no specialized hibernating forms.

In California, the most important citrus Eriophyid pest is the citrus bud mite, *Aceria sheldoni* (Ewing), which is to be found in practically all of the citrus-growing areas adjacent to the coast in Southern California. Severely damaged lemon trees show stunting and clustering of the young growth, and severe leaf and fruit malformation. These mites leave a characteristic brown condition in the buds in which they work. They may be found developing in large numbers under fruit buttons where they also leave a brown injury.

The citrus bud mite also works on oranges and grapefruit and seems to have a general range through the Pacific citrus-growing areas. Very similar or identical populations damage citrus in such places as Hawaii, Australia and Java.

Peach is infested by one Eriophyid, namely, the silver mite, *Vasates cornutus* (Banks). This mite winters around the lateral buds from 3 to 12 inches below the terminals, in the form of deutogynes. In the early spring, these mites invade the tender growing tips, and at that time, if the host plant lacks leaf glands, or if the leaf glands are not operating properly (these produce a sticky secretion), the mites cause an unhealthy longitudinal rolling of the leaves and, in some cases, numerous fine yellow dots on the leaves. This injury is not to be confused with the silvering of the peach leaf, which silvering occurs after prolonged feeding during spring and summer. The mite feeds on both leaf surfaces and produces deutogynes only in response to the temperature drop in the fall.

The plum nursery mite, *Vasates fockeui* (Nal. & Trt.), is found throughout the northern states and Canada. It severely damages young growth on
plums which accounts for its common name. This mite is closely similar
to the peach silver mite, no characters at the present time being available
to indicate a structural distinction between the two.

Filbert and currant suffer from the attacks of big-bud mites, *Phytoptus
avellanae Nal.,* and *Cecidophyes ribis* Nal., respectively. The terminal buds
on certain filbert varieties enlarge in the spring, and turn into galls never
producing shoots. The filbert mite is unique in having two types of nymphs,
a normal type developing in the big-buds, and a flattened nymph which
spends the summer on the undersides of the leaves.

The redberry mite on blackberries along the Pacific Coast, namely,
Aceria essigi (Hassan), insures itself a breeding place in an unusual manner. Feeding in the developing berry by this mite causes either all of the
drupelets, or the basal ones, to remain red and unripe. The berry thus
hangs on the vine longer, and is unfit for eating.

The Eriophyid with the most peculiar habitat, that has come to notice
so far, is the onion or bulb Eriophyid, *Aceria tulipae* (K.). Liliaceous bulbs
such as onion, garlic and tulip are attacked, the mites living between the
bulb layers. Thus the mite lives underground, a habit not known to be
possessed by any other species. The activities of *Aceria tulipae* cause the
bulbs to shrink and dry out. These mites persist in storage.

References:

Baker, E. W. 1939. The fig mite, *Eriophyes ficus* Cotte, and other mites of
    the fig tree, *Ficus carica* Linn. Bull. Calif. Dept. Agr. 28(4):266–275.

Boyce, A. M., and R. B. Korsmeier. 1941. The citrus bud mite, *Eriophyes
    sheldoni* Ewing. J. Econ. Ent. 34(6):745–756.

Hodgkiss, H. E. 1930. The Eriophyidae of New York: II. The maple
    mites. N. Y. State Agr. Expt. Sta. Tech. Bull. 163.

Keifer, H. H. 1938. Eriophyid studies. Bull. Calif. Dept. Agr. 27(2):181–
    206, and subsequent publications.

——. 1942. Eriophyid studies XII. Bull. Calif. Dept. Agr. 31 (3):
    117–129.

——. 1946. A review of North American economic eriophyid mites.
    J. Econ. Ent. 39(5):563–570.

Parrott, P. J., H. E. Hodgkiss, and W. S. Schoene. 1906. The apple and
    pear mites. N. Y. State Agr. Expt. Sta. Bull. 283.

Yothers, W. W., and A. C. Mason. 1930. The citrus rust mite and its con-
    trol. U.S. Dept. Agr. Tech. Bull. 176.

TARSONEMINI CANESTRINI AND FANZAGO, 1877

The females possess a tracheal system behind the pedipalps; the males perhaps may have a rudimentary stigma. The females usually have a pair of latero-ventral, keglike pseudostigmatic organs between coxae I and II. The mouth parts are reduced. The two sexes are usually differentiated.

Key to the Tarsonemini

1. Both males and females with four pairs of legs   2

    Females with one to three pairs of legs; males with three, seldom four, pairs of legs   Podapolipodidae

2. Anterior dorsal body plate not forming a broad, rooflike covering over mite; leg IV not ending in many whiplike setae   3

    Anterior dorsal body plate forming broad rooflike covering over mite; leg IV ending in many whiplike setae, one "seta" may bear pair of claws, being merely extremely modified portion of tarsus   Scutacaridae

3. Leg IV of female with ambulacra (claws and cup)
         Pyemotidae (= Pediculoididae)

    Leg IV of female without ambulacra, ending in terminal and subterminal whiplike setae   Tarsonemidae

Podapolipodidae Oudemans, 1931

Figure 107

Diagnosis: Parasites of insects. The females lack spherical pseudostigmatic organs and are without the complete number or with deformed legs; the female may be legless in the adult stage. The chelicerae are needle-like, the palpi are rudimentary, and the legs have claws and caruncle.

This family shows the greatest degeneration or specialization of all the mites, remaining more or less in the larval stage. The first stage is a sexually undifferentiated larva which has three pairs of legs, the posterior pair separate from the other two and almost on the end of the body; on the posterior of the body is a small tubercle bearing two adhering, long, whiplike setae which are lost in the adults.

In *Locustacarus trachealis* Ewing the sexually mature female retains the appearance of the larvae and the posterior setae, which are lost in the other members of the family. The *Tarsopolipus* are the least degenerate. The male has four pairs of normal legs but appears similar to the males of the other genera which have only three pairs of legs. The female has three pairs of legs, the third pair being on the posterior portion of the body. During the parasitic life the body becomes strongly swollen. Both the males and females of *Eutarsopolipus* are

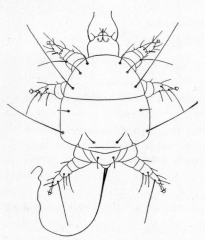

similar to the larvae in having three pairs of legs. In the female during the parasitic stage the hysterosoma stretches so that the third pair of legs moves posteriorly to give the mite a flasklike shape. In the *Tetrapolipus* the male has three pairs of legs but the female loses the third pair. Legs I and II are quite short but maintain the normal segmentation. During parasitism the body swells to about three times its length. The male of *Podapolipus* has the three pairs of legs but the female develops from the larva into a completely degenerate form with only the first pair of legs present. These legs are extremely short but are divided into three to five segments. In the position

Figure 107 *Locustacarus trachealis* Ewing. Young female.

where legs II would join the body are two diverticulae which flank the sides of the gnathosoma to give the anterior end of the body a characteristic appearance. The body may become rather swollen and the shape depends upon gravity and other external influences.

Genera:

1. *Podapolipus* Rovelli and Grassi, 1888 (= *Pimelofia* Trägårdh, 1902)
   Type. *Podapolipus reconditus* Rovelli and Grassi, 1888
2. *Eutarsopolipus* Berlese, 1913
   Type. *Eutarsopolipus lagenaeformis* Berlese, 1913
3. *Locustacarus* Ewing, 1924
   Type. *Locustacarus trachealis* Ewing, 1924
4. *Tarsopolipus* Berlese, 1911
   Type. *Tarsopolipus corrugatus* Berlese, 1911

5. *Tetrapolipus* Berlese, 1911

　　Type. *Tetrapolipus batocerae* Berlese, 1911

Discussion: These mites are parasitic on other arthropods. *Locustacarus trachealis* Ewing is found in the tracheae of grasshoppers in the United States and South Africa. *Tetrapolipus rhynchophori* Ewing was taken from beneath the elytra of *Rhynchophorus palmarum,* a palm weevil from Panama. *Podapolipus reconditus* Rovelli and Grassi is to be found under the elytra of certain European beetles; *Podapolipus grassi* Berlese, *P. bacillus* Berlese, and *P. diander* Volkonsky are external parasites of grasshoppers.

The most complete study of these mites has been made by Volkonsky 1940 on *Podapolipus diander,* a parasite of *Locusta migratoria* L. in Algeria. Young females of the mites are usually found under the posterior extension of the pronotum in the first three instars of the grasshopper. In the fourth and fifth instars the mites attach and lay eggs on the body under the rudimentary elements of the elytra and wings. When the grasshopper molts, the immature mites that have hatched from the eggs and the females that have not yet engorged and oviposited leave the cast skin and attach to the host grasshopper again. The adult grasshoppers harbor these mites in the folds between the mesothorax and metathorax and on the parts of the thorax covered with the elytra, on the underside of the elytra near the base, and along the main veins of the wings, usually on the ventral side. The first-stage females of the mites transform into adults. These adults mature and produce parthenogenetically an egg from which a "small" male immediately hatches. This "small" male mates with the parent female, and the latter begins to lay eggs which hatch within five or six days to produce females and "large" males. These males are parasitic on the females, perforating the abdomen of the female mites and at times killing them. These first-stage females attach to the intersegmental membranes of the grasshopper, feeding by piercing the integument, and gradually migrate toward the posterior segments and congregate at the genitalia. Mites are spread from one grasshopper to another when the grasshoppers mate. If the temperature rises to about 80.6 F many of the mites leave the host at night and crawl into crevices in the soil or to the tips of grass blades, attempting to attach to any object with which they come into contact. If they attach to *Locusta migratoria* the life cycle is continued; otherwise they die. The mites may develop continuously during the summer and pass the winter as eggs or as first-stage females attached to the grasshoppers.

Locustacarus trachealis Ewing lives in the principal tracheae and air sacs of grasshoppers, all stages being found in this habitat. The mites probably obtain nourishment by piercing the walls of the tracheae and air sacs and sucking the blood of the host. The body of the female, when gravid, extends to several times its former size. The eggs are laid in the tracheae; the female sometimes contains six to eight fully developed eggs and many more in different stages of development.

References:

Ewing, H. E. 1924. New tarsonemid mites (Order Acarina, family Tarsonemidae). Proc. Ent. Soc. Wash. 26(3):66–69.

Rovelli, G., and B. Grassi. 1888. Di un singolare acaride, *Podapolipus reconditus,* nobis. Bol. Soc. Ent. Ital. 20:59–63, Pl. XV.

Volkonsky, M. 1940. *Podapolipus diander,* n. sp., acarien hétérostygmate parasite du criquet migrateur (*Locusta migratoria* L.) Archiv. Inst. Pasteur Algérie 18(3):321–340.

Wehrle, L. P., and P. S. Welch. 1925. The occurrence of mites in the tracheal system of certain orthoptera. Ann. Ent. Soc. Amer. 28(1):35–44.

Scutacaridae Oudemans, 1916

Figure 108

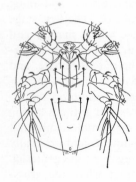

Diagnosis: The dorsal plates of the female are divided into tergites, the anterior plate covering the gnathosoma like a roof. These mites are usually round and flat. Female leg IV is elongated and may or may not have claws which end in strong setae.

Figure 108 *Scutacarus mediocritarsus* Vitzthum. Venter of female. (After Vitzthum 1925)

Genera:

1. *Scutacarus* Gros, 1845 (= *Disparipes* Michael, 1884)
   Type. *Acarus acarorum* Goeze, 1780 (= *Scutacarus femoris* Gros, 1845 = *Disparipes bombi* Michael, 1884)
2. *Acarapis* Hirst, 1921
   Type. *Tarsonemus woodi* Rennie, 1921

3. *Diversipes* Berlese, 1903
   a. *Diversipes* s. str.
      Type. *Disparipes exhamulatus* Michael, 1886
   b. *Microdispus* Paoli, 1911
      Type. *Microdispus obovatus* Paoli, 1911
4. *Imparipes* Berlese, 1903
   a. *Imparipes* s. str.
      Type. *Imparipes hystricinus* Berlese, 1903
   b. *Heterodispus* Paoli, 1911
      Type. *Imparipes elongatus* Trägårdh, 1904
5. *Microdispodides* Vitzthum, 1914
   Type. *Pediculoides amaniensis* Oudemans, 1912
      (= *Microdispodides wichmanni* Vitzthum, 1914)
6. *Pygmodispus* Paoli, 1911
   a. *Pygmodispus* s. str.
      Type. *Pygmodispus equestris* Paoli, 1911
   b. *Allodispus* Paoli, 1911
      Type. *Pygmodispus* (*Allodispus*) *latisternus* Paoli, 1911
7. *Variatipes* Paoli, 1911
   Type. *Disparipes nudus* Berlese, 1886

Discussion: These mites are minute, bizarre creatures, found in moss, soil, and sod samples throughout the world, and on various insects such as *Formica* and *Lasius*. One member of this family is a pest of honey bees. *Acarapis woodi* (Rennie) is the cause of the "Isle of Wight Disease" which is to be found in Europe. This scutacarid infests the tracheal tubes of bees and causes the eventual death of the host. The life cycle takes place within the tracheal tubes, although adult mites are to be found crawling through the hair of infested bees whereby they can be transferred from bee to bee. The mite causes injury to the bee by: (1) the parasite living upon the host fluids causing active injury; (2) possibly a toxic secretion; (3) mechanical stoppage of the tracheae which prevents air from reaching the individual organs or cutting off the air supply to the nerve centers which control the bee's activities. This mechanical disturbance is probably the most important. Since the bees can neither fly nor feed this becomes a nutrition problem.

References:

Hirst, S. 1922. Mites injurious to domestic animals. Brit. Mus. (Nat. Hist.) Econ. Ser., No. 13.

Jacot, A. P. 1936. Two unrecorded species of Scutacaridae from the Southern Appalachians. Canad. Ent. 68:225–229, Figs. 1–3.

Paoli, Guido. 1911. Monografia del "Tarsonemidi." Redia 7:215–281, Pls. VII–XI.

Rennie, J., *et al.* 1921. Isle of Wight Disease in hive bees. Trans. Roy. Soc. Edinburgh 52(4), No. 29:737–779.

Pyemotidae Oudemans, 1937

(= Pediculoididae Berlese, 1907)

Figures 109–112

Diagnosis: The anterior dorsal shield does not project anteriorly like a roof. Leg IV of the female is similar to legs II and III. The females have a capitate organ between coxae I and II except in *Acarophenax*. The chelicerae are stylet-like and the palpi are small and simple.

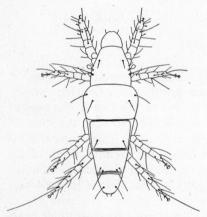 

Figure 109 *Pyemotes* (= *Pediculoides*) *ventricosus* (Newport). Dorsum of female.

Figure 110 *Pyemotes* (= *Pediculoides*) *ventricosus* (Newport). Dorsum of male.

Genera:

1. *Pyemotes* Amerling, 1862 (= *Heteropus* Newport, 1850, *nom. prae-occ.* = *Pediculoides* Targioni-Tozzetti, 1878)
   Type. *Pyemotes eccoptogasteri pruni* Amerling, 1862
2. *Acarophenax* Newstead and Duvall, 1918
   Type. *Acarophenax tribolii* Newstead and Duvall, 1918
3. *Pavania* Lombardini, 1949
   Type. *Pavania fusiformis* Lombardini, 1949

4. *Phthiroides* Oudemans, 1937
   Type. *Phthiroides megnini* Oudemans, 1937
5. *Pygmephorus* Kramer, 1877
   Type. *Pygmephorus spinosus* Kramer, 1877
6. *Resinacarus* Vitzthum, 1927
   Type. *Resinacarus resinatus* Vitzthum, 1927
7. *Siteroptes* Amerling, 1861 (= *Therismoptes* Amerling, 1861 = *Pediculopsis* Reuter, 1907)
   Type. *Acarus graminisugus* Hardy, 1851
8. *Tarsonemoides* Trägårdh, 1904
   Type. *Tarsonemoides termitophilus* Trägårdh, 1904

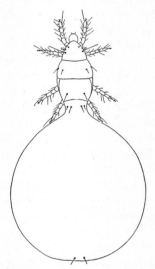

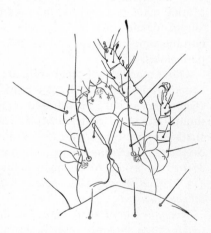

Figure 111 *Pyemotes* (= *Pediculoides*) *ventricosus* (Newport). Partially gravid female.

Figure 112 *Siteroptes* (= *Pediculopsis*) *graminum* (Reuter). Respiratory system of gravid female.

Discussion: The life cycle of *Pyemotes* (= *Pediculoides*) *ventricosus* (Newport) is as follows. Males and females are produced viviparously and are sexually mature at birth. The female is fertilized immediately after emergence and seeks a suitable host and pierces it with the stylet-like chelicerae. As it feeds the tip of the abdomen becomes enormously distended and the eggs develop and hatch within the swollen bag. The developing mites complete all their stages within the parent and do not emerge until mature. The first to emerge are the males, usually only a small number. These males feed very little and pierce the parent "sphere" in order to obtain food. They do not leave the mother but remain clustered about the genital opening and fertilize the females as they emerge. A full-sized gravid female is capable of producing 200 to 300 offspring, and retains its vitality throughout the birth of its progeny.

The life cycle of *Siteroptes* (= *Pediculopsis*) *graminum* (Reuter) is even more interesting than that of the preceding species. During attachment to food the hysterosoma of the female swells from 100 to 500 times the original body volume and within this sack the eggs are formed and develop into adult mites. In this species, however, there is a mass birth marked by a breakdown of the hysterosoma, although an early larva, nymph, or especially male may be extruded before the mass birth. Only a few males are born, each brood containing at least one male. Mating takes place within the sack before birth, as well as after birth. Virgin females give rise to males, which have the haploid number of chromosomes. This species, as well as *Pyemotes,* possesses heteromorphic males.

Other members of this family are little known and apparently of no economic importance. Banks 1915 stated that migratorial forms of a *Pygmephorus* have been found on a mole, flies, and thrips, and Vitzthum states that *Pygmephorus* is carnivorous. *Pygmephorus americanus* Banks has been reported as a "pseudoparasite" of *Musca domestica* and *Stomoxys calcitrans*. Jacot 1936 has described a few east coast species and given a key to distinguish the more common genera *Pyemotes* (= *Pediculoides*), *Siteroptes* (= *Pediculopsis*), *Pygmephorus,* and *Resinacarus*.

Pyemotes (= *Pediculoides*) *ventricosus* (Newport) is the causative agent of the hay or grain itch. Normally it is an ectoparasite of various insect larvae such as the Angoumois grain moth, *Sitotroga cerealella* (Olivier), the satin moth, *Stilpnotia salicis* (L.), the peach twig borer, *Anarsia lineatella* Zeller, and of many other insects. When grain infested with the parasitized grain moth larvae is handled at threshing, in storage, or on the docks, these mites will attack man, especially in hot weather when the need for moisture is great, and cause an intense itching. All parts of the body are affected, although the arms and neck are the regions usually attacked. As many as a thousand bites have been recorded from one individual. They cannot burrow under the skin or persist long on man, however. Swan 1934 describes the eruptions as follows: "The wheals vary in size and form with different subjects. They present, especially after rubbing, a raised whitish area with a small central vesicle, which marks the seat of the puncture. The blanched area is surrounded by a rosy red areole. The lesions may itch severely, especially when warm in bed, or when the body is heated by exertion. Rubbing and scratching usually break the central vesicle and the possibility of secondary infection then arises. Itching usually subsides in two to three days, but the marks may last longer." Webster 1910 states that some severe cases show general systemic symptoms such as a "rise of temperature from 99° to 102°; in one case the temperature rose to 103.8°; the pulse rate is accelerated to 100, or as high as 110—in one case to 130. Other symptoms were intense headache, anorexia, nausea, in some cases vomiting, and a mild form of diarrhoea. In severe cases some complained of general joint pains and backache; in these the urine was examined and albumin in small amount was found, but no casts or blood. When the acute symptoms disappeared so did the albumin." Asthma due to these mites has also been reported. Generally, the mite is not considered important in controlling insect pests, although in isolated cases or in the laboratory, colonies of larvae may be completely eradicated by this mite. The distribution of this species appears to be world-wide. Until recently only one species, *Pyemotes* (= *Pediculoides*) *ventricosus,* was recognized but Oudemans 1937 has described several more.

Siteroptes (= *Pediculopsis*) *graminum* (Reuter) superficially resembles the preceding species, but is a pest of grasses and grains, causing considerable damage to wheat, oats, barley, and rye, as well as being the active agent in the dissemination of the spores of the carnation bud rot, *Sporotrichum poae,* in the United States. Infested cereals may be malformed and stunted, and often silvered, leading to the common name of "silver top."

References:

Cooper, K. W. 1937. Reproductive behaviour and haploid parthenogenesis in the grass mite, *Pediculopsis graminum* (Reut.) (Acarina, Tarsonemidae). Proc. Natl. Acad. Sci. 23(2):41–44.

——. 1940. Relations of *Pediculopsis graminum* and *Fusarium poae* to central bud rot of carnation. Phytopathology 30(10):853–859.

Herfs, A. 1926. Okologische Untersuchungen an *Pediculoides ventricosus* (Newp.). Berl. Zoologica, Heft 74, Stuttgart.

Jacot, A. P. 1936. An undescribed mite from the southern Appalachians. Canad. Ent. 68(4):82–85.

Oudemans, A. C. 1937. Tijdschr. v. Ent. 80, Verslag IV–VIII.

Swan, D. C. 1934. The hay itch mite, *Pediculoides ventricosus* (Newp.) (Acarina, Pediculoididae) in South Australia. J. Agr. South Austral. 37:1289–1299.

Webster, F. M. 1910. A predaceous and supposedly beneficial mite, *Pediculoides*, becomes obnoxious to man. Ann. Ent. Soc. Amer. 3(1): 15–39, Pls. III–V.

Tarsonemidae Kramer, 1877

Figures 113–115

Diagnosis: The tarsonemids have a segmented body and an anterior dorsal shield which lacks a rooflike projection. Leg IV of female differs from legs II and III in that it ends in an apical and subapical whiplike

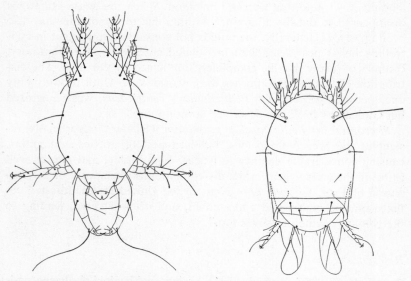

Figure 113 *Tarsonemus setifer* Ewing. Dorsum of male.

Figure 114 *Tarsonemus setifer* Ewing. Dorsum of female.

setae. *Tarsonemella* and *Tarsonemus typhae* Oudemans 1929 lack the clavate organ between coxae I and II while others have such an organ. The chelicerae are stylet-like and the palpi simple. Heteromorphic males are present in this family. The group of genera now included under the tarsonemids is heterogeneous and probably needs further revision.

Genera:

1. *Tarsonemus* Canestrini and Fanzago, 1876
   Type. *Chironemus minusculus* Canestrini and Fanzago, 1876
2. *Avrosia* Oudemans, 1928
   Type. *Acarus translucens* Nietner, 1861
3. *Hemitarsonemus* Ewing, 1939
   Type. *Tarsonemus tepidariorum* Warburton, 1904
4. *Pseudotarsonemoides* Vitzthum, 1921
   Type. *Pseudotarsonemoides eccoptogasteris* Vitzthum, 1921
5. *Tarsonemella* Hirst, 1923
   Type. *Tarsonemella africana* Hirst, 1923

Discussion: The tarsonemids illustrate a highly simplified type of life cycle. There are only four stages: egg, larva, quiescent nymphal stage in which the larva transforms into a mature adult (there being no active nymph), and the adult. The males are heteromorphic and the fourth pair of legs is used for clasping the female during copulation. This pair of legs is extremely important in the identification of the species. The females lay one egg at a time, the hysterosoma being adapted with a series of overlapping segments to allow for the expansion of the body. The mites appear to prefer humid, sheltered conditions and disappear in many cases after the onset of high temperatures.

Figure 115
Tarsonemus phyllopherus Ewing. Leg iv of male. (After Ewing 1939)

This is a widely distributed group of mites, being found throughout the warmer parts of the world. Although some of the species appear to be scavengers and predators, many are of economic importance because they cause serious injury to plants. The following species which have proved to be injurious to their hosts indicate the wide range of host plants and the importance of this family.

Tarsonemus pallidus Banks is a serious pest of cyclamens in the United States and of strawberries in Europe; *T. waitei* Banks injures the peach tree in various parts of the United States; *T. spirifex* Marchal damages oats in Europe and has been reported from Arizona and Kansas in the United States; *T. laticeps* Halbert, the bulb scale mite, is a pest of narcissus bulbs in Europe and the United States, causing reduction in the number of flowers produced; *T. ananas* Tryon is an agent in the transmission of a pineapple rot in Australia. *Hemitarsonemus latus* (Banks) is listed as being a pest of a wide assortment of plants throughout the world, such as tea in Ceylon, *Cinchona* sp. in

Sumatra, *Hevea* sp. in the Netherlands Indies, tomato, cyclamen, delphinium in the United States, and cotton in the Belgian Congo.

Tarsonemus sp. have also been recorded as being taken from lungs of persons suffering from asthma and other respiratory ailments.

References:

Carter, H., G. Wedd, and V. St. E. D'Abrera. 1944. The occurrence of mites (Acarina) in human sputum and their possible significance. India Med. Gaz. 79(4):163–168.

Ewing, H. E. 1939. A revision of the mites of the subfamily Tarsoneminae of North America, the West Indies, and the Hawaiian Islands. U.S. Dept. Agr. Tech. Bull. 653.

Hambleton, E. J. 1938. A ocorrencia do ácaro tropical *"Tarsonemus latus* Banks,"* (Acar. Tarsonemidae). Causador da rasgadura das folhas nos algodoais de S. Paulo. Arch. Inst. Biol. [Sao Paulo] 9(19):201–209, Pls. 19–23.

Moznette, G. F. 1917. The cyclamen mite. J. Agr. Res. 10(8):373–390.

Soysa, E., and M. Jayawardena. 1945. Pulmonary acariasis: a possible cause of asthma. Brit. Med. J. No. 4383, pp. 1–6.

Vrydagh, J. M. 1942. Etude de l'acariose du cotonnier, causee par *Hemitarsonemus latus* (Banks) au Congo Belge. Pubs. Inst. Natl. pour l'Etude Agron. Congo Belge, Sér. Sci., No. 28.

PROSTIGMATA KRAMER, 1877

These mites have a respiratory system with the stigma opening at or near the base of the chelicerae.

Key to the Prostigmata

1. Body normal; shape neither wormlike nor annulate   2

    Body small, wormlike, annulate; with eight legs; parasites in skin pores   Demodicidae

2. Living on land   3

    Living in water   Hydrachnellae [1]

3. Without thumb-claw process on palpus   4

    With thumb-claw process on palpus composed of spine or claw on palpal tibia and ventrally placed palpal tarsus   21

4. Gnathosoma extended into very long, conelike process   5

    Gnathosoma short, not conelike   7

[1] The "water mites" are included as a complete unit with keys to simplify presentation.

5. Gnathosoma free, not enclosed in sheath 6

   Gnathosoma enclosed in sheath formed by extension of body wall; body hard; no suture between propodosoma and hysterosoma; chelicerae elongated with small, equal, distal shears; with two pairs of genital suckers Cryptognathidae

6. Palpi long, turned inward; distal segment clawlike, adapted for grasping; body with external plates; with two pairs of genital suckers Cunaxidae

   Palpi long, elbowed, sensory organ; distal segment of palpus with usually two long, sensory setae; chelicerae elongated with small, equal, distal shears; body soft without surface plates; with three pairs of genital suckers Bdellidae

7. Movable chela sharp, small, for piercing; not opposed to fixed chela 8

   Movable chela usually with teeth; opposed to fixed chela and adapted for biting and grasping 12

   Movable chela long, whiplike, for piercing; with stylophore; small mites; allied to the Tetranychidae but without thumb-claw process Phytoptipalpidae

8. With two pairs of genital suckers 9

   Without genital suckers 10

9. With a pair of long, fine, sensory setae on both propodosoma and hysterosoma; without peritremes Ereynetidae

   With sensory setae only on propodosoma; with peritremes; with small, clawlike pulvillus Paratydeidae

10. Without peritremes, legs I normal; free-living 11

    With peritremes; chelicerae needle-like, extrusible, for piercing; palpi minute, difficult to see; legs I highly specialized for grasping hairs in many cases (rather heterogeneous group of genera related to Cheyletidae but lacking strongly developed palpi; thumb-claw complex present but difficult to see because of reduction in size) Myobiidae

11. Legs with netlike armor; movable chela minute, almost invisible; found in nasal passage of birds Speleognathidae

    Legs without netlike armor; movable chela large, visible; free-living Tydeidae

12. Without well-developed pseudostigmata or pseudostigmatic organs on propodosoma   13

    With well-developed pseudostigmatic and pseudostigmatic organs on propodosoma (Endeostigmata of Grandjean 1939)   16

13. With "Rhagidia organ" on tarsus I; coxae I–II and III–IV in two separate groups   14

    Without "Rhagidia organ" on tarsus I; coxae platelike, contiguous; armored with lenslike eyes and usually with large, lenslike organs behind eyes; with two pairs of genital suckers; palpal end segment small, pointed, with long end setae   Labidostommidae

14. With small, distorted cheliceral shears, not for grasping   15

    With large, cheliceral shears, for grasping; body soft, with two pairs of genital suckers; palpal end segment large, rounded, with many short setae   Rhagidiidae

15. Soft-bodied, without projection over rostrum; with two pairs of genital suckers   Eupodidae

    Hard-armored, with projection or shield over rostrum; with two pairs of genital suckers   Penthalodidae

16. With three pairs of genital suckers; eyes present or absent   17

    With two pairs of genital suckers; eyes present or absent   18

17. With single pair of sensory setae on propodosoma   Terpnacaridae

    With two pairs of sensory setae on propodosoma   Pachygnathidae

18. With two pairs of sensory setae on propodosoma   19

    With single pair of sensory setae on propodosoma; tarsi monodactyle; no eyes   Alicorhagiidae

19. Tarsi with two or three claws   20

    Tarsi monodactyle; body clearly segmented; legs IV adapted for jumping; eyes probably present in all genera   Nanorchestidae

20. Legs I–IV tridactyle; no eyes; anterior pair of sensory setae in special depression; fixed chela almost lacking   Lordalychidae

    Leg I bidactyle; legs II–IV tridactyle; two pairs of eyes; no special depression for sensory setae; fixed chela normal   Sphaerolichidae

21. Movable chela developed into a straight, stylet-like, extrusible piercing organ   22

    Movable chela strong, hinged non-extrusible piercing organ   26

22. Movable chela straight, stiff, of varying lengths, no stylophore (mandibular plate)   23

    Movable chela long, whiplike, curving within body; basal cheliceral segments fused and form stylophores (mandibular plates); without crista and with lenslike eyes; no genital suckers (Phytoptipalpidae related to this family but do not possess thumb-claw process on palpus)   Tetranychidae

23. Chelicerae long, slender, capable of being withdrawn deeply into the body; dorsal sensory areas and sensory setae present   24

    Chelicerae short and not capable of being extended to such extent; with M-like prominent peritreme on gnathosoma; no dorsal sensory areas; with large pincer-like palpi for grasping   Cheyletidae

24. Without genital suckers; with sensillary area and/or crista   25

    With genital suckers; no sensillary areas; palpi small, entire mouth parts capable of being withdrawn into body cavity   Calyptostomidae

25. Mouth parts small, capable of being withdrawn into the body; propodosoma usually drawn out into long nose   Smaridiidae

    Mouth parts large, not capable of being withdrawn into body; propodosoma not drawn out into long nose or snout   Erythraeidae

26. Without strong body armor; with normal leg setae   27

    With several strongly sclerotized dorsal plates; legs I and II, especially I, with several large spines on tubercles giving rake effect
    Caeculidae

27. Palpal thumb not large; inconspicuous, at times hard to see   28

    Palpal thumb large and conspicuous   29

28. With three pairs of genital suckers; dorsal sensory setae in some cases set in characteristic pits or pseudostigmata; tarsal claws large, serrate   Teneriffiidae

    Without genital suckers; no specialized sensory setae on dorsum; tarsal claws not serrate; usually modified to live beneath scales of lizards; no suture between propodosoma and hysterosoma
    Pterygosomidae

    Without genital suckers; two pairs of sensory setae on propodosoma; with tarsal suckers or claws; free-living; body divided by suture   Pseudocheylidae

29. Palpal tarsus ventral   30

    Palpal tarsus distal; large red mite, with radiating legs; free peritremes   Anystidae

30. Large mites with sensory areas on propodosoma   32

    Small mites; no dorsal sensory areas   31

31. With three pairs of genital suckers; without eyes; tarsi with claws but without pulvillus; tarsus ɪ with seven rodlike sensory setae
           Pomerantziidae

    Without genital suckers; with one or two pairs of eyes; tarsi with claws and pulvillus; tarsus ɪ with only one rodlike sensory seta
           Raphignathidae

32. Adults not figure-8-shaped and with numerous setae on tectum if present; larvae usually with more than one dorsal plate; setae on pedipalpal coxa usually anterior to palpal femur   Trombidiidae

    Adults usually figure-8-shaped, with only one or two setae on tectum; larvae with a single dorsal plate (with exception of one genus with a pygidial plate); seta on pedipalpal coxa posterior to palpal femur   Trombiculidae

Eupodidae Koch, 1842

(= Penthaleidae Oudemans, 1931)

Figure 116

Diagnosis: The eupodids are yellowish or greenish, and occasionally flecked in color. Their legs are usually reddish or black flecked with red (*Penthaleus, Halotydeus*). They are small- to medium-sized mites from 0.160 to 1 mm. long. Fast moving and extremely fragile the

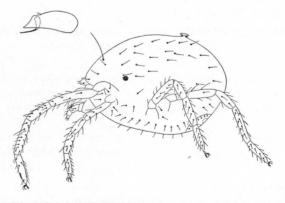

Figure 116 *Penthaleus major* (Dugès). Lateral view of female showing dorsal anus. Somewhat flattened by mounting. Upper left, chelicera.

eupodids are more or less pear-shaped with the narrow end to the rear. Either a strong or weak suture separates the propodosoma from the hysterosoma. Their skin is soft, finely striated, and weakly haired. An eye spot appears on each side of propodosoma and a pair of pseudo-stigmata with weakly differentiated sensory setae is present. Leg I of *Linopodes* is up to four times as long as the body while leg IV of *Eupodes* is somewhat thicker than the other legs and often has a very thick femora. The tarsi have two claws and a haired empodium. The palpi have four movable segments and the chelicerae are shearlike but have small, somewhat deformed, or modified chelae. Two pairs of genital suckers are present. In *Penthaleus* the anus is dorsal, while in *Halotydeus* it is terminal, and in other genera ventral.

Genera:

1. *Eupodes* Koch, 1836
   Type. *Eupodes hiemalis* Koch, 1838
2. *Cocceupodes* Thor, 1934
   Type. *Eupodes clavifrons* R. Canestrini, 1886
3. *Halotydeus* Berlese, 1891
   Type. *Notophallus hydrodromus* Berlese and Trouessart, 1889
4. *Linopodes* Koch, 1836
   Type. *Acarus motatorius* Linnaeus, 1758
5. *Penthaleus* Koch, 1836 (= *Notophallus* R. Canestrini, 1886)
   Type. *Tetranychus major* Dugès, 1834 (= *Penthaleus haemotopus* Koch, 1836)
6. *Protacarus* Hirst, 1923 (fossil)
   Type. *Protacarus crani* Hirst, 1923
7. *Protereunetes* Berlese, 1923
   Type. *Micrereunetes* (*Protereunetes*) *agilis* Berlese, 1923

The Eupodidae has been split into three families by European workers—Penthaleidae Oudemans, 1931, Penthalodidae Thor, 1933, and Eupodidae. The characters used to separate the Penthalodidae from the others appear to be substantial but those used for the family Penthaleidae do not give a clearly defined group. Because of this the Penthaleidae (*Penthaleus* and *Halotydeus*) are placed back into the Eupodidae.

Discussion: The life cycle of these mites is simple—egg, larva, nymph, adult. *Halotydeus destructor* (Tucker) has been studied in Australia. The dry season is bridged over by a resting egg laid in October. They are laid in great numbers on the soil surface, under clods or sticks, and are highly resistant to heat, drought, or desiccating winds. Moisture and sunshine are necessary for the hatching of these over-summering eggs. The adult is a soft-bodied mite whose front legs act as sensory organs. The leaf surfaces are broken by the rasping mouth parts and the sap is sucked up. The adult lives from twenty-five to fifty days and is killed off by heat and drought. The mite prefers light, well-drained soils.

Very few species are known. Of these *Linopodes antennaepes* Banks (?possibly *L. motatorius* L.) is a pest of mushrooms. This long-legged mite damages the mushrooms by chewing off the feeder roots of the growing plant, causing the stems to constrict at the base and injuring or killing the developing mushroom. The mites are found on or near the surface of the mushroom beds, and under boards and leaves out of doors. The eggs are laid in groups in the soil; they hatch in a short time into larvae which are similar to the adults except for the number of legs, genitalia, and other small differences; nymphs possess eight legs and are similar to the adult forms. The mite is found in the United States and in Europe.

Eupodes species are remarkable jumpers and the fourth pair of legs are enlarged for this purpose. They are usually to be found in moss and under leaves.

Penthaleus major (Dugès) has been reported attacking peas, clover, oats, wild mustard, and lupine in California, barley in Arizona, and wheat in Oklahoma and Texas. It is a pest of pasture and forage crops in Australia and South Africa, as well as of lettuce and peas in France.

Halotydeus destructor (Tucker) is a serious pest of vegetable and leguminous crops in Australia and South Africa.

References:

Baker, E. W. 1946. New species of North and Central American mites of the family Penthaleidae (Acarina). J. Wash. Acad. Sci. 36(12):421–425.

Solomon, M. E. 1937. Experiments on the effects of temperature and humidity on the survival of *Halotydeus destructor* (Tucker), Acarina fam. Penthaleidae. Austral. J. Expt. Biol. and Med. Sci. 15:1–16.

———. 1937. Behaviour of the red-legged earthmite, *Halotydeus destructor,* in relation to environmental conditions. J. Anim. Ecol. 6(2):340–361.

Thor, Sig. 1934. Einzelne neue, besonders Norwegische *Eupodes* Arten mit einigen alteren Arten verglichen. Zool. Anz. 105:201–215.

Womersley, H. 1941. The red-legged earth-mite (Acarina, Penthaleidae) of Australia. Trans. Roy. Soc. South Australia 65(2):292–294.

Penthalodidae Thor, 1933

Figure 117

Diagnosis: The body of these mites is black, usually with red flecks, and the leg segments are red. They are small to medium-sized mites from 0.330 to 1.5 mm. long and pear-shaped with the narrow end to the rear. The propodosoma and hysterosoma are not separated or at best are separated only by a shallow suture. The integument is strongly sclerotized, reticulate, or punctate. An eye is situated on each side of the propodosoma (missing in *Tectopenthalodes* according to Trägårdh). Setae on the legs and body are sparse and short; a pair of pseudostigmata with sensory setae is present. The legs are long and narrow, usually with six movable segments. All tarsi have haired empodia between the claws. The palpi are narrow with four movable segments and the chelae are small, shearlike, and somewhat distorted. There is a tectum-like projection over the rostrum. These mites possess two pairs of genital suckers.

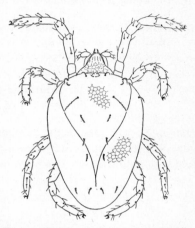

Figure 117 *Penthalodes turneri* Baker. Dorsum of female.

Genera:

1. *Penthalodes* Murray, 1877 (= *Penthaleus* Berlese, 1891 = *Chromotydeus* Berlese, 1903)
   Type. *Megamerus ovalis* Dugès, 1834
2. *Stereotydeus* Berlese, 1901
   Type. *Stereotydeus notophalloides* Leonardi, 1901
3. *Tectopenthalodes* Trägårdh, 1907
   Type. *Penthaleus villosus* Trouessart, 1903

Discussion: These mites are to be found in moss, debris, and such. They appear to be predaceous, but nothing is actually known of their biology or importance. The immature forms are similar to the adults but lack the heavy sclerotization. Several North American species have been described by Baker 1946, who at that time placed them in the family Penthaleidae which in this paper is considered to be a part of the Eupodidae.

References:

Baker, E. W. 1946. New species of North and Central American mites of the family Penthaleidae (Acarina). J. Wash. Acad. Sci. 36(12):421–425.

Womersley, H. 1935. On some Australian and South African species of Acarina of the genus *Stereotydeus* (Penthalodidae). Proc. Linn. Soc. New South Wales 60(1–2):79–82.

Bdellidae Dugès, 1834

Figure 118

Diagnosis: In general the bdellids are of reddish color, but owing to gut contents the mites may appear greenish, brown, or flecked with violet (seldom black as in *Trachymolgus*). They are medium-sized to large

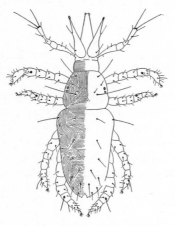

mites measuring from 0.450 to 3.50 mm. long (excluding the gnathosoma). Elongated and pear-shaped these mites possess a sharp rostrum which gives them the name of "Snout Mites." A suture is situated between the propodosoma and hysterosoma. In general the integument is thin and striated (*Trachymolgus* is armoured and possesses round tubercles); often a subcutaneous shield is to be found on the propodosoma. Four pseudostigmata with sensory setae are present and two pairs of separated eyes are located on the lateral margins of the propodosoma (*Cyta* and *Monotrichobdella* have an unpaired, anterior, median eye). The legs have six movable segments and all tarsi are provided with short pretarsus, two claws, and pulvillus. The palpi have five movable segments, the genu and tibia being very short, the femur very long, the tarsus either cylindrical and long or short and

Figure 118 Bdella willisi Baker and Balock. Dorsum of female with left half showing striae.

keglike with two end setae, except for *Monotrichobdella* which possesses one. Normally the genu and tibia are bent, giving the palpi an elbowed appearance. Chelicerae are elongated (more compact in *Cyta*) with one or more dorsal setae and very small, usually weak shears. Three pairs of genital suckers are present. Grandjean 1938 has divided the Bdellidae into four subfamilies.

Key to the Bdellidae

1. With well-developed genital tracheae; venter of rostrum with only two pairs of strong setae and two pairs of weak anterior setae   2

   Without well-developed genital tracheae; venter of rostrum with six pairs of strong setae and two pairs of weak anterior setae   3

2. With unpaired seta anterior to genital opening   Cytinae

   With pair of setae anterior to genital opening   Spinibdellinae

3. Trichoboth (long sensory seta) on tibiae I, II, and IV and tarsi III and IV   Odontoscirinae

   Trichoboth on tibiae I and IV and tarsi III and IV   Bdellinae

Cytinae Grandjean, 1938

Genera:

1. *Cyta* v. Heyden, 1826
   Type. *Scirus latirostris* Hermann, 1804
2. *Trachymolgus* Berlese, 1923
   Type. *Bdella nigerrima* G. Canestrini and Fanzago, 1876

Spinibdellinae Grandjean, 1938

Genera:

1. *Spinibdella* Thor, 1930
   Type. *Spinibdella reducta* Thor, 1930
2. *Biscirus* Thor, 1913
   Type. *Bdella silvatica* Kramer, 1881
3. *Monotrichobdella* Baker and Balock, 1944
   Type. *Monotrichobdella max-osburni* Baker and Balock, 1944

Bdellinae Grandjean, 1938

Genus:

Bdella Latreille, 1795 (= *Scirus* Hermann, 1804, *non* Thor, 1931)
   Type. *Acarus longicornis* Linnaeus, 1758 (= *Scirus vulgaris* Hermann, 1804)

Odontoscirinae Grandjean, 1938

Genera:

1. *Odontoscirus* Thor, 1913
   Type: *Bdella virgulata* G. Canestrini and Fanzago, 1876
2. *Bdellodes* Oudemans, 1937 (= *Scirus* Thor, 1931, *non* Hermann, 1804)
   Type. *Scirus longirostris* Hermann, 1804
3. *Neomolgus* Oudemans, 1937 (= *Molgus* Thor, 1931 *nom. praeocc.*)
   Type. *Acarus littoralis* Linnaeus, 1758
4. *Thoribdella* Grandjean, 1938
   Type. *Biscirus meridionalis* Thor, 1931

Unassigned genera: The following genera were not adequately described and cannot be placed under any of the above subfamilies.

1. *Caenobdella* Oudemans, 1937
   Type. *Bdella crassipes* C. L. Koch, 1839
2. *Hoplomolgus* Berlese, 1923
   Type. *Bdella capillata* Berlese, 1891 (*non* Kramer, 1881)
        (= *Molgus* (*Hoplomolgus*) *tuberculatus* Berlese, 1923)
3. *Hoploscirus* Thor, 1937
   Type. *Scirus dubitatus* Womersley, 1933
4. *Troglobdella* Oudemans, 1937
   Type. *Scirus obisium* Gervais, 1841

Discussion: Males and females are usually very similar, the differences lying in the genital organs, although occasionally there may be some slight differences in the palpi. The egg is slightly elliptical and is covered with a number of clavate spines or projections. They are laid on the soil, in leaf mold, or wherever the mite happens to be. They hatch into the six-legged larva, which is similar to the adult except in the number of legs and in lacking genital plates. The proto-, deuto-, and trito-nymphal stages have the genital plates, two pairs of genital suckers, fewer genital setae, and are smaller than the adult.

This family appears to be distributed throughout the world in both extremes of climate. They are predaceous on other mites and small insects. Little is known of the effect of these predators on their prey except for one species, *Biscirus lapidarius* (Kramer) which controls the lucerne flea *Sminthurus viridis* L. in certain localities in Western Australia. These mites are usually to be found in moss, lichens, leaf mold, and debris, wherever there is an abundance of small insects and other mites.

Paul DeBach reports in correspondence that a *Bdella* sp. occurring commonly on orange trees in Orange County, California, is predaceous on collembola. The mite, after capturing its prey by squirting onto it a liquid "silk" and enmeshing its appendages, would suck the body contents. When this mite was eliminated by a DDT application the collembola population increased tremendously.

The common North American species is *Bdella oblonga* Say, which is to be found along the east coast, west to Texas and as far south as Panama. It is one of the largest of the Bdellidae, measuring up to about 1300 μ in length and can be distinguished by its reticulate inverted U-shaped propodosomal shield. *Biscirus lapidarius* (Kramer), which is known from Europe and Australia, has also been taken in Mexico. *Bdella virgata* Ewing is to be found in the United States and Mexico.

References:

Baker, E. W., and J. Balock. 1944. Mites of the family Bdellidae. Proc. Ent. Soc. Wash. 46(7):176–184.

Currie, G. A. 1934. The Bdellid mite *Biscirus lapidarius* Kramer, predatory on the lucerne flea *Sminthurus viridis* L. in Western Australia. J. Austral. Council Sci. & Indus. Res. 7(1):9–20.

Grandjean, F. 1938. Observations sur les Bdelles (Acariens). Ann. Soc. Ent. France 107:1–24.

Thor, Sig. 1931. Bdellidae, Nicoletiellidae, Cryptognathidae. Das Tierreich 56, pp. 1–65.

Womersley, H. 1933. A preliminary account of the Bdellidae (Snout Mites) of Australia. Trans. Roy. Soc. South Austral. 57:97–107.

————. 1933. A possible biological control of the clover springtail or lucerne flea (*Sminthurus viridis* L.) in Western Australia. J. Austral. Council Sci. & Indus. Res. 6(2):83–91.

Rhagidiidae Oudemans, 1922

Figures 119–122

Diagnosis: The rhagidiids are whitish, yellow, or rosy-colored mites. Light-sensitive and fast-moving, they range from small to medium size (0.350 to 1.80 mm.). They are long, delicate, and without armor. A suture separates the propodosoma and hysterosoma. The setae are simple and long. A pair of poorly developed pseudostigmata with only slightly modified sensory setae is located on the propodosoma. Usually eye spots are present. The legs of these mites are relatively long and narrow and have five movable segments. The femora of legs I and II are divided ventrally and the femora of leg III and IV are divided completely into two parts. All tarsi have two claws and a haired empodium. Four movable segments comprise the palpi which have no thumb or claw. The palpal tarsus is cylindrical and about as thick as the tibia.

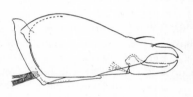

Figure 119   Rhagidia gelida Thorell. Dorsum of female. (After Oudemans 1928)

Figure 120   Rhagidia gelida Thorell. Chelicera and trachea. (After Oudemans 1926)

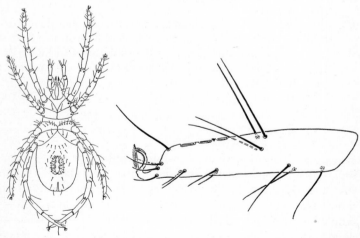

Figure 121   Rhagidia gelida Thorell. Venter of female. (After Oudemans 1928)

*Figure 122   Tarsus I of *Rhagidia* sp. showing profile of Rhagidia organ.

The chelicerae are strong with opposed, grasping chelae. The rhagidiids have two pairs of genital suckers.

Genera:

1. *Rhagidia* Thorell, 1871 (= *Scyphius* C. L. Koch, 1836 *nom. prae-occ.; = Noerneria* Canestrini, 1886)
   Type. *Rhagidia gelida* Thorell, 1871
2. *Coccorhagidia* Thor, 1934
   Type. *Noerneria clavifrons* R. Canestrini, 1886

Discussion: Very little information is to be found on these mites. They are known from Europe and North America, but future collecting will probably reveal them to be world-wide in distribution. They appear to be predaceous and, since they are rather common in certain localities, they may play a more important role in the general relationship of small insects and mites than has been thought. They live in soil, humus, and moss. *Rhagidia pallida* Banks is from New York, New Hampshire, and Washington, D.C., and is to be found on the ground under damp boards or stones; *R. cavicola* Banks is from Mammoth Caverns, Kentucky; Banks says this species is somewhat common and is often found under stones on which egg masses of the cave spider, *Anthrobia mammouthia* Telkpf. occur.

Nothing is known of the life cycle of these mites, other than that all stages are somewhat similar in appearance except for the larval forms which possess only six legs.

Cryptognathidae Oudemans, 1902

Figure 123

Diagnosis: The cryptognathids are small, scarlet-red mites measuring from 0.300 to 0.400 mm. in length. The body is oval and lacks a suture between the propodosoma and the hysterosoma. The dorsum has a net-like skin pattern and the skin is punctate. A pair of lenslike eyes is located on each side of propodosoma. The chitinous extensions of the body form a tube which is not closed ventrally and through which the gnathosoma is capable of being extruded or withdrawn into the body. The chelicerae are shearlike while the chelae are small, almost straight, untoothed, and sharp for piercing. No genital suckers are present.

Genus:

Cryptognathus Kramer, 1878
Type: *Cryptognathus lagena* Kramer, 1878

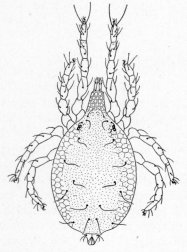

Discussion: These mites live in moss and under stones. Sig Thor 1931 lists only two species and one variety. *Cryptognathus lagena* Kramer is known from Germany, Holland, Switzerland, Italy, France, England, Ireland, and Norway and is to be found under stones and in moss. *C. cucurbita* Berlese was taken in Italy and specimens have been found in *Sciurus n. niger* nest in Florida. *C. cucurbita* var. *subnitida* Berlese was described from Somaliland, Africa. Nothing is known of their habits other than that they appear to be predaceous.

Figure 123 *Cryptognathus cucurbitae* Berlese. Dorsum of female.

Reference:

Thor, Sig. 1931. Bdellidae, Nicoletiellidae, Cryptognathidae. Das Tierreich 56:78–81.

Labidostommidae Oudemans, 1904

Figures 124–126

Diagnosis: These mites are free-living, completely armored, yellowish predators measuring from 0.57 to 1.5 mm. in length and are eggshaped. Their propodosoma is divided into two sections, the posterior portion shading into the hysterosoma but without a clear line of demarcation. There are two pairs of pseudostigmatic organs, one on each of the propodosomal plates. One lenslike eye is located on each side of propodosoma and at times an unpaired eye is placed in the middle of the propodosoma on the anterior margin. A large lenslike organ on lateral margins behind eyes may be present. The palpus has four segments and the chelicerae have large, strong, opposed chelae. The legs have six movable segments and the coxal plates are contiguous. All tarsi are provided with two claws and tarsi II, III and IV with a clawlike empodium. Two pairs of genital suckers are present. In the

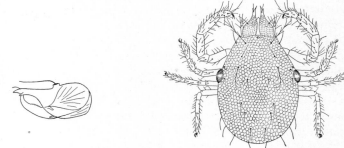

Figure 124 *Labidostomma luteum* Kramer. Lateral view of chelicera. (After Thor 1931)

Figure 125 *Labidostomma neotropica* Stoll. Dorsum of female.

female the genital and anal openings are united in a circular plate while the male genital opening is separate although in the same position.

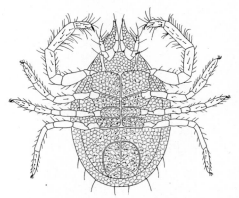

Figure 126 *Labidostomma neotropica* (Stoll). Venter of female.

Genera:

1. *Labidostomma* Kramer, 1879 [= *Panoplia* v. Heyden, 1826 (*nom. praeocc.*) = *Nicoletiella* R. Canestrini, 1882 = *Ceratoacarus* Ewing, 1913]

   Type. *Labidostomma luteum* Kramer, 1879 (Some believe this to be a synonym of *Acarus denticulatus* Schrank.)

2. *Eunicolana* Berlese, 1911
   Type. *Eunicolana tuberculata* Berlese, 1911

Discussion: Grandjean 1942 has studied the family in some detail and the following life history is based on his studies. The adults feed readily on Collembola and small, immature, oribatid mites. Eggs are laid separately and without protection. The adult is able to carry the egg from one place to another by seizing it between the first pair of legs and resting it on the extremity of the chelicerae. The egg, which is rather large, hatches in about twelve days into the larva. The larva does not feed and is mobile for only a few hours. It seeks a place to transform into the protonymphs. The proto-, deuto-, and tritonymphs greatly resemble the adult mites in structure and food habits.

The Labidostommidae is a small family of little known mites found in Europe, South Africa, North and Central America, and Brazil in South America. The mites live in moss, humus, and soil and are predaceous on other mites and small insects. Many species are characterized by a lateral protuberance behind the lateral eyes, the function of which is unknown. The family is represented in the United States by *Labidostomma pacifica* (Ewing) and from the southern United States to Panama by *L. neotropica* (Stoll).

References:

Grandjean, F. 1942. Observations sur les Labidostommidae. Bull. Paris Mus. Nat. d'Hist. Nat. Ser. 2, 14(2):118–125; (3):185–192; (5): 319–326; (6):414–418.

Thor, Sig. 1931. Bdellidae, Nicoletiellida, Cryptognathidae. Das Tierreich 56:66–77.

Ereynetidae Oudemans, 1931

Figure 127

Diagnosis: The ereynetids are reddish yellow or colorless white. They are small mites measuring from 0.220 to 0.500 mm. in length. The body has a suture located between the propodosoma and the hysterosoma. Their integument is soft and striated. *Ereynetes* has a complicated shield pattern on the propodosoma while *Opsereynetes* has a simpler pattern. Setae on the body are few but a pair of long sensory setae is situated on the propodosoma and another pair is located on the hysterosoma. *Opsereynetes* has eye spots but *Ereynetes* has a pair of lenslike eyes. The palpi are simple, lack either a thumb or a claw, and are three- to five-segmented. The digitus mobilis of chelicerae is sharp, for piercing, and extends beyond the digitus fixus. All tarsi have claws and haired pulvillus. Two pairs of genital suckers are present.

Genera:

1. *Ereynetes* Berlese, 1883 (= *Micrereunetes* Berlese, 1923)
   Type. *Ereynetes berlesei* Oudemans, 1928
2. *Opsereynetes* Thor, 1932
   Type. *Opsereynetes norvegicus* Thor, 1932
3. *Riccardoella* Berlese, 1923
   Type. *Acarus limacum* Schrank, 1781

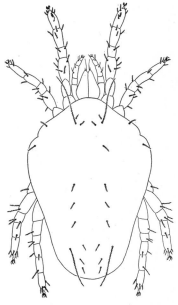

Figure 127 Opsereynetes robustus Baker. Dorsum of female.

Discussion: These mites are known from Europe, North America, Java, Sumatra, and Japan and are likely to be found wherever careful collecting is made. They are moss-lichen and sometimes leaf inhabitants and appear to be predaceous. The species, *Riccardoella limacum* (Schrank) is to be found in Europe and North America on the common snail, *Helix pomata* L. This mite is at times abundant on the slimy parts of the snail but apparently does not cause its host any harm. Turk and Phillips 1946 have studied the slug mite and have worked out the life history as follows. Eggs are laid in the mucus of the mantle cavity of the snail. The egg hatches into a six-legged larva which lacks the posterior pair of abdominal sensory setae and the genital suckers. The proto- and deutonymphs resemble the adults. However, these workers state that this species exhibits neotony in that the deutonymphal stage (nympha generans) contains the eggs, whereas the adults examined were never found with well-developed ova. The female deutonymph is either viviparous or ovoviviparous. The mites do not spend the entire time on the snail, but run along the ground and are able to find the host by following the slime trail. The food may be the slime or may be found off the snail. The mites and snails appear to live in perfect harmony with each other.

References:

Baker, E. W. 1945. Five mites of the family Ereynetidae from Mexico. J. Wash. Acad. Sci. 35(1):16–19.

Grandjean, F. 1939. Observations sur les Acariens (5 serie). Bull. Paris Mus. d'Hist. Nat., Ser. 2, 11(4):394–401.

Thor, Sig. 1933. Tydeidae, Ereynetidae. Das Tierreich 60:58–84.

Turk, F. A. and Stella-Maris Phillips. 1946. A monograph of the slug mite —*Riccardoella limacum* (Schrank). Proc. Zool. Soc. London 115 (3, 4):448–472.

Paratydeidae Baker, 1949

Figure 128

Diagnosis: These mites are prostigmatic and have peritremes as in the predaceous Cheyletidae. Their palpi are four-segmented, without the claw-thumb complex and with the tarsal segment terminal. The cheliceral bases are fused, and the movable chela is short and nonretractile for piercing. The body is elongated and both the propodosoma and the hysterosoma are without plates. The skin is striated. The hysterosoma is divided dorsally by a distinct suture behind the third pair of legs. A few simple setae are located on the body and the propodosoma has two pairs of long sensory (?) setae, one pair of short setae, two pairs of lenslike eyes, and two pairs of lateral, peglike setae. The anal opening is situated on the venter at the rear. The genital opening, separated from the anal opening, is located behind coxae IV, and has two pairs of genital suckers and from two to four pairs of genital setae. Coxae

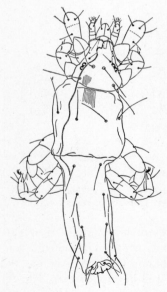

Figure 128 *Paratydeus alexanderi* Baker. Dorsum of female.

I-II and III-IV are in two widely separated groups; coxae of the legs are fused with the body and the legs are sparsely haired. All tarsi have two claws and a small clawlike pulvillus; tarsus I has two short, rodlike, sensory setae. The paratydeids measure 0.366 mm. in length.

Genus:

1. *Paratydeus* Baker, 1949
   Type. *Paratydeus alexanderi* Baker, 1949
2. *Neotydeus* Baker, 1950
   Type. *Neotydeus ardisannae* Baker, 1950
3. *Scolotydaeus* Berlese, 1910
   Type. *Scolotydaeus bacillus* Berlese, 1910

Discussion: These mites, which apparently are soil livers, appear to be predators. Only three species are known.

References:

Baker, E. W. 1949. Paratydeidae, a new family of mites (Acarina). Proc. Ent. Soc. Wash. 51(3):119–122.
——. 1950. Further notes on the family Paratydeidae (Acarina) with a description of another new genus and species. J. Wash. Acad. Sci. 40(9):289–291.

Speleognathidae Womersley, 1936

Figure 129

Diagnosis: The speleognathids are small, light yellowish-brown mites measuring about 0.80 mm. in length. The skin is soft and has no shields. A few short setae are present on the body while a pair of long sensory setae is to be found on the propodosoma. Short and simple palpi which lack the claw-thumb complex are present. The chelicerae are reduced and the movable chela is a tiny, sharp point. Lenslike eyes may or may not be situated on the propodosoma. There is no suture between the propodosoma and the hysterosoma. The legs are short, with netlike sclerotization and the coxae are divided into two groups. All tarsi have claws and a haired pulvillus. No genital suckers are present.

Genus:

Speleognathus Womersley, 1936
Type. *Speleognathus australis* Womersley, 1936

Discussion: *Speleognathus australis* Womersley has been collected in moss and from around cattle watering tanks in Australia. *Speleognathus sturni* Boyd is to be found in the nasal passages of starlings in

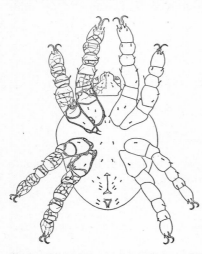

the eastern United States. Boyd 1948 found that the birds with these mites had more nasal secretion, or mucus, than those not parasitized. There is apparently a close relationship between this group and the Ereynetidae in structure and biology, for *Riccardoella limacum* (Schrank) inhabits the snail, whereas *S. sturni* is in the warm mucus of the nasal passage of the starling. Boyd points out the possibility of a common ancestor of the two mites. This species may be rather generally distributed and will probably be found wherever the starling or related birds are established.

Figure 129 *Speleognathus sturni* Boyd. Venter of female. (From Boyd 1948)

The larval form of *S. sturni* Boyd, although basically similar to the adult, shows an interesting deviation in that tarsus I does not possess claws or pulvillus but tibia I has a long, bifurcate, clawlike process.

References:

Boyd, Elizabeth. 1948. A new mite from the respiratory tract of the starling (Acarina, Speleognathidae). Proc. Ent. Soc. Wash. 50(1):9–14.
Womersley, H. 1936. On a new family of Acarina, with description of a new genus and species. Ann. Mag. and Nat. Hist. 18(104):312–315.

Tydeidae Kramer, 1877

Figures 130, 131

Diagnosis: The tydeids are weakly colored in yellow, brown, red, or green. They are very small mites measuring from 0.100 to 0.300 mm. in length (they are usually about 0.20 mm. long). They are of various shapes but usually an egg-shape predominates. The skin is soft with punctate striations, and in some species it has a punctate or reticulate pattern. There are few body setae and a pair of sensory setae is located on the propodosoma. The propodosoma and hysterosoma are usually separated by a distinct suture. The legs are five- or six-segmented and the tarsi have short pretarsus, two claws, and haired pulvillus (leg I

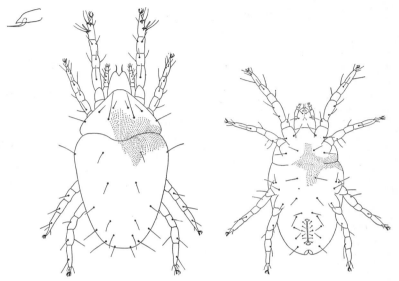

Figure 130 *Tydeus starri* Baker. Lateral view of chelicera and dorsum of female.

Figure 131 *Tydeus starri* Baker. Venter of female.

of *Pronematus* lacks the claws and pulvillus, and in *Proctotydaeus* leg I is without claws and pulvillus whereas legs II-IV lack the pulvillus). The chelicerae have a thick basal piece and a very sharp-pointed, fixed chela from which a dagger-like, almost straight, movable chela extends in such a way that the chelicerae are not truly chelate. Some species lack eye spots, while others have two and three eye spots. No genital suckers are present.

Genera and subgenera:

1. *Tydeus* Koch, 1836 (= *Microtydeus* Thor, 1931 = *Brachytydeus* Thor, 1931 = *Melanotydeus* Berlese, 1910 = *Stylotydeus* Thor, 1933 = *Lasiotydeus* Berlese, 1908? = *Calotydeus* Oudemans, 1937 = *Tectotydeus* Oudemans, 1937)

   a. *Tydeus* s. str.

      Type. *Tydeus kochi* Oudemans, 1928 (= *Tydeus croceus* Koch, 1836 (*non Acarus croceus* Linnaeus, 1758)

    b. *Tydaeolus* Berlese, 1910
       Type. *Tydaeus atomus* Berlese, 1908
    c. *Triophtydeus* Thor, 1932 (= *Tridilatydeus* Baker, 1946)
       Type. *Tydeus triophthalmus* Oudemans, 1929
  2. *Coccotydeus* Thor, 1931
     Type. *Coccotydeus globifer* Thor, 1931
  3. *Lorryia* Oudemans, 1925 (= *Raphitydeus* Thor, 1933)
     Type. *Lorryia superba* Oudemans, 1925
  4. *Coleotydaeus* Berlese, 1910
     Type. *Coleotydaeus rhombicus* Berlese, 1910
  5. *Pronematus* G. Canestrini, 1886
    a. *Pronematus* s. str.
       Type. *Pronematus bonatii* Canestrini, 1886
    b. *Pronecupulatus* Baker, 1944
       Type. *Pronecupulatus anahuacensis* Baker, 1944
    c. *Proctotydaeus* Berlese, 1911
       Type. *Proctotydaeus viator* Berlese, 1911
  6. *Retetydeus* Thor, 1931
     Type. *Retetydeus catenulatus* Thor, 1931

The family has been divided in the past into too many genera based on such characters as size, width, length of setae, type of setae, and presence or absence of eye spots. It is believed that the above presentation is a more correct and simpler one.

Discussion: These mites are world-wide in distribution and appear to be predaceous on small insects and mites and their eggs. There is an indication that certain species, however, may be plant feeders but more observation is necessary. One species, *Tydeus molestus* (Moniez), is a minor pest to man in an isolated region in Belgium. They cause irritation by the bite to human beings and to domestic animals. *Tydeus californicus* (Banks) is predaceous on the citrus bud mite, *Aceria sheldoni* (Ewing), in Southern California. *Pronematus ubiquitus* (McGregor), a mite found throughout California, is common on the fig trees where it preys on the fig mite, *Aceria ficus* (Cotte). *Lorryia superba* Oudemans, a European species, has been found in California, and *L. mali* (Oudemans), another European species, has been taken on apple leaves in Nova Scotia.

Most species are to be found in moss, lichens, or on plant leaves in association with other mite colonies. The life cycle is a simple one; each female deposits eggs singly. This develops into the larva, nymph, and adult, all stages being quite similar, and the adult acquiring the genital opening. The male is similar to the female except in having a much smaller genital opening. In no case has any species appeared to be of great importance in controlling a pest, although they may be of minor value.

Reference:

Thor, Sig. 1933. Tydeidae, Ereynetidae. Das Tierreich 60:1–57.

Cunaxidae Thor, 1902

Figure 132

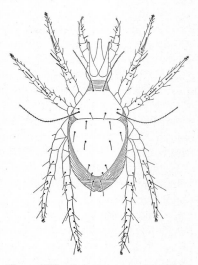

Diagnosis: These are small, red mites from 0.350 to 0.500 mm. long (not including the gnathosoma which is long and conelike). A suture separating the propodosoma from the hysterosoma is present. The integument is soft, finely striated, punctate in spots, and in many cases has extensive plates. There are four distinct sensory setae on propodosoma. Eyes may or may not be present. The legs have six movable segments; all tarsi have claws and pulvillus. The palpi are used for grasping and are large, pincerlike, and usually have apophyses and strong spines on the inner side. The palpal end segment is clawlike, and the chelicerae are elongated with a very small, distal, sickle-like digitus mobilis. Two pairs of genital suckers are present.

Figure 132   *Cunaxa capreolus* (Berlese). Dorsum of male.

Genera and subgenera:

1. *Cunaxa* v. Heyden, 1826 (= *Scirus sensu* Berlese = *Dactyloscirus* Berlese, 1916)
   Type. *Scirus setirostris* Hermann, 1804
2. *Bonzia* Oudemans, 1927
   Type. *Bonzia halacaroides* Oudemans, 1927
3. *Coleoscirus* Berlese, 1916
   Type. *Coleoscirus halacaroides* Berlese, 1916

Acarology

4. *Cunaxoides* Baker & Hoffmann, 1948 (= *Eupalus* Koch, 1838 *nom. praeocc.* = *Haleupalus* Radford, 1950)
   Type. *Eupalus croceus* Koch, 1838
5. *Rosenhofia* Oudemans, 1922
   Type. *Rosenhofia machairodus* Oudemans, 1922
6. *Scirula* Berlese, 1887
   Type. *Scirula impressa* Berlese, 1887

Discussion: No species has been reported as of great economic importance, although they are predators on other mites and small insects. The family is widely distributed and many species are more or less cosmopolitan. *Cunaxa capreolus* (Berlese) is a European species to be found in Africa, the United States, and Mexico; *C. setirostris* (Hermann) is another species which is distributed throughout the world, as is *C. inermis* (Trägårdh) and *C. taurus* (Kramer). This latter species is rather distinctive in having immensely long palpi with long inner spines and apophyses and is fairly common in leaves or leaf mold in the northeastern United States. *Cunaxoides parvus* (Ewing) is from Iowa, where it was described as a "real enemy of the oyster shell scale," although it was not numerous. *C. pectinatus* (Ewing) is distributed from the United States (Illinois) to Panama.

Larvae and nymphs are similar to the adults. Males are similar to females except in having much smaller genital plates and perhaps other minor variations, as in *Cunaxa capreolus* (Berlese) in which the male has a much smaller apophysis on the third palpal segment than does the female. Nymphal forms appear to have three pairs of genital setae rather than four, as do the adults. A nymph of *Cunaxoides pectinatus* (Ewing) has the three pairs of genital setae, a small body and long legs, and no dorsal shield but the entire body is striated. Otherwise it is similar to the adult. The mites are usually to be found in moss, humus, and on leaves.

The family appears to be closely related to the Halacaridae, and it has been stated that *Bonzia* is a "landgoing" halacarid.

References:

Baker, E. W., and Anita Hoffmann. 1948. Acaros de la familia Cunaxidae. Anales de la Escuela Nacional de Ciencias Biologicas V(3–4):229–273.
Ewing, H. E. 1917. New Acarina. Part II. Descriptions of new species and varieties from Iowa, Missouri, Illinois, Indiana, and Ohio. Bull. Amer. Mus. Nat. Hist. 37(2):151.

Thor, Sig, and C. Willmann. 1941. Acarina. Prostigmata 6–11 (Eupodidae, Penthalodidae, Penthaleidae, Rhagidiidae, Pachygnathidae, Cunaxidae). Das Tierreich 71 a.

Lordalychidae Grandjean, 1939

Figures 133–136

Diagnosis: The lordalychids are medium-sized mites measuring from 0.30 to 0.40 mm. long. They have a globular body which is constricted between the propodosoma and the hysterosoma. The propodosoma is rather small in relation to the hysterosoma. The skin is pebbled, ru-

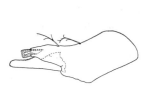

Figure 133 *Lordalychus peraltus* Grandjean. Lateral view of chelicera. (After Grandjean 1939)

Figure 134 *Lordalychus peraltus* Grandjean. Lateral view of female. (After Grandjean 1939)

gose, and not smooth but with striae. Two pairs of propodosomal sensory setae are present, the anterior pair being located in a special invaginated area. No eyes are present. The chelicerae are primitive with abortive, fixed chela. The palpus is simple and has no claw-thumb complex. The legs are situated at the anterior portion of the body; all

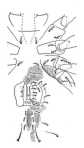

Figure 135 *Lordalychus peraltus* Grandjean. Dorsum of propodosoma. (After Grandjean 1939)

Figure 136 *Lordalychus peraltus* Grandjean. Venter of female. (After Grandjean 1939)

tarsi possess two claws and an empodium (the claws on *Lordalycus* have ventral rays; the pulvillus is rayed). The femur is divided into basi- and telofemur. Two pairs of genital suckers are present.

Genera:

1. *Lordalycus* Grandjean, 1939
    Type. *Lordalycus peraltus* Grandjean, 1939
2. *Hybalicus* Berlese, 1913
    Type. *Hybalicus flabelliger* Berlese, 1913

Discussion:　The discovery, with the aid of the phase microscope, of the prostigmatic type of tracheal systems opening at the base of the chelicerae in four families of the Endeostigmata of Grandjean indicates a definite relationship to the Prostigmata. The Endeostigmata form a closely knit group of families (Terpnacaridae, Pachygnathidae, Alicorhagididae, Nanorchestidae, Lordalychidae and Sphaerolichidae) and are at present retained within the Prostigmata. The families are little known and only a few species and genera have been described.

Reference:

Grandjean, F. 1939. Quelques genres d'acariens appartenant au groupe des Endeostigmata. Ann. des Sci. Nat., Zool., Ser. 11, 2: 1–122.

Sphaerolichidae Grandjean, 1937

Figures 137–139

Diagnosis:　These mites have a whitish or yellowish color (in alcohol). They are small to medium-sized (from 0.30 to 0.40 mm. long). The body is globular, thick, and round while the skin is soft and striated or has punctiform striae. The propodosoma has a

Figure 137　*Sphaerolichus barbarus* Grandjean. Dorsum of female. (After Grandjean 1939)

Figure 138　*Sphaerolichus barbarus* Grandjean. Lateral view of chelicera. (After Grandjean 1939)

tectum or anterior protuberance with an unpigmented ventral eye. There are also two pairs of lateral eyes. Two pairs of sensory setae are situated on the propodosoma. The body lacks a suture between the propodosoma and the hysterosoma. The legs are located anteriorly in two closely approximated groups: femur I is divided into three sections; femora II, III, and IV are divided into two sections; tarsus I is bidactyle; tarsi II, III, and IV are tridactyle (the claws and empodium are clawlike with short rays). The legs are adapted for jumping. The chelicerae have opposed chelae. The palpus has five segments and no claw-thumb complex. Two pairs of genital suckers are present.

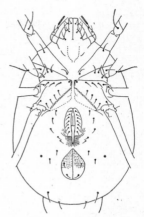

Figure 139 *Sphaerolichus barbarus* Grandjean. Venter of female. (After Grandjean 1939)

Genus:

Sphaerolichus Berlese, 1904
Type. *Sphaerolichus armipes* Berlese, 1904

Discussion: The sphaerolichids are little-known mites that live in a dry habitat in vegetable debris. A tracheal system opening at the base of the chelicerae was found in the only available species, an undescribed genus from California. Grandjean 1939 has also found tracheae in *Sphaerolichus.*

Reference:

Grandjean, F. 1939. Quelques genres d'acariens appartenant au groupe des Endeostigmata. Ann. des Sci. Nat., Zool., Ser. 11, 2:1–122.

Nanorchestidae Grandjean, 1937

Figures 140–141

Diagnosis: These colorless or reddish, with a brownish posterior, mites are small in size (from 0.165 to 0.350 mm. long). Their shape is more or less extended in length with a sacklike hysterosoma. The body is usually clearly (in *Oehserchestes* vaguely) segmented into gnathosoma, propodosoma, metapodosoma, and opisthosoma by sharply delineated constrictions. The skin is soft with fine striations and thirty-two specially formed setae are located on the dorsum. Palpi possess four or five segments, without thumb-claw complex. The chelicerae are chelate. Either no eyes are present (*Oehserchestes*) or a small, simple, lenslike eye is located on each side of the propodosoma. Four sensory setae are on the propodosoma. There is no tectum. The legs are situated far anteriorly; legs IV are specialized for jumping. The tarsi have only an empodial claw which can be withdrawn into a very deep claw-depression. Three pairs of genital suckers are present.

Figure 140 *Speleorchestes poduroides* Hirst. Dorsum of female. (After Hirst 1917)

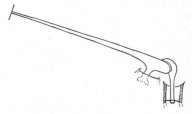

Figure 141 *Nanorchestes pulvinar* Grandjean. First pair of propodosomal sensory setae showing arrangement of the long "activating" seta and the short, true sensory seta. (After Grandjean 1942)

Genera:

1. *Nanorchestes* Topsent and Trouessart, 1890 (= *Monalichus* Berlese, 1904)

   Type. *Nanorchestes amphibius* Topsent and Trouessart, 1890
2. *Speleorchestes* Trägårdh, 1909 (= *Leptalicus* Berlese, 1910).

   Type. *Speleorchestes formicorum* Trägårdh, 1909
3. *Oehserchestes* Jacot, 1939 (= *Coccorchestes* Jacot, 1938 *nom. prae-occ.*)

   Type. *Coccorchestes humicolus* Jacot, 1938

4. *Caenonychus* Oudemans, 1903
   Type. *Caenonychus fallax* Oudemans, 1903

Discussion: There are only a few described species, but the distribution is probably world-wide and these mites have been overlooked because of their minute size. They are usually to be found in moss and soil and it has been stated that *Nanorchestes amphibius* Topsent and Trouessart is practically marine in habit. They are probably predaceous.

One species, *Nanorchestes pulvinar* Grandjean, presents an interesting arrangement in the forward pair of propodosomal sensory setae. The long "sense setae" activate a short seta which apparently is the true sensory organ.

Grandjean 1942 lists the stages of *Nanorchestes* as larva, three nymphal, and adult. The males are differentiated from the females by the larger number and position of the genital setae.

A *Speleorchestes* sp. from Mexico possesses a tracheal system opening at the base of the chelicerae.

References:

Grandjean, F. 1942. Observations sur les Acariens (7 Ser.). Bull. Paris Mus. d'Hist. Nat. Ser. 2, 14(4):264–267.

Womersley, H. 1944. Australian Acarina, families Alycidae and Nanorchestidae. Trans. Roy. Soc. South Austral. 68(1):133–143.

Pachygnathidae Kramer, 1877

Figures 142–144

Diagnosis: These are small, whitish mites ranging from 0.30 to 0.40 mm. in length. The skin is soft and may be striate, reticulate, or with diverse pattern. The pachygnathids possess an anterior protuberance or tectum which varies in shape. They have no median eye and may or may not have lateral eyes. The propodosoma is separated from the hysterosoma by a suture and has two pairs of sensory setae (in *Petralycus* the anterior pair is globose while in *Bimichaelia* the posterior pair is globose). The hysterosoma may or may not be segmented. The chelae of the chelicerae are opposed and the palpus is five-segmented without the claw-thumb complex. The legs are in two distinct groups. All tarsi are provided with two claws and a pulvillus (the claws are simple and the pulvillus rayed); in *Petralycus* femora I, II and III are entire while IV is divided into basi- and telofemur. Three pairs of genital suckers are present.

Figure 142 *Petralycus unicornis* Grandjean. Venter of female. (After Grandjean 1943)

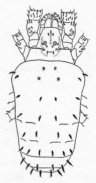

Figure 143 *Petralycus unicornis* Grandjean. Dorsum of female. (After Grandjean 1943)

Genera:

1. *Pachygnathus* Dugès, 1834
   Type. *Pachygnathus villosus* Dugès, 1836
2. *Bimichaelia* Thor, 1902 (= *Michaelia* Berlese, 1884 *nom. praeocc.*)
   Type. *Michaelia augustana* Berlese, 1884
3. *Petralycus* Grandjean, 1943
   Type. *Petralycus unicornis* Grandjean, 1943

Figure 144 *Petralycus unicornis* Grandjean. Lateral view of chelicera. (After Grandjean 1943)

Discussion: These mites are found in humus and vegetable debris and in the soil. They are probably predators but very little is known of them. *Bimichaelia diadema* Grandjean has a larva, two active nymphal stages, and an adult stage; *Bimichaelia arbusculosa* Grandjean and *Petraycus unicornis* Grandjean have three nymphal stages. A *Bimichaelia* sp. from southern United States was studied and found to have the tracheal system.

References:

Grandjean, F. 1942. Quelques genres d'acariens appartenant au groupe des Endeostigmata (2 Ser.) Premiere partie. Ann. des Sci. Nat., Zool., Ser. 11, 4:85–135.

——. 1943. Quelques genres d'acariens appartenant au groupe des Endeostigmata (2 ser.) Deuxieme partie. Ann. des Sci. Nat., Zool., Ser. 11, 5:1–59.

Terpnacaridae Grandjean, 1939

Figures 145–147

Diagnosis: Granular and reddish in color the terpnacarids are small mites about 0.35 mm. in length. They are soft-bodied and have a somewhat sacklike, segmented hysterosoma. A suture is situated between the propodosoma and the hysterosoma. One pair of propodosomal sensory setae, one pair of lateral, lenslike eyes, an unpaired, anterior median eye on the venter of the tectum or anterior protuberance of the propodosoma are present. The palpus is composed of five segments and does not have a claw-thumb complex. The chelicerae have opposed chelae. Divided into two groups, the legs are five-segmented and fairly long, especially legs I and IV; the femur is divided into two parts in legs I, III, and IV. All tarsi are provided with two claws and a pulvillus. Three pairs of genital suckers are present.

Figure 145 *Terpnacarus bouvieri* Grandjean. Dorsum of female. (After Grandjean 1939)

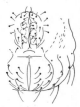

Figure 146 *Terpnacarus bouvieri* Grandjean. Genital-anal region. (After Grandjean 1939)

Figure 147 *Terpnacarus bouvieri* Grandjean. Palpus. (After Grandjean 1939)

Genera:

1. *Terpnacarus* Grandjean, 1939
   Type. *Terpnacarus bouvieri* Grandjean, 1939
2. *Alycosmesis* Grandjean, 1939
   Type. *Sebaia palmata* Oudemans, 1904

3. *Sebaia* Oudemans, 1903 (= *Monalichus* Berlese, 1904)
    Type. *Sebaia rosacea* Oudemans, 1903

Discussion: These small mites are to be found in more or less dry situations in vegetable debris. *Terpnacarus* and *Sebaia* are both jumpers but *Alycosmesis* is not. An apparently undescribed genus from Guatemala shows the prostigmatic tracheal system.

Reference:

Grandjean, F. 1939. Quelques genres d'acariens appartenant au groupe des Endeostigmata. Ann. des Sci. Nat., Zool., Ser. 11, 2:1–122.

Alicorhagiidae Grandjean, 1939

Figures 148–150

Diagnosis: These mites are small (about 0.22 to 0.30 mm. long) and whitish in color with a brownish posterior. The body is not very elongated and a light suture is located between the propodosoma and

Figure 148   *Alicorhagia fragilis* Berlese. Lateral view of chelicera (right) with detail (left). (After Grandjean 1939)

the hysterosoma. The skin is soft with tuberculate striae. One pair of propodosomal sensory setae is present and the large frontal protuberance of the propodosoma bears two setae. There are no eyes. The

Figure 149   *Alicorhagia fragilis* Berlese. Dorsum of female. (After Grandjean 1939)

Figure 150   *Alicorhagia fragilis* Berlese. Venter of female. (After Grandjean 1939)

chelicerae are opposed and there is no claw-thumb complex on the palpus. The legs are five-segmented and the femur is divided into basi- and telofemur; trochanters I and II are also divided. All tarsi have a single retractable claw (pulvillus). Two pairs of genital suckers are present.

Genus:

> *Alicorhagia* Berlese, 1910 (= *Willania* Oudemans, 1931 = *Epistomalycus* Thor, 1931)
>
> Type. *Alicorhagia fragilis* Berlese, 1910

Discussion: Grandjean 1939 reports *Alicorhagia fragilis* Berlese as being common in forest humus in France.

Reference:

Grandjean, F. 1939. Quelques genres d'acariens appartenant au groupe des Endeostigmata. Ann. des Sci. Nat., Zool., Ser. 11, 2:1–122.

Raphignathidae Kramer, 1877

(= Stigmaeidae Oudemans, 1931; Caligonellidae Grandjean, 1944)

Figures 151–154

Diagnosis: The raphignathids are small, red mites, round in shape, with no suture or no distinct suture between the propodosoma and the hysterosoma. They may or may not have various numbers of shields.

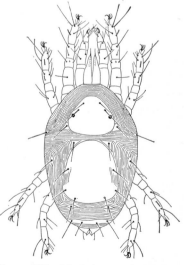

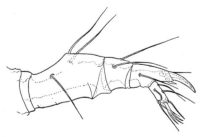

Figure 151 *Homocaligus* sp. Palpus showing thumb and claw. (After Grandjean 1946)

Figure 152 *Mediolata mali* (Ewing). Dorsum of female.

The integument is finely striated between the dorsal shields. One or two pairs of lenslike eyes may be present. The propodosomal sensory setae are undifferentiated. These mites have peritremes which at times enter into the basal portion of the chelicerae. The moderately long cylindrical palpal tarsus is located ventrally on the palpal tibia beneath a small to large tibial claw; the movable chela is stylet-like for piercing. All tarsi have two claws and a rayed pulvillus; tarsi I and II each have a single sensory organ. The coxae are either contiguous or separated into two groups. There are no genital suckers and the anal opening is either posterior or posterior dorsal.

Figure 153 *Raphignathus* sp. Dorsal view of gnathosoma.

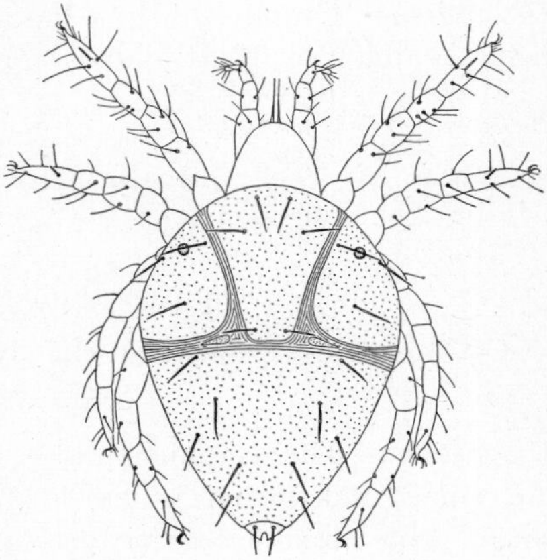

Figure 154 *Raphignathus cardinalis* (Ewing). Dorsum of female.

The discovery of two genera with the peritremes in the cheliceral bases but with large palpal claws and terminal anus has led to combining these three families, since they now grade into one another and since there are no clear-cut, so-called family characters.

Genera:

1. *Raphignathus* Dugès, 1834 (= *Syncaligus* Berlese, 1910)
   Type. *Raphignathus ruberrimus* Dugès, 1834
2. *Acheles* Oudemans, 1903
   Type. *Acheles mirabilis* Oudemans, 1903
3. *Apostigmaeus* Grandjean, 1944
   Type. *Apostigmaeus navicella* Grandjean, 1944
4. *Barbutia* Oudemans, 1927
   Type. *Stigmaeus anguineus* Berlese, 1910

5. *Caligonella* Berlese, 1910
   Type. *Stigmaeus humilis* Koch, 1838
6. *Caligonus* Koch, 1836
   Type. *Caligonus piger* Koch, 1838
7. *Eupalopsellus* Sellnick, 1949
   Type. *Eupalopsellus olandicus* Sellnick, 1949
8. *Eupalopsis* Canestrini, 1886
   Type. *Eupalus maseriensis* Canestrini and Fanzago, 1876
9. *Eustigmaeus* Berlese, 1910 (= *Liostigmaeus* Thor, 1930)
   Type. *Stigmaeus kermesinus* Koch, 1841
10. *Homocaligus* Berlese, 1910
    Type. *Stigmaeus scapularis* Koch, 1838
11. *Ledermulleria* Oudemans, 1923
    Type. *Caligonus segnis* Koch, 1836
12. *Macrostigmaeus* Berlese, 1910
    Type. *Stigmaeus (Macrostigmaeus) serpentinus* Berlese, 1910
13. *Mediolata* R. Canestrini, 1890 (= *Zetsellia* Oudemans, 1927)
    Type. *Stigmaeus longirostris* Berlese, 1887
14. *Neophyllobius* Berlese, 1886
    Type. *Neophyllobius elegans* Berlese, 1886
15. *Podaia* Oudemans, 1923
    Type. *Acarus rubens* Schrank, 1781
16. *Stigmaeus* Koch, 1836 (= *Stigmaeodes* Canestrini, 1890)
    Type. *Stigmaeus cruentus* Koch, 1836
17. *Storchia* Oudemans, 1923
    Type. *Caligonus robustus* Berlese, 1885
18. *Villersia* Oudemans, 1927
    Type. *Villersia vietsi* Oudemans, 1927

Discussion: Although distributed throughout the world only a few species are yet known. They are to be found in moss, lichens, straw, and leaves. At Santa Paula, California, *Mediolata terminalus* (Quayle) was seen preying on the citrus bud mite, *Aceria sheldoni* (Ewing) on lemon. The chelicerae were inserted into the bud mites and the body contents sucked out. Owing to the small numbers, its relative slowness, and the usual inaccessibility of the minute eriophyids beneath bud scales and fruit buttons, this predator is of no great value. No details of their biology are known other than that the eggs are red and laid singly beneath the fruit buttons. *Eupalopsis pinicola* Oudemans, a European species, has been collected in eastern Canada on apples and is probably predaceous on the other apple mites; it is predaceous on scale insects in Europe. *Mediolata nova-scotiae* Nesbitt has been collected on apples in Nova Scotia. *Neophyllobius* sp. has been observed preying on crawler stages of scales in southern California.

References:

Grandjean, F. 1944. Observations sur les Acarines de la famille des Stigmaeidae. Archives des Sciences physiques et naturelles. Periode 5, 26:103–131.

——. 1946. Au sujet de l'organe de Claparède. Archives des Sciences physiques et naturelles. Periode 5, 28:82–87.

McGregor, E. A. 1950. Mites of the genus *Neophyllobius*. Bull. South. Calif. Acad. Sci. 49(2):55–70.

Vitzthum, H. 1929. Acari. Die Tierwelt Mitteleuropas 3(3):50–52.

Pomerantziidae Baker, 1949

Figures 155–157

Figure 155 *Pomerantzia charlesi* Baker. Genital region of female.

Diagnosis: These mites have a palpal thumb-claw complex and movable short chelae which are stylet-like. The peritreme is short and does not reach to the inner base of the chelicerae. There are several dorsal shields but no eyes and no differentiated sensory setae on the propodosoma. The anus is terminal and there are three pairs of genital suckers. Seven rod-like and one conelike sensory setae appear on tarsus I and two rodlike sensory setae appear on tarsus II. All tarsi have claws but no pulvilli.

Genus:

Pomerantzia Baker, 1949
Type. *Pomerantzia charlesi* Baker, 1949

Discussion: This is a small (0.34 mm. long), raphignathid-like mite, which is to be found in peach orchard soil in Georgia, United States. The morphology and habitat indicate a predaceous life.

Reference:

Baker, E. W. 1949. Pomerantziidae, a new family of mites. J. Wash. Acad. Sci. 30(8):269–271.

Figure 156 *Pomerantzia charlesi* Baker. Dorsal view of female.

Figure 157 *Pomerantzia charlesi* Baker. Tarsus I showing sensory setae.

Pterygosomidae Oudemans, 1910

Figures 158, 159

Diagnosis: These mites are parasitic on lizards, with the exception of *Pimeliaphilus podapolipophagus* Trägårdh which is a parasite of cockroaches, and *P. isometri* Cunliffe, found on a scorpion. They are red and small to medium in size (from 0.160 to 1.30 mm. long). Those found on lizards are flat, baglike in outline, and about twice as wide as they are long. The body setae range from few to many and are usually rodlike, leaflike, or fanlike. A shield, either whole or divided, may or may not be present on the propodosoma. Also the pterygosomids may or may not possess a pair of lenslike eyes. The gnathosoma is terminal or deeply inserted into the body and the chelicerae are narrow, with a distorted, movable chela in the lizard parasites and a sharp, piercing, movable chela in the cockroach parasites. At the base of the gnathosoma are prominent peritremes. The palpus has a thumb-claw complex but the thumb is not prominent. The coxae are located anteriorly in the lizard parasites while they are more normal in those parasitizing the cockroach. The tarsi have a pair of claws, each with a pair of tenent hairs. No genital suckers are present and the anal opening is posterior.

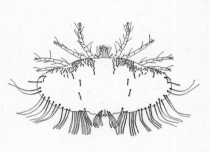

Figure 158 *Pimeliaphilus podapolipophagus* Trägårdh. Dorsum of female.

Figure 159 *Pterygosoma neumanni* Berlese. A typical lizard parasite form. (After Hirst 1925)

Genera:

1. *Pterygosoma* Peters, 1849
   Type. *Pterygosoma agamae* Peters, 1849
2. *Geckobia* Mégnin, 1878
   Type. *Geckobia latasti* Mégnin, 1878
3. *Geckobiella* Hirst, 1917
   Type. *Geckobia texana* Banks, 1915
4. *Hirstiella* Berlese, 1920
   Type. *Geckobiella* (*Hirstiella*) *trombidiformes* Berlese, 1920
5. *Ixodiderma* Lawrence, 1935
   Type. *Ixodiderma inverta* Lawrence, 1935
6. *Pimeliaphilus* Trägårdh, 1904 (= *Pimeliaphiloides* Vitzthum, 1942)
   Type. *Pimeliaphilus podapolipophagus* Trägårdh, 1904
7. *Scaphothrix* Lawrence, 1935
   Type. *Scaphothrix convexa* Lawrence, 1935
8. *Zonurobia* Lawrence, 1935
   Type. *Zonurobia cordylensis* Lawrence, 1935

Discussion: The Pterygosomidae, for the most part, are parasites of lizards, usually being found beneath the scales of their host. According to Hirst 1925: "When more than one form of *Geckobia* is found on the same host, one form usually lives beneath the ventral scales and is flattened, being considerably wider than long and having scales instead of hairs on the venter. The second form occurring on the same host is usually to be discovered between the claw and pad of the toes, between the laminae of the pad, or between the toes themselves: this form is normally practically spherical in shape and has hairs instead of scales on the venter." Lawrence 1935 states: "Generally speaking, therefore, mite parasites are absent (i) in families of lizards in which scales are entirely absent or which lack imbricating scales, (ii) in genera where degeneration of the limbs has taken place, whether these degenerate forms are burrowing as in the Scincidae, or surface living as in the Zonuridae and Gerrhosauridae, and (iii) in certain isolated species of genera in which the majority of forms are parasitized."

Very little is known about the biology of most of these species. The life cycle of all Pterygosomidae consists of larva, nymphochrysalis, nymph, teleiochrysalis, and adult in the female mites, but only the larva, chrysalis, and adult stages in the male mites. Lawrence 1935 figures the larval, nymphal, and adult stages of *Zonurobia cordylensis* Lawrence. The immature forms are very similar to the adult; larva and nymph each possess a small eye plate or shield containing one seta; the adult does not have such a plate but does have the two eyes. In *Pimeliaphilus podapolipophagus* Trägårdh, a parasite of cockroaches, all stages are very similar and differences are small. Although this species has been placed in other families by various workers, it is truly related to the lizard parasites, being the more primitive, free-living type. *P. isometri* Cunliffe is a parasite of scorpions in the Philippine Islands.

In the United States *Pimeliaphilus podapolipophagus* Trägårdh has proved to be a pest in cockroach-rearing cages, at times causing enough damage to hamper rearing. *Geckobiella texana* (Banks) was described from *Sceloporus floridanus* in Texas. *Hirstiella trombidiformes* Berlese is known from San Luis Potosí, Mexico, although its host is unknown.

References:

Hirst, S. 1925. On the parasitic mites of the suborder Prostigmata (Trombidioidea) found on lizards. J. Linn. Soc. London, Zool. 36:173–200.

Lawrence, R. F. 1935. The prostigmatic mites of South African lizards. Parasitol. 27(1):1–45.

Lawrence, R. F. 1936. The prostigmatic mites of South African lizards. Parasitol. 28(1):1–39.

Caeculidae Berlese, 1893

Figures 160, 161

Diagnosis: The caeculids are brownish black, moderately large mites from 1.0 to 2.60 mm. long. They are plump, short, broad, and somewhat trapeziform in shape. There is no suture between the propodosoma and the hysterosoma. The body is heavily armored, usually with

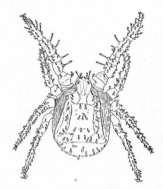

Figure 160 *Caeculus calechius* Mulaik. Palpus. (After Mulaik 1945)

Figure 161 *Caeculus pettiti* Nevin. Dorsum of female. (After Nevin 1943)

seven dorsal shields (three unpaired and two paired) surrounded by weakly striated or wrinkled skin. There are two pairs of lenslike eyes on each side of the propodosoma. An outstanding character is the row of tubercles on the inner side of leg ɪ which supports very long, strong spines giving them the name of "rake-legged mites"; a similar row is on leg ɪɪ. All tarsi lack pretarsi but have two ambulacral claws which are often of different sizes. There is no empodium. The short palpi have strong tibial claws and there is a ventrally placed tarsus or thumb on the tibia. The chelicerae are short and thick with a strong, sickle-like, movable chela and only a remnant of the fixed chela. No genital suckers are present.

Genera:

1. *Caeculus Dufour,* 1832
   Type. *Caeculus echinipes* Dufour, 1832
2. *Procaeculus* Jacot, 1936
   Type. *Procaeculus bryani* Jacot, 1936

Discussion: André 1935 states that the *Caeculus* are predators, sluggish and slow, to be found in the sun or bare earth and rocks in dry places. In cold periods they take refuge in the moss. When disturbed they play possum. The eight-legged nymphs are similar to the adults but less chitinized; the six-legged larvae are also similar to the other stages.

Most of the American species have been described by Mulaik 1945, from the southwestern United States.

References:

André, M. 1935. Notes sur le genre *Caeculus* Dufour (Acariens) avec descriptions d'espèces nouvelles africaines. Bull. Soc. d'Hist. Nat. de l'Afrique du Nord 26:79–127.

Jacot, A. P. 1936. Some rake-legged mites of the family Cheyletidae. J. N. Y. Ent. Soc. 44:17–31.

Lawrence, R. F. 1939. New South African species of the genus *Caeculus* (Acari). J. Linn. Soc. London, Zool. 40(273):537–545.

Mulaik, S. 1945. New mites in the family Caeculidae. Bull. Univ. Utah 35(17):1–23.

Nevin, F. R. 1943. *Caeculus pettiti,* a new species of mite from Virginia. Ann. Ent. Soc. Amer. 36(3):389–393.

Tetranychidae Donnadieu, 1875

Figures 162–164

Diagnosis: These mites are plant feeders. They vary in color from yellowish, greenish, orangish, reddish or red, and some are only red in winter. Of medium size, they measure up to 0.80 mm. in length. Pear-shaped, with the narrow portion toward the rear, these mites possess more or less marked shoulders. The propodosoma is not separated or is only weakly separated from the hysterosoma by a weak suture. The dorsal body surface is usually arched, but is flat in *Bryobia* and *Tetranycopsis*. The skin is soft and has no plates. A pair of eyes is located on each side of the propodosoma. A peritreme is present and at times protrudes. The palpus has a thumb-claw complex. The chelicerae are fused at the base, forming the stylophore and the movable chela is highly modified into a long, whiplike, piercing organ which is characteristic for this group (and the Phytoptipalpidae). The tarsi have claws or modified pulvilli. The claws possess tenent hairs and are used in the generic classification of the group. Tarsus I usually has a pair of du-

plex sensory setae. No genital suckers are present. The males possess
genitalia which are useful in species identification.

The spider mites receive their name from their ability to spin a
fine web over the leaves of the plant upon which they feed, and at

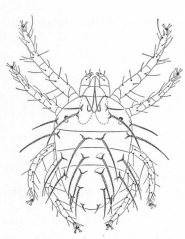 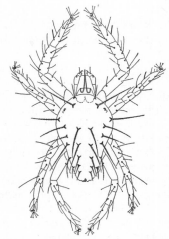

Figure 162   *Metatetranychus ulmi*
(Koch). Dorsum of female.

Figure 163   *Metatetranychus ulmi*
(Koch). Dorsum of male.

times the entire plant may be covered by this webbing. Blauvelt 1945
describes the silk glands as consisting of two groups, the tubular silk
glands and the reniform silk glands, both of which empty into a
common duct in the rostrum. Geijskes 1939 states that *Tetranychus,
Eotetranychus, Amphitetranychus* and *Schizotetranychus* spin freely;

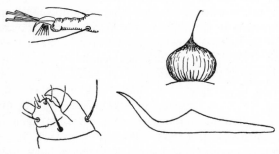

Figure 164   *Metatetranychus ulmi* (Koch). Upper row, tip of tarsus, egg; lower
row, tip of palpus, aedeagus.

Paratetranychus and *Metatetranychus* spin weakly; and *Bryobia, Petrobia* and *Tetranycopsis* do not spin. Grandjean 1948 believes the silk glands to be in the palps, opening on the palpal thumb through the broad, rounded, terminal "finger" or "spine."

Genera:

1. *Tetranychus* Dufour, 1832 (= *Epitetranychus* Zacher, 1916)
   Type. *Tetranychus lintearius* Dufour, 1832
2. *Allochaetophora* McGregor, 1950
   Type. *Allochaetophora californica* McGregor, 1950
3. *Amphitetranychus* Oudemans, 1931
   Type. *Tetranychus viennensis* Zacher, 1920
4. *Anatetranychus* Womersley, 1940
   Type. *Anatetranychus hakea* Womersley, 1940
5. *Aplonobia* Womersley, 1940
   Type. *Aplonobia oxalis* Womersley, 1940
6. *Apotetranychus* Oudemans, 1931
   Type. *Apotetranychus muscicola* Oudemans, 1931
7. *Bryobia* Koch, 1836 (= *Schmiedleinia* Oudemans, 1928)
   Type. *Bryobia praetiosa* Koch, 1836
8. *Eotetranychus* Oudemans, 1931
   Type. *Acarus telarius* Linnaeus, 1758
9. *Eutetranychus* Banks, 1917 (= *Anychus* McGregor, 1920)
   Type. *Tetranychus banksi* McGregor, 1914
10. *Eurytetranychus* Oudemans, 1931
    Type. *Tetranychus latus* Canestrini and Fanzago, 1876
11. *Hystrichonychus* McGregor, 1950
    Type. *Tetranychus gracilipes* Banks, 1900
12. *Linotetranus* Berlese, 1910
    Type. *Linotetranus cylindricus* Berlese, 1910
13. *Metatetranychus* Oudemans, 1931
    Type. *Tetranychus ulmi* Koch, 1836
14. *Monoceronychus* McGregor, 1945
    Type. *Monoceronychus californicus* McGregor, 1945
15. *Neotetranychus* Trägårdh, 1915
    Type. *Neotetranychus rubi* Trägårdh, 1915
16. *Oligonychus* Berlese, 1886 (Oudemans 1938 states = *Rhodaxes* Kirchner, 1863)
    Type. *Tetranychus minimus* Targioni-Tozzetti, 1878 (= *Oligonychus brevipodus* Berlese, 1886)
17. *Paratetranychus* Zacher, 1913
    Type. *Tetranychus ununguis* Jacobi, 1905
18. *Petrobia* Murray, 1877 (= *Tetranobia* Banks, 1917)

Type. *Acarus latens* Müller, 1776 (= *Trombidium lapidum* Hammer, 1804)

19. *Platytetranychus* Oudemans, 1931
    Type. *Tetranychus gibbosus* Canestrini, 1890
20. *Pseudobryobia* McGregor, 1950
    Type. *Pseudobryobia bakeri* McGregor, 1950
21. *Septanychus* McGregor, 1919
    Type. *Tetranychus tumidus* Banks, 1900
22. *Schizotetranychus* Trägårdh, 1915 (= *Stigmaeopsis* Banks, 1917 = *Divarinychus* McGregor, 1930)
    Type. *Tetranychus schizopus* Zacher, 1913
23. *Simplinychus* McGregor, 1950
    Type. *Neotetranychus buxi* Garman, 1935
24. *Tetranychina* Banks, 1917 (= *Tenuicrus* Womersley, 1940)
    Type. *Tetranychina apicalis* Banks, 1917
25. *Tetranycopsis* Canestrini, 1890
    Type. *Tetranychus horridus* Canestrini and Fanzago, 1876

Discussion: *Metatetranychus ulmi* (Koch) [known in this country as *Paratetranychus pilosus* (Canestrini and Fanzago)] can be used for illustrating one type of spider mite biology. The mite passes the winter as eggs, which are deposited on the branches and twigs, are bright red, and may be so numerous as to give the branches a reddish appearance. In the northwestern United States these eggs hatch in the spring, when the new leaves are appearing. The egg, which is stalked but without the guy wires found on legs of *M. citri* (McGregor), splits around its equator for most of its circumference, a small portion being left as a hinge. The upper half, or lid, is lifted by the six-legged larva, which crawls out, the lid usually springing back to its original position. The small, bright-red or orange larvae swarm to the young leaves and at once begin feeding. After a period of feeding, during which the larva moves about to some extent, it settles down, usually on the under side of the leaf near a vein or midrib, and remains quiescent for a time about equal to the feeding period. Afterward the skin becomes smooth and glossy in appearance and finally turns pearly white, an indication that the larva has loosened itself from the new skin underneath. Within a few hours the skin splits transversally across the dorsum, between the second and third pair of legs, and the eight-legged protonymph emerges. The molted skins remain adhering to the leaf, and if numerous enough give the leaf a silvery appearance. The protonymphal stage is shorter than the larval stage, and the feeding and quiescent stages are repeated. The mite then molts and becomes a deutonymph, which

Plate 2 Damage to citrus fruit and foliage by *Metatetranychus citri* (Mc-Gregor). Damaged fruit and foliage is shown in upper row and normal material in lower row. (From A. M. Boyce, Insects and mites and their control, The Citrus Industry, Volume II, 1948. Courtesy of The University of California Press.)

is slightly longer than either larval or protonymphal stages. The females become larger and more globose than the males during the deutonymphal stage and can thus be distinguished. The males complete each stage in a fraction of a day less than the females, the total in the Northwest for the immature stages averaging eight days for the males and nine days for the females. When the male emerges it runs about the leaf until it finds a quiescent female deutonymph. It then settles down beside the deutonymph to await emergence of the female. As soon as the nymphal skin of the latter splits across the back the male begins working at the posterior half of it with his fore legs and mouth parts. The female arches her back and within a few minutes her posterior legs are freed. She then backs out of the anterior half of the old skin and copulation takes place immediately, sometimes even occurring before the female has had time to free herself entirely from the nymphal skin. The male crawls under the female from the rear, the latter elevating the tip of her abdomen. The male clasps his front legs about her abdomen and his second pair of legs about her hind legs, and then curves the end of his abdomen upward and forward until it meets the end of the female's abdomen. Copulation lasts from ten to fifteen minutes. Eggs are laid within a day or two after emergence in hot weather, while in cool weather oviposition may begin several days or a week later. Eggs are laid on both surfaces of the leaf, usually along the midribs and veins and near the edges of the leaves. These summer eggs hatch on an average in about eight to ten days. The number of generations per year depends on climate and season. Four generations are reported in Sweden, probably six in Connecticut, and from six to eight in the Northwest. Overwintering eggs are deposited over a rather long period, beginning about the middle of August, until the cold weather kills the mites or causes the leaves to drop, sometimes as late as November. Individual females of the sixth, seventh, and eighth broods may deposit these eggs.

The life cycle of *Metatetranychus citri* (McGregor) is very similar to that of *M. ulmi,* except that in California the adults overwinter on the host and there may be from twelve to fifteen generations a year.

Tetranychus bimaculatus Harvey overwinters chiefly as mature females. During mild weather in the southern United States eggs are laid and considerable development may take place. This species overwinters on wild plants and in the spring, when the mites develop rapidly and the food plants become too crowded to support them properly, they migrate to other hosts, such as cotton. There appears to be a predominance of the females during the summer, but as cold weather approaches the numbers of the sexes become more nearly equal. The female lives from seventeen days in midsummer to several months in winter, whereas the male is shorter lived. The female is not active, but the male, when not mating, moves rapidly about. The male is smaller and narrower than the female and the abdomen can be telescoped considerably, as during mating. Parthenogenesis, the giving birth to males by unfertilized females, has been reported.

Little work has been done on the transmittal of plant diseases by the spider mites. Moskovetz 1940 reports a virus disease of cotton being transmitted by *Tetranychus telarius* (L.).

Of the plant-feeding mites, the Tetranychidae are probably the most important economically. Hardly a plant is free from at least one species, and practically all species of the family are or appear to be potential pests. The mites damage the plants by piercing the leaves with their stylet-like chelicerae and draining out the cellular material near the puncture. When the mite population is large the leaves may be killed and drop from the tree. Populations of red spiders may build up to fantastic numbers if left uncontrolled. In Porterville, California, *Tetranychus pacificus* McGregor has reproduced so rapidly in the summer on chinaberry (umbrella) trees that they were defoliated within a few days, and the dropping mites completely covered the entire surface of the ground as well as fence posts. The use of DDT for agricultural pests apparently has upset a spider mite-predator complex, causing the tetranychids to become serious problems in areas where they had been of no or of secondary importance. Little known or undescribed species are not only becoming pests, but some are building up resistance to the newer acaricides. In many cases, however, no reason can yet be given for increased populations of these mites.

There are many species of importance in the United States, but only a few are listed here. *Metatetranychus ulmi* (Koch) is distributed over continental Europe from Italy to Sweden and Norway, and from France to Russia. In the United States it is distributed generally along the Atlantic coast from Nova Scotia to North Carolina and west to Ontario, Michigan, Indiana, Tennessee, Kentucky, Wisconsin, Illinois, and Missouri. In the West it is found from British Columbia to central California and east to Idaho and northern Utah. The favorite food plants are the deciduous fruits, especially the plum, prune, apple, and pear, but this mite has been found on many other plants. *M. citri*

(McGregor) is one of the major pests of citrus in California. Although found in Florida, it is of little importance there, perhaps owing to climatic differences.

Tetranychus bimaculatus Harvey (also known as *T. telarius* L.) occurs throughout the country and is a major pest of cotton in the southeastern United States as well as a pest of fruit trees and truck crops throughout the country.

Bryobia praetiosa (Koch) is a pest of crops in the United States, being serious on almonds, peach, prune, alfalfa, clover, and peas. This species overwinters in the north in the egg stage and in southern regions as adults on clover and other plants. It is common in Europe.

The Tetranychidae are not usually host specific, and on citrus, as well as on other plants, there are several species on the one plant. *Tetranychus lewisi* McGregor, *T. yumensis* McGregor, *Metatetranychus citri* (McGregor), and *Eutetranychus clarki* McGregor are all to be found on citrus.

References:

Blauvelt, W. E. 1945. The internal morphology of the common red spider mite (*Tetranychus telarius* Linn.) N. Y. (Cornell) Agr. Expt. Sta. Mem. 270.

Cagle, L. R. 1949. Life history of the two-spotted spider mite. Virginia Agr. Expt. Sta. Tech. Bull. 113.

Garman, P. 1940. Tetranychidae of Connecticut. Conn. (State) Agr. Expt. Sta. Bull. 431.

——., and J. F. Townsend. 1938. The European red mite and its control. Conn. (State) Agr. Expt. Sta. Bull. 418.

Geijskes, D. C. 1939. Beiträge zur Kenntnis der Europaischen Spinnmilben (*Acari, Tetranychidae*), mit Besonderer Berucksichtigung der Niederlandischen Arten. Mededeelingen van de Landbouwhoogeschool 42(4).

Grandjean, F. 1948. Quelques caracteres des Tétranyques. Bull. du Mus. Ser. 2, 20(6):517–524.

McGregor, E. A. 1950. Mites of the family Tetranychidae. Amer. Mid. Nat. 44(2):257–420.

——., and F. L. McDonough. 1917. The red spider on cotton. U.S. Dept. Agr. Bull. 416.

Moskovetz, S. N. 1940. Plant virus diseases and their control. Trans. Conf. on Plant Virus Disease. Moscow 4–7/11. Moscow, Inst. Mikrobiol. Izd. Akad. Nauk U.S.S.R. 1941.

Newcomer, E. J., and M. A. Yothers. 1929. Biology of the European red mite in the Pacific Northwest. U. S. Dept. Agr. Tech. Bull. 89.

Phytoptipalpidae Ewing, 1922

(= Pseudoleptidae Oudemans, 1928; Trichadenidae Oudemans, 1938; Tenuipalpidae Sayed, 1950)

Figures 165, 166

Diagnosis: These mites are reddish plant feeders of very small size (from about 0.20 to 0.30 mm. in length) and of various shapes. A suture may or may not separate the propodosoma and hysterosoma.

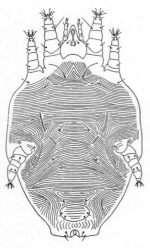 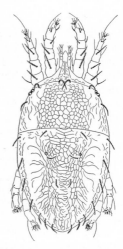

Figure 165 *Phytoptipalpus paradoxus* Trägårdh. Venter of adult female. (After Sayed 1942)

Figure 166 *Brevipalpus cardinalis* (Banks). Dorsum of female.

The skin may be striated or it may have a reticulated pattern. There are two pairs of lenslike eyes, a few body setae, and no sensory setae present. The palpi are cylindrical, small, and simple without thumb-claw complex. The chelicerae are U-shaped, long, slender, needle-like, and protrusible as in the Tetranychidae. A stylophore (mandibular plate) is present. There are three or four pairs of legs in the adults. All tarsi have claws, tenent hairs and pulvilli. Tarsi I and II have rod-like sensory setae. No genital suckers are present. The genital opening is transverse as in the Eriophyidae.

Genera:

1. *Phytoptipalpus* Trägårdh, 1904
   Type. *Phytoptipalpus paradoxus* Trägårdh, 1904
2. *Brevipalpus* Donnadieu, 1875
   Type. *Brevipalpus obovatus* Donnadieu, 1875
3. *Dolichotetranychus* Sayed, 1938
   Type. *Stigmaeus floridanus* Banks, 1900
4. *Pentamerismus* McGregor, 1949 (= *Aegyptobia* Sayed, 1950)
   Type. *Tenuipalpus erythreus* Ewing, 1917
5. *Phyllotetranychus* Sayed, 1938 (according to Vitzthum may be the same as *Raoiella* Hirst)
   Type. *Phyllotetranychus aegyptium* Sayed, 1938.
6. *Pseudoleptus* Bruyant, 1911
   Type. *Pseudoleptus arechavalatae* Bruyant, 1911
7. *Raoiella* Hirst, 1924 (= *Rondaniacarus* Oudemans, 1938)
   Type. *Raoiella indica* Hirst, 1924
8. *Tegopalpus* Womersley, 1940
   Type. *Tegopalpus conicus* Womersley, 1940
9. *Tenuipalpus* Donnadieu, 1875
   Type. *Tenuipalpus palmatus* Donnadieu, 1875
10. *Trichadenus* Rondani, 1879
    Type. *Trichadenus sericariae* Rondani, 1879

Discussion: The life history of this family may be illustrated by that of *Brevipalpus inornatus* (Banks) as worked out by McGregor 1916. The egg is thickly elliptical in outline, is about 96 μ long by 67 μ wide, and is deposited with the long axis perpendicular to the leaf. The female usually lays the egg in a crevice or abrasion, in old molted skins, or in the groove by the midvein. They are often closely packed in clusters of several hundred, each female laying approximately twenty eggs. In South Carolina during the summer the eggs hatch in about eight days and the six-legged larva emerges. The average larval duration is 4.7 days. The larvae molt into protonymphs whose duration is about 4.5 days. The deutonymphal stage lasts about four days, the total being about twenty-one days. There are possibly six to seven generations per year in South Carolina, the mite being found throughout the entire year. All stages are more or less similar.

The genus *Phytoptipalpus* Trägårdh is a typical phytoptipalpid but lacks the fourth pair of legs. Sayed 1942 records it as having two "larval" stages before it attains sexual maturity. This genus, along with *Tenuipalpus eriophyoides* Baker nymph, indicates the phylogenetic relationship between the Eriophyidae, which are elongate, annulate and with two pairs of legs, and the typical plant-feeding Tetranychidae.

Although many members of this family appear to do little damage to the plants upon which they feed, some are of distinct economic importance. McGregor 1916 reports defoliation of privet throughout Florida, South Carolina, Alabama, Mississippi, and Louisiana by *Brevipalpus inornatus* (Banks). Green 1900 records a species as causing serious damage to tea plants in Ceylon; the mites denude branches and even whole bushes of their leaves, terminal buds are damaged, and at times the bush is killed. Lewis 1944 found *Brevipalpus lewisi* McGregor scarring lemon fruit at Porterville, California; in parts of an infested grove, which had received no commercial spray treatment for about ten years, more than twenty-five per cent of the fruit was scarred, whereas in adjacent treated orchards these mites were hard to find. Jones *et al.* 1941 describes a *Brevipalpus* (*B. phoenicis* Geijskes) as sometimes causing serious damage to papaya fruits in Hawaii, T. H. The fruits develop gray, scaly, or cracked areas, most frequently at points where they are in contact with the trunk. This same species also damages citrus in Spain. Blanchard 1940 reports *B. pseudocuneatus* (Blanchard) as a pest of citrus in Argentina. Another is found damaging passion fruit in Australia.

Tenuipalpus pacificus Baker is a pest of orchids as is *Brevipalpus australis* (Tucker). Sayed 1942 reports *Tenuipalpus granati* Sayed as causing browning of the leaves in vineyards in Egypt; it has also been taken on leaves, branches and occasionally on fruits of pomegranates.

Pseudoleptus and *Dolichotetranychus* are to be found in various salt grasses throughout the world; the two species at times cause distortion of the grass heads.

References:

Baker, E. W. 1945. Mites of the genus *Tenuipalpus* (Acarina: Trichadenidae). Proc. Ent. Soc. Wash. 47(2):33–38.
———. 1948. A new trichadenid mite which further indicates a phylogenetic relationship between the Tetranychidae and Eriophyidae. Proc. Ent. Soc. Wash. 50(3):59, 60.
———. 1949. The genus *Brevipalpus* (Acarina: Pseudoleptidae). Amer. Midland Nat. 42(2):350–402.
Blanchard, E. E. (1939) 1940. Tres acaros dañino para los cultivos argentinos. Rev. Fac. Agron. La Plata (3)24:11–18.
Green, E. 1900. Tea-mites, and some suggested experimental work against them. Roy. Bot. Gard., Ceylon. Cir. 17(Ser. 1):202, 203.

Jones, W. W., W. B. Storey, G. K. Parros, and F. G. Holdaway. Papaya production in the Hawaiian Islands. Bul. Hawaii Agri. Expt. Sta. 87: 46.

Lawrence, R. F. 1943. New South African mites of the genus *Tenuipalpus* Donnadieu (Tetranychidae). Trans. Roy. Soc. South Africa 30(1): 35–48.

Lewis, H. 1944. Injury to citrus by *Tenuipalpus* mites. Calif. Citrograph 29(4):87.

McGregor, E. A. 1916. The privet mite in the south. J. Econ. Ent. 9:556–560.

————. 1949. Nearctic mites of the family Pseudoleptidae. Mem. South. Calif. Acad. Sci. 3(2):1–45.

Planes, S. (1944) 1945. La roña de los frutos citricos. Bol. Patal. Veg. y Ent. Agr. 13:47–54.

Sayed, M. T. 1942. Contribution to the knowledge of the Acarina of Egypt: II. The genus *Tenuipalpus* Donnadieu. Bull. Soc. Found 1er Ent. 24:93–113.

Teneriffiidae Thor, 1911

Figures 167, 168

Diagnosis: These are medium-sized mites from 0.70 to 0.90 mm. long. The body is elongated with legs adapted for running. The integument is lined, lacks a crista but has a propodosomal shield. There

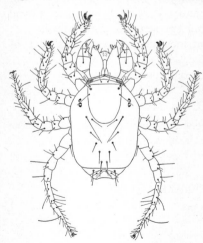

are two pairs of widely separated eyes. The anal opening is ventral (almost terminal) and the long genital opening has weak, sickle-like flaps with few setae and three pairs of weakly developed genital suckers. The legs are simply built and haired; the two ambulacral

Figure 167   *Austroteneriffia hirsti* Womersley. Dorsum of female.

Figure 168   *Austroteneriffia hirsti* Womersley. Distal portion of palpus.

claws at least on legs I and II are pectinate; legs III and IV occasionally have a clawlike empodium. The rostrum is short and broad. The chelicerae are sickle-like, with two small setae on the dorsal surface of the basal segment. The palpus is five-segmented, thick, strongly bent, with a long tibial claw and weak setae. The palpal tarsus is almost rudimentary with setae of various lengths. Peritremes opening at base of chelicerae are present.

Genera:

1. *Teneriffia* Thor, 1911 (= *Teneriffiola* Strand, 1911)
   Type. *Teneriffia quadripapillata* Thor, 1911
2. *Austroteneriffia* Womersley, 1935
   Type. *Austroteneriffia hirsti* Womersley, 1935
3. *Heteroteneriffia* Hirst, 1926
   Type. *Heteroteneriffia marina* Hirst, 1926
4. *Neoteneriffiola* Hirst, 1924
   Type. *Neoteneriffiola luxoriensis* Hirst, 1924
5. *Parateneriffia* Thor, 1911
   Type. *Parateneriffia bipectinata* Thor, 1911

Discussion: *Heteroteneriffia marina* Hirst, 1926 was collected in Malaya under rocks and stones on a rocky bank which was submerged at half-tide every day and at full tide was under four to six feet of water. At low tide there was a permanent pool of sea-water about twenty feet wide between the bank and the shore. The mites moved rapidly and were hard to catch. Other species and genera have been described from such widely divergent localities as the Island of Teneriffe, Paraguay, Egypt, and Australia.

The structure of the mites indicates a predaceous habit.

Reference:

Womersley, H. 1935. On the occurrence in Australia of Acarina of the family Teneriffiidae (Trombidoidea) Rec. South Austral. Mus. 5: 333–338.

Pseudocheylidae Oudemans, 1909

Figure 169

Diagnosis: The pseudocheylids are colorless or reddish, small to medium-sized mites from 0.23 to 1.1 mm. long. They are more or less elongated and somewhat rhombic, with a strong furrow between the propodosoma and the hysterosoma. The propodosomal shield is either weak or entirely lacking as is usually the case. The peritreme is present at the base of the chelicerae. There are two pairs of sensory setae on the propodosoma. Two pairs of lenslike eyes may be found on each side of the propodosomoa (*Pseudocheylus*), or two pairs of pigment spots with

a mutual cornea (*Neocheylus*), or there may be no eyes. The palpi are short and usually somewhat thicker than the legs. The palpal femur is longer than the other segments and thickened on the outer side so that the palpi are forceps-like. The palpal tibia has a strongly bent claw, and the ventral palpal tarsus is weak (or entirely gone?). Tarsi of the legs have either a long stalked triangular caruncle or sucker and no claws (*Pseudocheylus, Neocheylus*), or have a bell-like caruncle or lobe between two claws (*Tarsocheylus*), or lack an empodium and have normal but very small claws on tarsi ı and comblike claws on the other tarsi (*Stigmocheylus*). No genital suckers are present. The genus *Heterocheylus* has only one pair of propodosomal

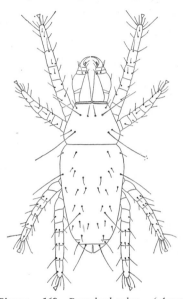

Figure 169 *Pseudocheylus* (*Anoplocheylus*) *europaeus* Berlese. Dorsum of female. (After Berlese 1910)

sensory setae. Tarsi ı lack ambulacra, but ıı, ııı, and ıv have caruncles or lobes only. Trägårdh 1950 has divided these mites into two subfamilies.

Key to the Pseudocheylidae
(from Trägårdh)

1. Chelicerae stylet-like; palps with large, sharply pointed, dentate terminal tooth and varying number of comb-shaped or sickle-shaped setae; all legs with claws   Pseudocheylinae

    Chelicerae with strongly curved, sharp terminal tooth of the same type as in the larvae of the *Trombidiidae*. Palps with blunt, edentate terminal tooth, no comb-shaped or sickle-shaped setae. Legs ı antenniform, legs ıı-ıv with tooth-shaped, subterminal bristle and large, disk-shaped empodium   Heterocheylinae

Pseudocheylinae Tragårdh, 1950

Genera:

1. *Pseudocheylus* Berlese, 1888
   a. *Pseudocheylus* s. str. (= *Rhagina* Womersley, 1935)
      Type. *Pseudocheylus biscalatus* Berlese, 1888
   b. *Anoplocheylus* Berlese, 1910
      Type. *Pseudocheylus* (*Anoplocheylus*) *europaeus* Berlese, 1910
2. *Neocheylus* Trägårdh, 1906
   Type. *Neocheylus natalensis* Trägårdh, 1906
3. *Stigmocheylus* Berlese, 1910
   Type. *Stigmocheylus brevisetus* Berlese, 1910
4. *Tarsocheylus* Berlese, 1904
   Type. *Tarsocheylus paradoxus* Berlese, 1904

Heterocheylinae Tragårdh, 1950

Genus:

Heterocheylus Lombardini, 1926
Type. *Heterocheylus fusiformis* Lombardini, 1926

Discussion: This is a small family consisting of only a few described species. A single species has been described from the United States, *Pseudocheylus americanus* (Ewing), which was taken under the bark of a hard maple tree at Urbana, Illinois. Another species, *Pseudocheylus biscalatus* Berlese, was collected under the bark of trees in Paraguay and Brazil in South America. *Neocheylus natalensis* Trägårdh is from damp moss, Natal, South Africa. *Pseudocheylus protea* (Womersley) is from moss, Australia. The other genera are represented by species from soil, moss, humus, and rotten debris in Italy. The family as a whole appears to be predaceous, with the exception of *Heterocheylus* which is an ectoparasite of arthropods.

Reference:

Trägårdh, I. 1950. Description of a new species of *Heterocheylus* Lombardini from Africa, with notes on the classification of the Pseudocheyletidae. Ent. Tidskrift 71, hft. 2:104–110.

Anystidae Oudemans, 1902

Figure 170

Diagnosis: Of red or reddish color, the anystids are medium-sized mites from 0.55 to 1.35 mm. long. They have a soft integument and may or may not possess a propodosomatic shield (actually a lack of or differentiation in skin striations rather than a sclerotization). No suture is present between the propodosoma and the hysterosoma. The peritreme, at times freely protruding and located at the base of the chelicerae, is present. The rostrum is short and conelike. A movable chela which is distal and hook-like is also present. The palpal tibia has one to three internal claws and the palpal tarsus is located disto-ventrally on the tibia. A smooth tubercle-like projection on the anterior portion of the propodosoma bears a pair of sensory setae; the propodosoma has a pair of sensory setae. The legs radiate from the body and the coxae are in one or two closely separated

Figure 170 *Anystis baccarum* (Linnaeus). Dorsum of female. (After Oudemans 1936)

groups. All tarsi are either entire or divided into many segments; the tarsi have two claws which may be combed, toothed, or pilose and which have a clawlike, brushlike or bell-like empodium. There are no genital suckers. There are two subfamilies.

Key to the Anystidae

1. Short, broad; with two pairs of eyes; palpal tibia with three claws
    Anystinae

    Longer than broad; with one to two pairs of eyes; palpal tibia with one smooth claw or two feathered claws   Erythracarinae

Anystinae Oudemans, 1936

Genera:

1. *Anystis* v. Heyden, 1826 (= *Actineda* Koch, 1836)
    Type. *Trombidium cornigerum* Hermann, 1804
2. *Autenriethia* Oudemans, 1936
    Type. *Actineda velox* Berlese, 1905
3. *Barella* Oudemans, 1936
    Type. *Anystis sinensis* Berlese, 1923
4. *Scharfenbergia* Oudemans, 1936
    Type. *Actineda hilaris* Koch, 1836
5. *Snartia* Oudemans, 1936
    Type. *Snartia nepenthus* Oudemans, 1936

6. *Tencateia* Oudemans, 1936
   Type. *Tencateia besselingi* Oudemans, 1936
7. *Walzia* Oudemans, 1936
   Type. *Actineda antiguensis* Stoll, 1886

Erythracarinae Oudemans, 1936

Genera:

1. *Erythracarus* Berlese, 1903
   Type. *Trombidium parietinum* Hermann, 1804 (= *Erythraeus comes* Berlese, 1886)
2. *Absoloniana* Willmann, 1940
   Type. *Absoloniana diversipes* Willmann, 1940
3. *Anandia* Hirst, 1927
   Type. *Anandia alticola* Hirst, 1927
4. *Bechsteinia* Oudemans, 1936
   Type. *Bechsteinia schneideri* Oudemans, 1936
5. *Chabrieria* Oudemans, 1936
   Type. *Tarsotomus terminalis* Banks, 1916
6. *Chaussieria* Oudemans, 1937 (= *Schellenbergia* Oudemans, 1936, nom. praeocc.)
   Type. *Erythraeus domesticus* Koch, 1847
7. *Erythrocheylus* Berlese, 1903
   Type. *Pseudocheylus erythraeoides* Leonardi, 1901
8. *Siblyia* Oudemans, 1936
   Type. *Erythraeus ignipes* Dugès, 1834
9. *Tarsolarkus* Thor, 1912
   Type. *Tarsolarkus articulosus* Thor, 1912
10. *Tarsotomus* Berlese, 1882
    Type. *Erythraeus hercules* Berlese, 1882

Discussion: These are long-legged, fast moving mites, predaceous on other mites and many small insects. They are to be found on plants, tree leaves, branches, and grass. Although they are not usually abundant, they occasionally may be found in great numbers. *Anystis agilis* (Banks) is described from the United States and *Walzia antiguensis* (Stoll), a Venezuelan species, has been found in Florida.

The larval, nymphal, and adult stages are similar; two nymphal stages are known. The mites apparently have the power of spinning and the young can enclose themselves in a cocoon (nymphochrysalis or teleiochrysalis). Banks has found freshly molted specimens encased in little silken white cocoons.

Reference:

Oudemans, A. C. 1936. Neues uber Anystidae (Acari). Archiv. f. Natur-gesch. neue folge 5:364–446.

Myobiidae Mégnin, 1877

Figures 171, 172

Diagnosis: These are small to medium-sized mites that are unar-mored and have striated skin and peritremes. The chelicerae are mi-nute and stylet-like. The palpi are simple, minute, and not used for grasping; they may or may not have a claw and if a thumb is present

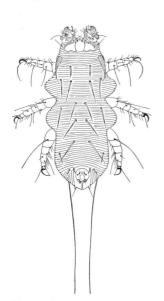

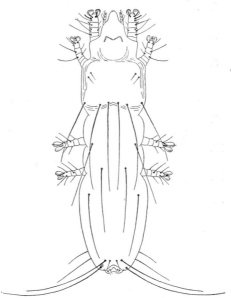

Figure 171 *Myobia muscu-linus* (Schrank). Dorsum of female.

Figure 172 *Syringophilus columbae* Hirst. Dorsum of female. (After Hirst 1922)

it is hard to see. The first pair of legs may be modified for grasping hairs; the other legs have one or two claws. The male genital opening may be dorsal. This is a rather heterogeneous group of mites and may be further separated upon study. *Harpirhynchus, Ophioptes, Picobia, Psorergates,* and *Syringophilus* may form a distinct family intermediate between the Myobidiidae and Cheyletidae but probably closer to the latter.

Genera:

1. *Myobia* v. Heyden, 1826
   Type. *Pediculus musculi* Schrank, 1781
2. *Amorphacarus* Ewing, 1938
   Type. *Myobia elongata* Poppe, 1896
3. *Calcarmyobia* Radford, 1948
   Type. *Myobia rhinolophia* Radford, 1940
4. *Eadiea* Jameson, 1949
   Type. *Eadiea condylurae* Jameson, 1949
5. *Eutalpacarus* Jameson, 1949
   Type. *Eutalpacarus peltatus* Jameson, 1949
6. *Ewingana* Radford, 1948
   Type. *Ewingana bispinosa* Radford, 1948
7. *Foliomyobia* Radford, 1948
   Type. *Myobia chiropteralis* Michael, 1884
8. *Harpirhynchus* Mégnin, 1877 (= *Harpicephalus* Canestrini, 1885 = *Sarcopterinus* Railliet, 1893 = *Sarcopterus* Giebel, 1871 = *Sarcoborus* Oudemans, 1904)
   Type. *Sarcoptes nidulans* Nitzsch, 1818
9. *Neomyobia* Radford, 1948
   Type. *Myobia rollinati* Poppe, 1908
10. *Ophioptes* Sambon, 1928
    Type. *Ophioptes parkeri* Sambon, 1928
11. *Picobia* Haller, 1878
    Type. *Picobia heeri* Haller, 1878
12. *Protomyobia* Ewing, 1938
    Type. *Myobia claparedei* Poppe, 1896
13. *Psorergates* Tyrrell, 1883
    Type. *Psorergates simplex* Tyrrell, 1883
14. *Radfordia* Ewing, 1938
    Type. *Myobia ensifera* Poppe, 1896
15. *Syringophilus* Heller, 1880
    Type. *Syringophilus bipectinatus* Heller, 1880

Discussion: The mites forming the *Myobia* complex are found on mammals of three orders—Rodentia, Insectivora, and Chiroptera. This group of mites has legs I greatly modified for hair clasping. According to Ewing 1938 they feed at the bases of the hairs on the secretions in the hair follicles and seldom, if ever, suck blood. Grant 1942, working with *Myobia musculi* (Schrank), has observed feeding and states, "Feeding appears to occur at other places than in the hair follicles, at least the beak seems often to be inserted into the skin where no hair can be seen to arise even with the aid of a dissecting microscope. It may be mentioned that what appeared to be red blood corpuscles were observed in the oral tube of one specimen." Jameson 1948 states that *Myobia simplex* Ewing has been found full of blood. Skidmore 1934 found *Radfordia ensifera* (Poppe) (= *Myobia ratti* Skidmore) causing injury to white rats. He states, "These rats were scratching themselves about the head, nose and neck. Many had small dry scabs on the head, about the ears, and upper sides of the neck. Some had bloody scabs due to bleeding caused by severe scratching."

These mites are probably distributed throughout the world. In Australia *Psorergates ovis* Womersley, 1941 is parasitic on sheep producing a chronic irritation of the skin along the sides and flanks of the body. The genus *Syringophilus* contains species which are to be found inside the quills of bird feathers in North America and Europe: they are believed to feed on the internal cones of the feathers. *Harpirhynchus nidulans* (Nitzsch) lives in colonies in the follicles of feathers and causes tumors or cysts in the skin of the host; the mite is to be found on numerous birds including the pigeon. The genus *Ophioptes* contains mites which are parasitic on South American snakes. They live in small pits which they produce in the heavily cornified layer of the snake scales. Ewing 1933 described a species which forms pits in the scales; both Ewing and Sambon described two forms—one is a sacklike nymph without legs, and within this swollen nymphal form is a fully formed, eight-legged individual which Sambon described as a male and which Ewing believed to be a nymph or a female; examination of the type in the United States National Museum shows the form to be an adult but with the sex unknown. The life cycle is otherwise unknown.

References:

Ewing, H. E. 1938. North American mites of the subfamily Myobiinae, new subfamily (Arachnida). Proc. Ent. Soc. Wash. 40(7):180–197.

Grant, D. C. 1942. Observations on *Myobia musculi* (Schrank) (Arachnida: Acarina: Cheyletidae). Microentomology 7(3):64–76.

Jameson, E. W. 1948. Myobiid mites (Acarina: Myobiinae) from Shrews (Mammalia: Soricidae) of Eastern North America. J. Parasitol. 34 (4):336–342.

——. 1949. Myobiid mites (Acarina: Myobiidae) from *Condylura cristata* (Linnaeus) and *Neurotrichus gibbsii* (Baird) (Mammalia: Talpidae). J. Parasitol. 35(3):423–430. •

Radford, C. D. 1934. Notes on the genus *Myobia*. North Western Naturalist 356–364. 1935: 248–258. 1936 a:34–39. 1936 b:144–151.

——. 1948. A revision of the fur mites Myobiidae (Acarina). Bull. Paris Mus. d'Hist. Nat. Ser. 2, 20(5):458–464; (6):525–531.

Womersley, H. 1941. Notes on the Cheyletidae (Acarina, Trombidoidea) of Australia and New Zealand with descriptions of new species. Rec. South Austral. Mus. 7(1):51–64.

Cheyletidae Leach, 1814

Figure 173

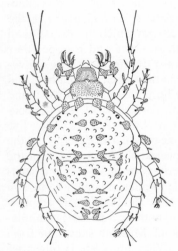

Figure 173 *Cheletogenes ornatus* (Canestrini and Fanzago). Dorsum of female.

Diagnosis: The cheyletids are yellowish or reddish, small to medium-sized mites measuring from about 0.20 to 0.80 mm. in length. Their body is oval, plump, and in the feather-inhabiting mites, elongate. The propodosoma and the hysterosoma are usually plainly delineated and usually they have one or more dorsal shields. Lenslike eyes may be present or lacking. The dorsal body setae are simple, serrate, rodlike, or clavate. A strong peritreme which more or less frames the gnathosoma is present. The chelicerae are short and stylet-like for piercing while the palpi are large and pincer-like for grasping. The palpal thumb is short and may or may not have a comb and sickle-like setae. A large terminal claw, usually toothed, is located on the palpal tibia. The tarsi of the legs have two claws and an empodium (tarsus I of *Cheletogenes* has no claws or pulvillus; tarsus I of *Cheletomorpha* lacks claws but has a pulvillus). There are no genital suckers. The genital opening of the male is in some cases dorsal but usually posterior and ventral.

Genera:

1. *Cheyletus* Latreille, 1796
   Type. *Acarus eruditus* Schrank, 1781

2. *Acaropsis* Moquin-Tandon, 1862
   Type. *Tyroglyphus mericourti* Moquin-Tandon, 1851
3. *Chelacaropsis* Baker, 1949
   Type. *Chelacaropsis moorei* Baker, 1949
4. *Cheletogenes* Oudemans, 1905
   Type. *Cheyletus ornatus* Canestrini and Fanzago, 1876
5. *Cheletoides* Oudemans, 1904
   Type. *Syringophilus uncinatus* Heller, 1880
6. *Cheletomimus* Oudemans, 1904
   Type. *Cheletes berlesei* Oudemans, 1904 (= *Cheletomimus trux* Oudemans, 1904)
7. *Cheletomorpha* Oudemans, 1904
   Type. *Acarus lepidopterorum* Shaw, 1794 (= *Cheyletus venustissimus* Koch, 1839)
8. *Cheletophanes* Oudemans, 1904
   Type. *Cheyletus montandoni* Berlese and Trouessart, 1889
9. *Cheletophyes* Oudemans, 1914
   Type. *Cheletophyes vitzthumi* Oudemans, 1914
10. *Cheletopsis* Oudemans, 1904
    Type. *Cheyletus norneri* Poppe, 1888
11. *Cheletosoma* Oudemans, 1905
    Type. *Cheletosoma tyrannus* Oudemans, 1905
12. *Chelonotus* Berlese, 1893
    Type. *Chelonotus selenirhynchus* Berlese, 1893
13. *Cheyletia* Haller, 1884
    Type. *Cheyletia laureata* Haller, 1884
14. *Cheyletiella* Canestrini, 1886 (= *Ewingella* Vail and Augustson, 1944)
    Type. *Cheyletus parasitivorax* Mégnin, 1878
15. *Eucheyletia* Baker, 1949
    Type. *Eucheyletia bishoppi* Baker, 1949
16. *Eutogenes* Baker, 1949
    Type. *Eutogenes foxi* Baker, 1949
17. *Neoeucheyla* Radford, 1950 (= *Eucheyla* Berlese, 1913. *nom. praeocc.*)
    Type. *Cheyletia (Eucheyla) loricata* Berlese, 1913
18. *Neocheyletiella* Baker, 1949
    Type. *Neocheyletiella rohweri* Baker, 1949

Discussion: These mites develop normally from egg, larval, and nymphal stages to adults. Nymphs may have more dorsal plates than adults. In the genus *Cheyletus* the male often is dissimilar from the female in the nature of the gnathosoma. In these species the palpi are greatly elongated and have few or no basal teeth on the palpal claw;

an aedeagus is present, the larger female genital opening is lacking, and the sensory organ on tarsus I of the male is greatly enlarged. In *Cheyletiella parasitivorax* (Mégnin) the male genital opening is dorsal. In other genera where the two sexes are known the males are more or less similar to the females, varying in the characteristics mentioned above. Ewing 1912 has studied the life cycle of a *Cheyletus*. Eggs are laid near each other but not in clusters and the female remains near them for some time after oviposition has ceased. One female laid twenty-five eggs over a six-day period, another twenty-two eggs in two days and another laid only a single egg. At laboratory temperature, on an average, the duration of the incubation period was 4.3 days, the larval stage 7.66 days, the first nymphal stage 4.5 days, the second nymphal stage at least 5 days, and the adult stage 13 days. The larva is similar to the adult but has only six legs; the nymphs are likewise similar to the adult but have four pairs of legs. Ewing found that the young mites prefer eggs of other mites such as Acaridae with which they are associated. In the milled wheat samples he found that about 95 per cent of the acarids were killed in a short time by these cheyletids. Rodionov and Furman 1940 in a study of *Cheyletus eruditus* (Schrank) for control of granary mites (*Acarus siro* L., *Tyrophagus castellanii* Hirst and *Glycyphagus destructor* (Schrank), in Russia found that the cheyletids are not of great value in the control of grain mites in granaries and that their presence only lowers the purity of the grain. Their developmental period is longer than that of the grain mites, and although they are more resistant to desiccation, they are more susceptible to hydrocyanic gas. The strongly armored hypopial stages of the grain mites were not attacked by the cheyletids.

The Cheyletidae, as a whole, are free-living predators, although some are to be found in bird feathers, in squirrel, rabbit, or cat fur, and sometimes appear to injure the host. The free-living forms are to be found in association with infestations of other mites such as the Acaridae and Tetranychidae, and with scale insects, but as yet they do not appear to be of great importance in controlling mites or insects. Because of their free-living habits many species are world-wide in distribution.

References:

Baker, E. W. 1949. A review of the mites of the family Cheyletidae in the United States National Museum. Proc. U. S. Natl. Mus. 99(3238): 267–320.

Cooper, K. W. 1946. The occurrence of the mite, *Cheyletiella parasitivorax* (Mégnin) in North America, with notes on its synonymy and "parasitic" habits. J. Parasitol. 32(5):480–482.

Ewing, H. E. 1912. The life history and habits of *Cheyletus seminivorus* Packard. J. Econ. Ent. 5(5):416–420.

McGregor, E. A. 1944. A new potential enemy of the bud mite. Calif. Citrograph 30(2):53.

Olsen, S. J., and H. Roth. 1947. On the mite *Cheyletiella parasitivorax*, occurring on cats, as a facultative parasite of man. J. Parasitol. 33 (5):444–445.

Oudemans, A. C. 1906. Revision des Cheletines. Mem. Soc. Zool. de France 19:36–219.

Demodicidae Nicolet, 1855

Figures 174, 175

Diagnosis: The demodicids are weakly colored, very small mites from 0.10 to 0.39 mm. long. They are vermiform, annulate, and eight-legged. The legs are short, stumpy, five-segmented, and located on the anterior portion of the body. The chelicerae are stylet-like as in the

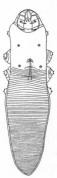

Figure 174 *Demodex muscardini* Hirst. Dorsal view of male. (After Hirst 1919)

Figure 175 *Demodex muscardini* Hirst. Ventral view of female. (After Hirst 1919)

Cheyletidae. A capitulum which covers the palpi and the chelicerae is present. The palpi are three-segmented and the distal segment has four or five rodlike setae. There is a pair of minute openings located on the venter of the capitulum near the base. The female genital opening is situated between or behind coxae IV, while the male genital opening is dorsal in the center of the podosoma. No genital suckers are present.

Genus:

> *Demodex* Owen, 1843
> Type. *Acarus folliculorum* Simon, 1842

Discussion: *Demodex muscardini* Hirst, a parasite of the dormouse, *Muscardinus avellanarius,* illustrates a complete life cycle of these mites. The eggs hatch into a larva which is very much like the early nymphal stage, except that there are three instead of four pairs of legs which consist of a chitinous plate or epimeron; each epimeron bears a pair of very minute and inconspicuous denticulate tubercles. The protonymph has four pairs of legs or epimera, each bearing two tiny but distinct tubercles of equal size, each with three or four minute but distinct denticles. There are four pairs of curious epidermal structures present nearer the middle of the ventral surface of the body. These are semicircular in shape, and the posterior margin is curved and furnished with sharp denticles. The deutonymph has the appendages or legs similar to those of the protonymph, but they are more leglike with several segments visible and with two clusters of denticles present. The four pairs of semicircular structures in the ventral surface are present but are much smaller. The adult has the genital opening, five-segmented legs, and has lost the semicircular structures on the ventral surface of the body.

Hirst 1919 gives an excellent review of the family from which the following information is taken. *Demodex folliculorum* Owen, which is to be found in the pores of man, especially around the nose and eyelids, has been implicated in various skin diseases. It has been noted, however, that these mites occur in normal as well as diseased tissue and are to be found infesting most people. It is now believed to be of no importance in man. Like the following species it is more or less world-wide in distribution. *D. canis* Leydig is present in the follicular, demodectic, or red mange of dog. In typical cases the mite is to be found in great numbers in association with a bacterium (*Staphylococcus pyogenes albus* or some allied form), which is the actual cause of the disease. The mite plays an important role in that it dilates the follicles and sweat glands and even possibly carries the germ into the pores. The mange may be pustular, accompanied by various crusts; it may be a "squamous affection with numerous epidermal pellicles. In a typical case there are small hairless patches, together with reddish pimples and pustules, skin hot and thickened in the affected places." There is a foul and disgusting odor accompanying this mange. The presence of the mite distinguishes this mange from sarcoptic mange or fungus infections. *D. equi* Railliet, although present on horses free of any disease, can also cause a "pathological condition of the skin, characterized either by pruritus, varying greatly in intensity, or by definite lesions. The coat is poor, with the hair very sparse in places." The disease usually commences on the saddle or neck of the animal but does not appear to be infectious. In the advanced stage pustules are present and the skin thickens. *D. phylloides* Csokor "causes a pustular skin disease in pigs, the pustules varying from the size of a grain of sand to a walnut." "Sometimes they may become confluent, and may rupture and cause sores and ulcers on the skin." They are to be found only where the skin is fine in texture, spreading "from the snout over the neck and under part of the chest and abdomen, and over the flanks and inner parts of the legs." Usually the general health of the animals is not affected. *D. bovis* Stiles causes nodules or pustules in cattle, these pustules varying in size from a head of a pin to as large as a hen's egg. They are to be found around the ears, sides, shoulders, and intercrural space. Various stages of development are to be found in the cheesy or fluid contents of the nodules. The disease appears to be infectious but does not seem to affect the general health of the animal. However, holes caused by these mites reduce the value of the hides. Other species have been found on sheep, hedgehogs, field mice, cats, rabbits, voles, and rats and are probably to be found on many other hosts.

References:

Hirst, S. 1919. The genus *Demodex* Owen. Brit. Mus. (Nat. Hist.) Studies on Acari No. 1.

———. 1922. Mites injurious to domestic animals. Brit. Mus. (Nat. Hist.) Econ. Series No. 13.

Lombardini, G. 1942. Contributo alla conoscenza della morfologia dei Demodicidae. Chiave analitica del genere *Demodex* Owen. Redia 28: 89–102.

Erythraeidae Oudemans, 1902

Figures 176, 177

Diagnosis: The adults of this family are reddish, predaceous mites with legs adapted for running. The larvae are heteromorphic, lack urstigma, and are parasitic on arthropods. The adult body is oval and arched with large numbers of setae. A shallow furrow separates the propodosoma from the hysterosoma. The propodosoma has a median, longitudinal crista metopica (Vitzthum lists *Fallopia* and *Neosmaris* as exceptions) which may reach posteriorly to the middle of the dorsum. There are two sensillary areas on crista; the anterior one is often far forward on a "nose," while the posterior one is usually on the

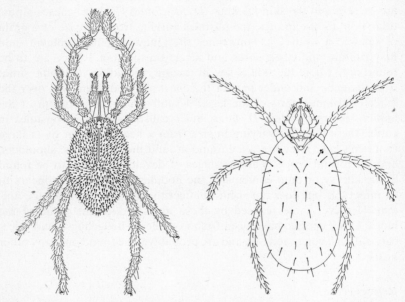

Figure 176 *Leptus hirtipes* Berlese. Dorsum of female. (After Vitzthum 1926)

Figure 177 *Leptus tenebrans* Vitzthum. Larva. (After Vitzthum 1926)

posterior end of the crista; the sensillary areas each have a pair of sensory setae. In mites lacking the crista, the sensory setae are located in a corresponding location. Either one or two pairs of lenslike eyes are present. Coxae I and II and III and IV are in two groups; the legs are long, slender and have six movable segments; the tarsi have two claws, but no empodium. Five movable segments comprise the palpi and the palpal tibia has a strong claw. The palpal thumb is usually pear-shaped but sometimes ball-like. The chelicerae are unsegmented, stylet-like, very long, capable of being withdrawn into the body, and usually toothed distally. No genital suckers are present.

Genera and subgenera:

1. *Erythraeus* Latreille, 1806 (= *Rhyncholophus* Dugès, 1834)
   a. *Erythraeus* s. str.
      Type. *Acarus phalangioides* DeGeer, 1778
   b. *Corerythrolophus* Radford, 1950 (= *Erythrolophus* Berlese, 1920, *nom. praeocc.*)
      Type. *Erythraeus* (*Erythrolophus*) *froggatti* Berlese, 1920
   c. *Ctenerythraeus* Berlese, 1918
      Type. *Erythraeus* (*Ctenerythraeus*) *trombidioides* Berlese, 1918
   d. *Ptilolophus* Berlese, 1916
      Type. *Erythraeus* (*Ptilolophus*) *claviger* Berlese, 1916
2. *Balaustium* v. Heyden, 1826 (= *Monotrombidium* Krauss, 1925)
   Type. *Trombidium murorum* Hermann, 1804
3. *Bochartia* Oudemans, 1910
   Type. *Bochartia kuyperi* Oudemans, 1910
4. *Caeculisoma* Berlese, 1888
   Type. *Caeculisoma tuberculatum* Berlese, 1888
5. *Callidosoma* Womersley, 1936
   Type. *Caeculisoma ripicola* Womersley, 1934 (larva)
6. *Claverythraeus* Trägårdh, 1937
   Type. *Claverythraeus mongolicus* Trägårdh, 1937
7. *Erythrellus* Southcott, 1946
   Type. *Erythrellus imbricatus* Southcott, 1946
8. *Erythroides* Southcott, 1946
   Type. *Erythraeus serratus* Womersley, 1936
9. *Erythrombium* Berlese, 1910
   Type. *Erythrombium eusisyrum* Berlese, 1910
10. *Euplatylophus* Radford, 1950 (= *Platylophus* Berlese, 1910, *nom. praeocc.*)
    Type. *Platylophus argasoides* Berlese, 1910
11. *Fallopia* Oudemans, 1905 (= *Microsmaris* Hirst, 1926)
    Type. *Rhyncholophus poriferus* Kramer, 1898
12. *Hauptmannia* Oudemans, 1910
    Type. *Achorolophus longicollis* Oudemans, 1910
13. *Leptus* Latreille, 1795 (= *Achorolophus* Berlese, 1891)
    Type. *Pediculus coccineus* Scopoli, 1763
14. *Lucasiella* Banks, 1910
    Type. *Rhyncholophus plumipes* Koch, 1856
15. *Neosmaris* Hirst, 1926
    Type. *Neosmaris novaezealandiae* Hirst, 1926
16. *Parawenhoekia* Paoli, 1937
    Type. *Parawenhoekia dectici* Paoli, 1937
17. *Parerythraeus* Southcott, 1946

Type. *Parerythraeus gregoryi* Southcott, 1946
18. *Sphaerolophus* Berlese, 1910
  a. *Sphaerolophus* s. str.
    Type. *Rhyncholophus globiger* Berlese, 1885
  b. *Cavannea* Berlese, 1910
    Type. *Rhyncholophus cavannae* Berlese, 1885
  c. *Eupodolophus* Berlese, 1914 (= *Fessoniella* Hirst, 1924)
    Type. *Sphaerolophus* (*Eupodolophus*) *chubbi* Berlese, 1914

Grandjean 1947 has separated the Erythraeidae into two families—Erythraeidae and Balaustiidae—but this arrangement is not followed here.

Discussion: The larvae of these mites are parasitic on insects much as the larvae of the Trombiculidae are parasitic on vertebrates. In one case Lawrence 1940 found as high as 400 larvae of *Erythraeus swazianus* Lawrence on a locust. Usually the number infesting an arthropod is much smaller. Lawrence states that the "larvae seem to attach themselves by the mouth-parts at all stages" and some of the molted skins can be found still adhering to the host. Most of the larvae are attached to the undersurface of the wings, and even to the tympanic membrane within the organ and under the rim of the opening. They are rarely found on the legs. *Leptus atticolus* Lawrence was taken from the legs of a spider, *Saitis* sp., Attidae, in Natal, South Africa. A mite identified as a *Leptus* sp. has been reared from lizards in Bougainville in the South Pacific. This is the first record of an erythraeid being parasitic on a vertebrate. Most species are known either from the larva or the adult, very few having the different stages correlated.

Adults are free-living predators and may be found on foliage, in humus or among leaves, and on the shore and sands. *Balaustium aonidaphagus* (Ebeling) is reported as a predator of the red scale on citrus in California. Ebeling 1934 states, "these mites are not ordinarily abundant and the writer has found them only in certain groves. As high as thirty mites were found on a single tree, but ordinarily only one or two, if any, are found. They may also be seen running about on the ground beneath the trees, which may, in part, be due to the difficulty they experience in clinging to the foliage." They are cannibalistic and if a number are left together in a sealed container invariably only one live mite will remain after a day or two. "The writer once observed a mite thrusting its mandibles and finally its entire cephalothorax beneath the armor of a red scale and feeding on the body of the insect. These mites also prey on red scale crawlers and other small insects and mites. If more abundant they might be an important enemy of the red scale."

An interesting erythraeid mite is *Ptilophus namaquensis* (Lawrence) which is from South Africa. The posterior pair of legs are rather long and the tibia is furnished with a large plume of long setae. The mites hold these legs, when running, either horizontally behind them or vertical, not using them for locomotion. The mite runs very rapidly and vibrates this last pair of legs. Several functions of this posterior pair of legs have been proposed by Lawrence 1937—(a) an aid in locomotion, (b) sensory, (c) defence, (d) sexual.

References:

Ebeling, W. 1934. A new predaceous mite from southern California. Pan-Pacific Ent. 10(1):33–34.

Grandjean, F. 1947. Étude sur les *Smarididae* et quelques autres Erythroides (Acariens). Arch. de Zool. Expt. et Gén. 85(1):1–126.

Lawrence, R. F. 1937. A new species of plume-footed mite from South Africa. Ann. South African Mus. 32(3):269–279.

——. 1940. New larval forms of South African mites from arthropod hosts. Ann. Natal Mus. 9(3):401–408.

Southcott, R. V. 1946. Studies on Australian Erythraeidae (Acarina). Proc. Linn. Soc. New South Wales 71(1–2):6–48.

Smaridiidae Kramer, 1878

Figures 178, 179

Diagnosis: These mites have a longish, oval body which is pointed anteriorly and moderate shoulders. The propodosoma is usually drawn out into a long "nose" and a shallow furrow separates it from the hysterosoma. The dorsal surface of body is slightly convex and occasionally has several longitudinal and transverse depressions. Two sensillary areas, each with a pair of sensory setae, are located on the dorsum of the propodosoma. The crista metopica may be present or absent. One or two eyes are situated on each side of the propodosoma. The setae are of peculiar structure; they are usually in the shape of a leaf with thorns or hairs which are strongly curved and folded longitudinally. Coxae I and II, and III and IV are united, but the two groups are separated. The legs are slender, occasionally extremely long, and have six movable segments. Two claws are present on the tarsi but both pretarsus and empodium are lacking. The palpi have five segments with a thumb-claw complex. The chelicerae are long and stylet-like. The gnathosoma is capable of being projected far anteriorly or withdrawn into the body. No genital suckers are present. According to Grandjean there is no protonymph. Heteromorphic without urstigma the larvae possess trichoboths or sensory setae on the first pair of legs. The larvae also have a scutum which possesses two pairs of sensory setae and two pairs of ordinary setae.

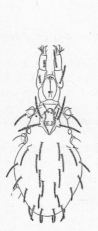

Figure 178 *Smaris latreillei* Grandjean. Larva. (After Grandjean 1947)

Figure 179 *Smaris mamillatus* (Say). Dorsum of female, gnathosoma partially extruded.

Genera:

1. *Smaris* Latreille, 1796 (= *Smariidia* Latreille, 1817 = *Dugèsia* Berlese, 1883)
   Type. *Trombidium squamatum* Hermann, 1804
2. *Aecosmaris* Grandjean, 1947
   Type. *Aecosmaris callitricha* Grandjean, 1947
3. *Fessonia* v. Heyden, 1826
   Type. *Trombidium papillosa* Hermann, 1804
4. *Hirstiosoma* Womersley, 1934
   Type. *Hirstiosoma scalaris* Womersley, 1934

5. *Phanolophus* André, 1927
   Type. *Phanolophus nasica* André, 1927
6. *Sclerosmaris* Grandjean, 1947
   Type. *Sclerosmaris philopempta* Grandjean, 1947
7. *Sphaerotarsus* Womersley, 1936
   Type. *Sphaerotarsus allmani* Womersley, 1936

Southcott 1946 revised the family and divided it into four subfamilies—the Smaridiinae, Fessoniinae, Hirstiosominae, and Phanolophinae. This system is not followed here.

Discussion: This is a little known group of mites in which the larval forms are parasitic on insects and the adult forms are predaceous. Very few species are known, the best known fauna being that of Australia and Europe. The family is little known in North America, Ewing having described *Hirstiosoma longilinealis* (Ewing) from the Middle West, and Say another species from the East Coast—*Smaris sericeum* Say.

Womersley and Southcott 1941 have studied the life history of a few of these mites and have been able to rear nymphs of *Smaris prominens* (Banks), an Australian species, from larvae found attached to psocids. They state, "when fully gorged the mites left their hosts and wandered freely about the tube for several days before becoming dormant. After several more days the skin splits transversely, revealing the pupa. Three to four weeks later the nymph emerges from a rent towards the posterior end of the pupa. Whether a second resting stage and nymph occurs has not been ascertained, but seems to be unlikely." The presence of only one nymphal stage agrees with Grandjean's statement that the protonymph stage is lacking. Womersley and Southcott have also been able to correlate nymphs of *Hirstiosoma* and *Sphaerotarsus* with adults on morphological grounds, as Grandjean has been able to do with the larvae and adults found associated together.

References:

Grandjean, F. 1947. Étude sur les Smaridiidae et quelques autres Erythroides (Acariens). Arch. de Zool. Expt. et Gén. 85(1):1–126.

Southcott, R. V. 1946. On the family Smaridiidae (Acarina). Proc. Linn. Soc. New South Wales 70(3–4):173–178.

Womersley, H., and R. V. Southcott. 1941. Notes on the Smaridiidae (Acarina) of Australia and New Zealand. Trans. Roy. Soc. South Austral. 65(1):61–78.

Calyptostomidae Oudemans, 1923

Figures 180, 181

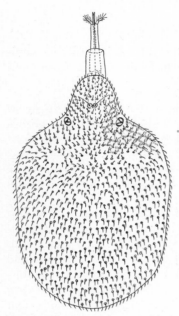

Figure 180 *Calyptostoma velutinus* (Müller). Dorsum of female; legs not shown.

Diagnosis: These are land-dwelling mites usually to be found in very wet places. Their body is square, plump, and truncate posteriorly with a dull or blunt point anteriorly. No suture separates the propodosoma and hysterosoma. The dorsal body surface is flat with numerous depressions, lacking setae, which are places of muscle attachment. No crista metopica or area sensilligerae are present, but on the anterior portion of the propodosoma there is a pair of pseudostigmata in the shape of a roundish cup from the bottom of which arise the short sensory setae. A pair of lenslike eyes are located on each side of the propodosoma. The dorsal setal bases are connected by sclerotized stripes in such a manner that the integument presents a design of stars, usually with a slender, leaf-shaped seta in the center of each star. The legs are slender, proportionately long, and have six movable segments. All tarsi lack pretarsus and empodium but have two claws. The palpi have five movable segments and the palpal tibia has a very short, weak tibial claw. The palpal tarsus is joined distally and directed anteriorly. The

Figure 181 *Calyptostoma velutinus* (Müller). Propodosomal sensory setae.

chelicerae are unsegmented, very long, and needle-like. The gnathosoma is highly projectile, and when in a state of rest it is retracted into the body. There are two pairs of genital suckers. The larvae are homomorphic, do not have urstigma, and probably are parasites of arthropods.

Genus:

Calyptostoma Cambridge, 1875 (= *Smaris* Berlese, 1887)
Type. *Acarus velutinus* Müller, 1778 (= *Calyptostoma hardyi* Cambridge, 1875)

Discussion: A little-known group of predaceous mites.

Trombidiidae Leach, 1815

Figure 182

Diagnosis: Nymphal and adult trombidiids can usually be recognized by their dense coat of setae that gives them a velvet-like appearance and by the division of their body into three more or less distinct sec-

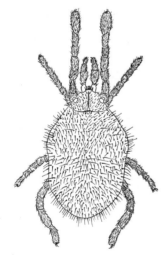

tions—gnathosoma, propodosoma, and hysterosoma. The body, however, is never 8-shaped. The chelicerae consist of two segments, a basal muscular one and a curved, bladelike distal segment that is provided with sawlike teeth on its

Figure 182 a *Microtrombidium* hystricinum (Canestrini). Dorsal view of adult. (After Vitzthum 1926)

Figure 182 b *Allothrombium neapolitanum* Oudemans. Dorsal view of larva. (After Oudemans 1912)

dorsal edge The stigmata open near the median, dorsal, proximal surface of the chelicerae and usually do not have free peritremes. The palps have five segments, and the palpal tarsus opposes a terminal tibial claw in thumblike fashion. The legs have six (exceptionally five) segments. A dorsal scutum or crista metopica is found on the median portion of the propodosoma. One (exceptionally two) pairs of sensillae are on the lateral expansions of the scutum. Anteriorly the scutum ends in an expanded plate that may project over the gnathosoma as a tectum. This plate bears numerous setae, or the plate may be lacking and the scutum rudimentary, consisting of little more than areas for the origin of the sensillae. One subfamily (Stygothrombiinae) is extremely degenerate and lacks numerous setae, and typical mouth parts, and its body shape is long and worm-like.

Larval trombidiids have a single urstigmen associated with leg I, usually more than one dorsal plate, and the seta on the pedipalpal coxa is usually anterior to the base of the palpal femur. These mites are parasitic on invertebrates.

Thor and Willmann 1947 have divided the family into fifteen sub-families. One of these subfamilies, the Trombiculinae, is now recognized as a family and will be considered in the next section. A key to the subfamilies, based on adults, modified from Thor and Willmann, follows:

Key to the Trombidiidae

1. Propodosoma with crista enclosed in plates of various shapes or free in integument   2

    Propodosoma without crista; scutum rudimentary; sensillae attenuate and nude   Trombellinae

2. One pair of sensillae   4

    Two pairs of sensillae   3

3. Three hysterosomal plates   Notothrombiinae

    Hysterosomal plates lacking   Johnstonianinae

4. Sensillae arising from sensillary area   6

    Sensillae not arising from sensillary area   5

5. Scutum expanded   Calothrombiinae

    Scutum straight   Tanaupodinae

6. Peritreme associated with cheliceral stigmata; eyes on movable peduncles   7

    No peritreme present; eye if present not on movable peduncle   8

7. Pulvillus present between ambulacral claws   Allothrombiinae

    Pulvillus absent   Trombidiinae

8. Sensillary area not anterior; two claws on legs   9

    Sensillary area in anterior region of scutum; three claws on legs
                    Stygothrombiinae

9. Sensillary area at the posterior end of scutum   10

    Sensillary area in mid region of scutum   11

10. Single eye on either side of crista   Tanaupodasterinae

    Double eye (exceptionally no eyes) on either side of crista
                    Microtrombidiinae

11. Setae nude   12

    Setae feathered   13

12. Scutum with free anterior projection   Rhinothrombiinae

    Scutum without free anterior projection   Ocypetinae

13. With dorsal pygidial plate   Eutrombidiinae

    Without dorsal pygidial plate   Holcotrombidiinae

Trombidiinae Thor, 1935

Genera:

1. *Trombidium* Fabricius, 1775 (= *Sericothrombium* Berlese, 1910)
   Type. *Acarus holosericeus* Linnaeus, 1758
2. *Austrothrombium* Womersley, 1934
   Type. *Allothrombium* (*Mesothrombium*) *australiense* Hirst, 1929
3. *Caenothrombium* Oudemans, 1927
   Type. *Caenothrombium caloris* Oudemans, 1927
4. *Dinothrombium* Oudemans, 1910
   Type. *Acarus tinctorius* Linnaeus, 1767
5. *Phyllotrombidium* Cooreman, 1946
   Type. *Trombidium barbarum* Lucas, 1846
6. *Xenothrombium* Oudemans, 1927
   Type. *Xenothrombium insulare* Oudemans, 1927

Allothrombiinae Thor, 1935

Genera:

1. *Allothrombium* Berlese, 1903 (= *Mesothrombium* Hirst, 1926)
   Type. *Trombidium fuliginosum* Hermann, 1804
2. *Corethrothrombium* Oudemans, 1929
   Type. *Corethrothrombium vandermeermohri* Oudemans, 1929

Calothrombiinae Thor and Willmann, 1947

Genus:

Calothrombium Berlese, 1918
Type. *Parathrombium paolii* Berlese, 1918

Eutrombidiinae Thor, 1935

Genera:

1. *Eutrombidium* Verdun, 1909
   Type. *Pediculus rostratus* Scopoli, 1763 (= *Trombidium trigonum* Hermann, 1804)
2. *Leptothrombium* Berlese, 1912
   Type. *Trombidium oblongum* Trägårdh, 1904

Johnstonianinae Thor, 1935

Genera:

1. *Johnstoniana* George, 1909 (= *Rohaultia* Oudemans, 1911)
   Type. *Rhyncholophus errans* Johnston, 1852
2. *Centrotrombidium* Kramer, 1896
   Type. *Centrotrombidium schneideri* Kramer, 1896
3. *Diplothrombium* Berlese, 1910
   Type. *Trombidium longipalpe* Berlese, 1887
4. *Hirstithrombium* Oudemans, 1940
   Type. *Diplothrombium australiense* Hirst, 1928
5. *Myrmicotrombium* Womersley, 1935
   Type. *Myrmicotrombium brevicristatum* Womersley, 1935

Microtrombidiinae Thor, 1935

Genera:

1. *Microtrombidium* Haller, 1882 (= *Manriquia* Boshell and Kerr, 1942)
   Type. *Trombidium purpureum* Haller, 1882
2. *Anomalothrombium* André, 1936
   Type. *Anomalothrombium nasigerum* André, 1936
3. *Camerotrombidium* Thor, 1936
   Type. *Ottonia vesiculosa* Thor, 1900
4. *Campylothrombium* Krausse, 1916
   Type. *Microtrombidium langhofferi* Krausse, 1916
5. *Dendrotrombidium* Thor, 1916
   Type. *Trombidium perligerum* Berlese, 1888
6. *Dromeothrombium* Berlese, 1912
   Type. *Trombidium macropodum* Berlese, 1903

7. *Echinothrombium* Womersley, 1937
   Type. *Ottonia spinosa* Canestrini, 1877
8. *Enemothrombium* Berlese, 1910
   Type. *Trombidium bifoliosum* Canestrini, 1884
9. *Eutrichothrombium* Womersley, 1937
   Type. *Trombidium euthrichum* Berlese, 1904
10. *Georgia* Hull, 1918
    Type. *Ottonia ramosa* George, 1909
11. *Foliotrombidium* Womersley, 1945
    Type. *Enemothrombium evansi* Womersley, 1937
12. *Hiotrombidium* Womersley, 1945
    Type. *Calothrombium tubbi* Womersley, 1937
13. *Laminothrombium* Womersley, 1937
    Type. *Microtrombidium myrmicum* Womersley, 1934
14. *Pedotrombidium* Womersley, 1945
    Type. *Pedotrombidium kohlsi* Womersley, 1945
15. *Neotrombidium* Leonardi, 1901
    Type. *Neotrombidium turcigerum* Leonardi, 1901
16. *Platyseta* Wharton, 1938
    Type. *Platyseta yucatanicus* Wharton, 1938
17. *Platytrombidium* Thor. 1936
    Type. *Trombidium vagabundum* Berlese, 1903
18. *Spelaeothrombium* Willmann, 1940
    Type. *Spelaeothrombium caecum* Willmann, 1940
19. *Valgothrombium* Willmann, 1940
    Type. *Ottonia valga* George, 1909

Notothrombiinae Thor and Willmann, 1947
Genus:

Notothrombium Storkán, 1934
Type. *Notothrombium regis-borisi* Storkán, 1934

Ocypetinae Vitzthum, 1941
Genus:

Ocypete Leach, 1814 (= *Podothrombium* Berlese, 1910)
Type. *Ocypete rubra* Leach, 1814

Rhinothrombiinae Thor and Willmann, 1947
Genus:

Rhinothrombium Berlese, 1910
Type. *Trombidium nemoricola* Berlese, 1886

Holcotrombidiinae

(new name for Scalothrombiinae Thor and Willmann, 1937)
Genus:

> *Holcotrombidium* Womersley, 1945 (= *Scalothrombium* Thor and Willmann, 1947)
> Type. *Euthrombium scalaris* Womersley, 1936 (*Euthrombium* is a *lapsus* for *Eutrombidium*)

Stygothrombiinae Thor, 1935

Genera.

1. *Stygothrombium* Viets, 1932
   Type. *Stygothrombium karamani* Viets, 1932
2. *Cerberothrombium* Viets, 1934
   Type. *Stygothrombium* (*Cerberothrombium*) *armatum* Viets, 1934

Tanaupodasterinae Thor and Willmann, 1947

Genus:

> *Tanaupodaster* Vitzthum, 1933
> Type. *Tanaupodaster montezuma* Vitzthum, 1933

Tanaupodinae Thor, 1935

Genera:

1. *Tanaupodus* Haller, 1882
   Type. *Tanaupodus steudeli* Haller, 1882
2. *Eothrombium* Berlese, 1910
   Type. *Eothrombium echinatum* Berlese, 1910
3. *Neotanaupodus* Garman, 1925
   Type. *Neotanaupodus tuberculatus* Garman, 1925
4. *Tignyia* Oudemans, 1937
   Type. *Acarus sulcatus* Müller, 1776
5. *Typhlothrombium* Berlese, 1910
   Type. *Trombidium histricinum* Leonardi, 1901

Trombellinae Thor, 1935

Genera:

1. *Trombella* Berlese, 1887
   Type. *Trombella glandulosa* Berlese, 1887
2. *Chyzeria* G. Canestrini, 1897
   Type. *Chyzeria ornata* G. Canestrini, 1897
3. *Parachyzeria* Hirst, 1926 (=*Thaumatotrombium* André, 1938)
   Type. *Parachyzeria indica* Hirst, 1926

Genera proposed for larvae whose subfamilial relationships are unknown.

1. *Astigma* Bruyant, 1911
   Type. *Astigma oudemansi* Bruyant, 1911
2. *Atomus* Latreille, 1795
   Type. *Acarus parasiticus* DeGeer, 1778
3. *Cercothrombium* Methlagl, 1928
   Type. *Cercothrombium loricatum* Methlagl, 1928
4. *Ettmülleria* Oudemans, 1911
   Type. *Trombidium sucidum* Trägårdh, 1910
5. *Heterotrombidium* Verdun, 1910
   Type. *Thrombidium granulatum* Oudemans, 1902
6. *Hexathrombium* Cooreman, 1944
   Type. *Hexathrombium spatuliferum* Cooreman, 1944
7. *Hoplothrombium* Ewing, 1925
   Type. *Hoplothrombium quinquescutatum* Ewing, 1925
8. *Monunguis* Wharton, 1938
   Type. *Monunguis streblida* Wharton, 1938
9. *Neothrombium* Oudemans, 1909
   Type. *Allotrombidium neglectum* Bruyant, 1909 (*Allotrombidium* is a *lapsus* for *Allothrombium*)
10. *Nothotrombicula* Dumbleton, 1947
    Type. *Nothotrombicula deinacridae* Dumbleton, 1947
11. *Paratrombium* Bruyant, 1910
    Type. *Paratrombium egregium* Bruyant, 1910
12. *Polydisca* Methlagl, 1928
    Type. *Polydisca squamata* Methlagl, 1928
13. *Womersleyia* Radford, 1946
    Type. *Womersleyia minuta* Radford, 1946

Discussion: The trombidiids are extremely numerous in both numbers and kinds. Thor and Willmann include 304 species in their section on the family in "Das Tierreich." That this is only a fraction of the species that await description is proved by the fact that almost every collection of mites from litter will contain new species of trombidiids. The next family, the Trombiculidae, has been studied more extensively than the Trombidiidae. Thor and Willmann included these forms in their account of the Trombidiidae as the subfamily Trombiculinae. They listed 150 species of trombiculid, in addition to their 304 species of trombidiids. Even with 150 species they failed to include all the new species discovered during World War II. The total number of trombiculids is now about 300, and many parts of the world have not yet been carefully surveyed for these mites. As a conservative estimate then, there are at least several thousand species of trombidiids, most of which await description.

Trombidiids are world-wide in distribution and have been found on every major land mass except those covered by ice and snow the year around. They are more abundant in the tropics than in temperate climes and are a conspicuous portion of the mite faunas found on oceanic islands.

The life history of trombidiid mites is as follows: egg, deutovum, larva, nymphochrysalis, nymph, imagochrysalis, imago. The life cycle of *Eutrombidium rostratus* has been well worked out by Severin 1944. Michener 1946 has found that microtrombidiids may undergo several postimaginal molts. The sex ratio is 1:1 in the cases investigated. The penis of the males will serve to distinguish them from females.

Trombidiid larvae parasitize arthropods and because of this habit they may potentially be important not only in the control of arthropods but also in the transmission of micro-organisms from one arthropod to another. The nymphal and adult stages feed on the eggs and early larval instars of many arthropods, and thus aid in keeping down their numbers. *Eutrombidium rostratus* is an important enemy of the locust. Its larvae feed on the locusts and its adults feed on the eggs of locusts.

References:

Berlese, A. 1912. Trombidiidae. Redia 8:1–291.

Feider, Z. 1950. Cercetǎri asupra aparatului respirator la Trombidiidae și prostigmatele superioare și lista speciilor de Trombidiidae din Republica Popularǎ Românǎ. Ann. Acad. Repub. Pop. Române, Vol. 3, mem. 5:1–185, Pls. 1–21.

Michener, C. D. 1946. The taxonomy and bionomics of some Panamanian trombidiid mites (Acarina). Ann. Ent. Soc. Amer. 39:349–380.

Severin, H. C. 1944. The grasshopper mite *Eutrombidium trigonum* (Hermann) an important enemy of grasshoppers. S. Dak. Agr. Expt. Sta. Tech. Bull. 3:1–36.

Thor, S., and C. Willmann. 1947. Trombidiidae. Das Tierreich Lfg. 71 b: 187–541 + Pls. XXIX–XXXVI.

Womersley, H. 1945. A revision of the Microtrombidiinae (Acarina, Trombidiidae) of Australia and New Guinea. Rec. South Austral. Mus. 8:293–355.

Trombiculidae Ewing, 1944

Figures 183, 184

Diagnosis: *Nymphs* and *adults*. They are about 1 mm. long and oval or more usually figure-8-shaped. The body is divided into three more or less distinct sections—gnathosoma, propodosoma, and hysterosoma. The cuticle is striated frequently with enlarged, platelike, setal bases. Eyes may be present or absent but if present are always located on

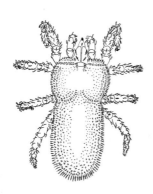

Figure 183 *Euschöngastia indica* (Hirst). Dorsal view of nymph. (After Wharton 1946)

Figure 184 *Euschöngastia indica* (Hirst). Dorsal view of larva. (After Wharton 1946)

the propodosoma. The setae are filiform and densely pilose, covering the legs and body to give a velvety appearance. Made of five segments, the palps are well developed and a tibial claw is present. The palpal tarsus opposes the claw in a thumblike fashion. The chelicerae have a stout basal segment and a bladelike distal segment that bears a row of saw-like teeth on its dorsal edge. The legs have six segments, and each tarsus is provided with a pair of ambulacral claws. The genital opening is located between coxae IV. The males have a bladelike penis and numerous setae on the longitudinal genital valves, while the females have a similar opening but lack a penis and have few setae on the valves; the genital openings of both sexes have three pairs of genital suckers. The stigmata open on the basal segment of the chelicerae. A scutum is present with a posterior sensillary area that bears a pair of pseudostigmata from which arise elongated sensillae. The anterior end of the crista is expanded to form a tectum that bears one or two setae.

Larvae. (The taxonomy of trombiculids is based primarily on the larvae.) The chelicerae have two segments; the basal segment is stout and muscular while the distal segment is a sclerotized, curved blade with or without projections called teeth. The palps have five segments; the basal segments are fused along the midline and have a median, anterior, laminar projection that extends beyond the basal segment of the chelicerae and a pair of lateral wings or galeae that curl dorsal about the chelicerae and bear a seta on each side; each basal segment also bears a seta posterior to the junction with the palpal femur. The second palpal segment or femur bears a single seta; the third or genu bears a single seta; the fourth, or tibia, has three setae; one is dorsal, one lateral, one ventral, and there is a terminal palpal claw. The fifth, or tarsus, articulates ventrally with the tibia and opposes the palpal claw in thumblike fashion. It bears several setae (usually eight), the basal one of which is a striated sensory seta. The body is usually red but may be almost colorless; it bears a dorsal plate or scutum at the level of the anterior two pairs of legs, usually two pairs of eyes that flank the scutum, several rows of dorsal setae, several rows of ventral setae, occasionally a posterior plate or a posterior group of specialized setae, a ventral anus, three pairs of legs, an urstigma or sclerotized pit associated with the posterior distal angle of coxa I, and at times a pair of tracheal trunks that open through stigmata in the region of the gnathosoma. The scutum bears from three to six marginal scutal setae or infrequently more, and a pair of pseudostigmata from which the sensillae or pseudostigmatic organs arise. The legs are composed of six segments if the femur is undivided and of seven if the femur consists of a basifemur and telofemur.

Wharton 1947 recognizes four subfamilies based on the larval morphology.

Key to the Trombiculidae

1. First pair of legs with seven segments   2

    All legs with six segments; two setae on coxa I   Leeuwenhoekiinae

2. Legs II and III with seven segments   3

    Legs II and III with six segments   Walchiinae

3. Paired, anterior, submedian, scutal setae and/or anteriormedian scutal projection   Apoloniinae

    Not as above   Trombiculinae

Leeuwenhoekiinae Womersley, 1944

Genera and subgenera:

1. *Leeuwenhoekia* Oudemans, 1911
   a. *Leeuwenhoekia* s.str.
      Type. *Heterothrombidium verduni* Oudemans, 1910
   b. *Comatacarus* Ewing, 1942
      Type. *Comatacarus americanus* Ewing, 1942
2. *Acomatacarus* Ewing, 1942
   a. *Acomatacarus* s. str.
      Type. *Acomatacarus arizonensis* Ewing, 1942
   b. *Austracarus* Lawrence, 1949
      Type. *Austracarus procaviae* Lawrence, 1949
   c. *Austrombicula* Lawrence, 1949
      Type. *Leeuwenhoekia womersleyi* Lawrence, 1949
   d. *Hyracarus* Lawrence, 1949
      Type. *Hyracarus typicus* Lawrence, 1949
3. *Hannemania* Oudemans, 1911
   Type. *Heterothrombidium hylodeus* Oudemans, 1910
4. *Odontacarus* Ewing, 1929
   Type. *Trombicula dentata* Ewing, 1925
5. *Whartonia* Ewing, 1944
   Type. *Hannemania nudosetosa* Wharton, 1938

Walchiinae Ewing, 1946

Genera:

1. *Walchia* Ewing, 1931
   Type. *Trombidium glabrum* Walch, 1927
2. *Gahrliepia* Oudemans, 1912
   Type. *Typhlothrombium nanus* Oudemans, 1910
3. *Gateria* Ewing, 1938
   Type. *Gahrliepia fletcheri* Gater, 1932
4. *Schöngastiella* Hirst, 1915
   Type. *Schöngastiella bengalensis* Hirst, 1915

Apoloniinae Wharton, 1947

Genera:

1. *Apolonia* Torres and Braga, 1938
   Type. *Apolonia tigipioensis* Torres and Braga, 1938
2. *Sauracarella* Lawrence, 1949 (placement uncertain)
   Type. *Sauracarella whartoni* Lawrence, 1949

3. *Womersia* Wharton, 1947
 Type. *Womersia strandtmani* Wharton, 1947

Trombiculinae Ewing, 1929
Genera and subgenera:
1. *Trombicula* Berlese, 1905
 a. *Trombicula* s. str. (= *Crotiscus* Ewing, 1944)
 Type. *Trombicula minor* Berlese, 1905 (a collection of members of the genus *Trombicula* of uncertain affinities)
 b. *Blankaartia* Oudemans, 1911 (= *Tragardhula* Berlese, 1912 = *Pentagonella* Thor, 1936 = *Megatrombicula* Michener, 1946)
 Type. *Trombidium niloticum* Trägårdh, 1905
 c. *Eutrombicula* Ewing, 1938 (= *Trombiculoides* Jacot, 1938 and *Acariscus* Ewing, 1943)
 Type. *Microthrombidium alfreddugèsi* Oudemans, 1910
 d. *Fonsecia* Radford, 1942
 Type. *Trombicula ewingi* Fonseca, 1932
 e. *Leptotrombidium* Nagayao *et al.,* 1916
 Type. *Trombidium akamushi* Brumpt, 1910
 f. *Neotrombicula* Hirst, 1925
 Type. *Acarus autumnalis* Shaw, 1790
 g. *Trombiculindus* Radford, 1948
 Type. *Trombiculindus squamosus* Radford, 1948
2. *Ascöschongastia* Ewing, 1946
 Type. *Neoschöngastia malayensis* Gater, 1932
3. *Doloisia* Oudemans, 1910
 Type. *Doloisia synoti* Oudemans, 1910
4. *Endotrombicula* Ewing, 1931
 a. *Endotrombicula* s. str.
 Type. *Endotrombicula penetrans* Ewing, 1931
 b. *Phrynacarus* Lawrence, 1949
 Type. *Phrynacarus fitzsimonsi* Lawrence, 1949
5. *Euschöngastia* Ewing, 1938
 Type. *Euschöngastia americana* Ewing, 1938
6. *Guntherana* Womersley and Heaslip, 1943
 Type. *Neoschöngastia kallipygos* Gunther, 1939
7. *Heaslipia* Ewing, 1944 (= *Trombiculoides* Womersley and Heaslip, 1943)
 Type. *Trombiculoides gateri* Womersley and Heaslip, 1943
8. *Myotrombicula* Womersley and Heaslip, 1943
 Type. *Myotrombicula vespertilionis* Womersley and Heaslip, 1943
9. *Neoschöngastia* Ewing, 1929 (= *Paraschöngastia* Womersley, 1939)
 Type. *Schöngastia americana* Hirst, 1921

10. *Novotrombicula* Womersley and Kohls, 1947
   Type. *Novotrombicula owiensis* Womersley and Kohls, 1947
11. *Oenoschöngastia* Womersley and Kohls, 1947
   Type. *Oenoschöngastia cana* Womersley and Kohls, 1947
12. *Riedlinia* Oudemans, 1914
   Type. *Riedlinia coeca* Oudemans, 1914
13. *Sauriscus* Lawrence, 1949
   Type. *Sauriscus ewingi* Lawrence, 1949
14. *Schöngastia* Oudemans, 1910
   Type. *Thrombidium vandersandei* Oudemans, 1905
15. *Tecomatlana* Hoffmann, 1947
   Type. *Tecomatlana sandovali* Hoffmann, 1947
16. *Trisetica* Traub and Evans, 1950
   Type. *Trisetica melvini* Traub and Evans, 1950

Unassigned genus:

Speotrombicula Ewing, 1946
   Type. *Trombicula trifurca* Ewing, 1933 (based on an adult)

Discussion: Trombiculids are very similar in their behavior to trombidiids. As nymphs and adults they feed on eggs and early larval instars of small arthropods. The stages in their life history are the same as those of trombidiids, with the exception that no trombiculid is known to undergo postimaginal molts. The big difference in their behavior is the host preference of the larvae. Trombiculids, with few exceptions, e.g. *Acomatacarus paradoxa* André, parasitize terrestrial vertebrates including man and his domestic animals.

Larvae (chiggers or red-bugs) belonging to the genera *Trombicula* and *Schöngastia* are insufferable human pests in many parts of the world. In the United States, *T.* (*E.*) *alfreddugèsi* (Oudemans), *T.* (*E.*) *splendens* Ewing, and *T.* (*E.*) *batatas* (Linnaeus) are responsible for an irritating dermatitis. Some individuals are immune from the effects of these chigger bites, while others will develop a blister measuring several inches across at the site of a bite.

In the Orient, species of *Trombicula* (*Leptotrombidium*) are the vectors of a rickettsial disease known as scrub typhus or tsutsugamushi disease. This disease caused a total of over 7,000 casualties in the United States armed forces during World War II. No estimates are available as to how prevalent the disease is in natives of many areas.

Trombiculids are not only pests and vectors of disease from one animal to another but are also damaging parasites of economically important birds and animals. In Australia *Trombicula* (*Eutrombicula*) *sarcina* is an important pest of sheep. *Apolonia tigipioensis* deplumes chickens. Species of *Neoschöngastia* are also harmful to poultry, as are the common pest chiggers.

Trombiculids are as well known as any of the other mites and yet the 300 or more described species probably do not represent more than half the species that will eventually be known.

References:

Berlese, A. 1912. Trombidiidae. Redia 8:1–291.
Ewing, H. E. 1944. The trombiculid mites (chigger mites) and their relation to disease. J. Parasitol. 30:339–365.
Lawrence, R. F. 1949. The larval trombiculid mites of South African vertebrates. Ann. Natal Mus. 11:405–486.
Philip, C. B. 1948. Tsutsugamushi disease (scrub typhus) in World War II. J. Parasitol. 34:169–191.
Thor, S., and C. Willmann. 1947. Trombidiidae. Das Tierreich Lfg. 71 b: 187–541 + Pls. XXIX–XXXVI.
Wharton, G. W. 1947. Studies on North American chiggers II. The subfamilies and *Womersia strandtmani,* n. gn., n. sp. J. Parasitol. 33: 380–384.
———, D. W. Jenkins, J. M. Brennan, H. S. Fuller, G. M. Kohls, and C. B. Philip. 1951. The terminology and classification of trombiculid mites (Acarina: Trombiculidae). J. Parasitol. 37(1):13–31.

CHAPTER VI

Hydrachnellae Latreille, 1802

(Hydracarina)

THE water mites form an ecological rather than a morphological group. Some are swimming, while others are nonswimming. They are inhabitants of fresh water except for the marine Pontarachnidae. The marine Halacaridae, although closely allied to the Cunaxidae, are also included here because of the habitat. The Hydrachnellae have cuticular glands, stigmata and tracheae (with the exception of the Pontarachnidae). Two pairs of eyes are present and may be either separate or coalesced; an imperfectly developed median eye is also present at times. The tarsi usually possess two claws but are without empodium or pretarsus. The palpi usually have five movable segments. The chelicerae have only the movable digit which is usually sickle-shaped. The larvae, with the exception of Hydrovolziidae and Halacaridae, are heteromorphous and have urstigma between coxae I and II.

The information on this group is taken from the works of Lundblad, Viets, and Vitzthum. Although the European species are well known, little has been done in this country except by Wolcott and later by Marshall. However, neither of them has published comprehensive works which will give the student an over-all grasp of the subject. Little is known about the biology of the group as a whole, although a few common species have been studied. Some work has been done on the immature stages but here, as in many other groups, much rearing work is needed.

The brightly colored watermites are to be found in lakes or ponds, along shores and in streams. A few are parasitic in the gills of fresh-water mussels, and the larvae of other forms are parasitic on aquatic insects much as chiggers are on vertebrates. Adult forms are preda-

259

ceous and feed on crustacea, insect larvae, and other water animals which are small enough to be captured. Some watermites are also parasitic in all stages in the gill chambers of crabs and are adapted for grasping the gill filaments. They are to be found at all times of the year but usually most of the species appear as adults in late summer and fall.

The Halacaridae, although closely related to the Cunaxidae, are treated here with the true watermites because of the similarity of habitat and the relative ease of identifying them by their habits.

Keys (from Viets 1936) to the superfamilies and families are given. Those who are interested in keys to the numerous subfamilies are referred to Viets.

References:

Only a few references are given. No attempt is made to make the list comprehensive, since this is one of the most extensively worked groups and a complete list is beyond the scope of this work. However, in the few papers cited it is hoped that the reader can find the necessary leads to understand the group better.

Lundblad, O. 1927. Die Hydracarinen Schwedens. I. Zool. Bidr. Uppsala 11:185–535.

——. 1931. Südamerikanische Hydracarinen. Zool. Bidr. Uppsala 13:1–86.

——. 1941. Eine Übersicht des Hydrachnellensystems und der bis jetzt bekannten Verbreitung der Gattungen dieser Gruppe. Zool. Bidr. Uppsala 20:359–379.

——. 1941. Die Hydracarinenfauna Südbrasiliens und Paraguays. Kungl. Svenska Vetenskapsakademiens Handlinger, Ser. 3, 19(7):1–183.

——. 1942. Ibid. 20(2):1–175; 20(8):1–171.

Marshall, R. The complete works are needed for the study of the United States fauna; not comprehensive in nature.

Viets, K. 1936. Wassermilben oder Hydracarina (Hydrachnellae und Halacaridae). Die Tierwelt Deutschlands 31:1–288; 32:289–574.

Wolcott, R. H. 1918. The Water Mites (Hydracarina). Chapter XXVI, pp. 851–875. In Ward and Whipple's Fresh Water Biology, John Wiley and Sons, Inc.

Key to the Hydrachnellae Superfamilies [1]

1. Without genital suckers; red, nonswimming, living in the upper courses of brooks   Hydrovolziae

    With genital suckers (except marine forms)   2

[1] From Viets 1936.

2. With narrow subulate rostrum; chelicerae on the whole dagger-like, without distinct separation between the claw and basal segment (fresh water forms) Hydrachnae

   Without narrow subulate rostrum; chelicerae not dagger-like, with claws and basal segments distinctly separated from one another (except marine forms) 3

3. Genital suckers often very small, not lying on the plates or lobes, nor under them, but free in the skin (then usually minute), or more or less enclosed by sclerotic clasps (then frequently stalked and acorn-shaped); eyes in eye capsules Limnocharae

   Genital suckers usually distinct, lying on or under the lobes or on the plates or connected to sucker areas in the ventral armor (except certain *Piona* spp. with scattered discoidal suckers lying in the ventral skin) 4

4. Genital organ with movable valves or lobes 5

   Genital organ without movable valves or lobes 6

5. Genital suckers more or less knobbed, lying on lobes or united with them, isolated when lying free Hydryphantae

   Genital suckers under or beside inner margin of lobes in region of genital opening, not sclerotically united with lobes Lebertiae

6. Palpi without apical claw between more or less spiniform palpal segment v and distal end of broadened segment iv 7

   Palpi with apical claw between palpal segment iv (whose distal margin more or less broadened and whose distal corner on the curved side more or less drawn out forwards) and clawlike segment v Arrhenurae

7. Genital organ with more or less distinct sucker plates and with disklike or porelike suckers lying on them 8

   Genital organ with swelling similar to lobes but firmly fused with ventral armor; suckers, which are few, in region of genital opening (except in *Midea* with sucker plates; palpal segment iv subulate and reduced) Mideopsae

8. Bodies generally with soft skin, rarely with more or less extensive dorsal plates or still more rarely completely armored; palpal segment iv generally with frequently minute sclerotic process on curved side at distal median corner Pionae

   Body always armored, with narrow dorsal arch; palpal segment iv without sclerotic process on curved side at distal median corner
   Axonopsae

List of superfamilies and families:

Hydrovolziae
  Hydrovolziidae Thor, 1905
Hydrachnae
  Hydrachnidae Leach, 1815
Limnocharae
  Limnocharidae Kramer, 1877
  Eylaidae Leach, 1815
  Protziidae Viets, 1926
Hydryphantae
  Hydryphantidae Thor, 1900
  Clathrosperchonidae Lundblad,
    1936
  Ctenothyasidae Lundblad, 1936
  Eupatrellidae Viets, 1935
  Hydrodromidae Viets, 1936
  Rhynchohydracaridae Lundblad,
    1931
  Thermacaridae Sokolow, 1927
Lebertiae
  Lebertiidae Thor, 1900
  Anisitsiellidae Viets, 1929
  Atractideidae Thor, 1902
  Mamersopsidae Lundblad, 1930
  Pseudohydryphantidae Viets,
    1926

  Rutripalpidae Sokolow, 1934
  Sperchonidae Thor, 1900
  Teutoniidae Lundblad, 1927
Arrhenurae Oudemans, 1902
  Arrenuridae Thor, 1900
Mideopsae
  Mideopsidae Thor, 1928
  Acalyptonotidae Thor, 1929
  A-Thienemanniidae Lundblad,
    1930
  Krendowskiidae Lundblad, 1930
  Mideidae Viets, 1929
Pionae Viets, 1930
  Pionidae Thor, 1900
  Astacocrotonidae Thor, 1927
  Feltriidae Thor, 1929
  Hygrobatidae Koch, 1842
  Limnesiidae Thor, 1900
  Nautarachnidae Viets, 1935
  Neotorrenticolidae Lundblad,
    1936
  Pontarachnidae Thor, 1929
  Unionicolidae Oudemans, 1909
Axonopsae
  Axonopsidae Viets, 1929

Key to the Hydrachnellae [1]

1. Body strongly armored with several plates; genital suckers not present; anal opening lying in plate of intermediate or large size   2

   Body may or may not be strongly armored but not as above; with genital suckers (exception: Pontarachnidae); anal opening almost without exception not lying in large plate; legs (except in Oxinae) more or less radial   3

   Body strongly armored with several plates; three pairs of genital suckers present; genital and anal openings in same ventral plate; legs I and II point anteriorly; legs III and IV point posteriorly; no swimming hairs; found in ocean   Halacaridae

2. Legs III and IV attached laterally so that epimera project beyond edge of body and can be seen from above; epimera separated by

[1] From Viets 1936.

well-defined sutures; anal opening in large plate; epimera I not
forming tube   Hydrovolziidae

Legs II and IV arranged so epimera not seen from above; epimera
not separated by suture; anal opening in small plate; epimera I
closes together anteriorly to form tube   Rhynchohydracaridae

3. Rostrum not elongate or awl-like, but conelike or other form and
    essentially shorter than palpus; chelicerae definitely two-segmented
    and with sickle-like cheliceral claw and basal segment   4

    Rostrum long, narrow, awl-like, more or less pointing ventrally
    and reaching about to tip of palpus; chelicerae, on the whole,
    slightly curved and stylet-like, the cheliceral claw and basal seg-
    ment not noticeably separated; chelicerae with posterior end reach-
    ing far into interior of body   Hydrachnidae

4. Genital organ without valvelike flaps or plates but with ledgelike
    or clasplike sclerotic structure surrounding genital suckers; genital
    suckers fastened in soft body skin, very small or more or less
    stalked and posteriorly often acorn-like   5

    Genital organs with valvelike or platelike sclerotic sections, on or
    under which are more or less distinct genital suckers (exception:
    a *Piona* species with dispersed, disklike suckers on ventral skin)   7

5. Double eyes either located medially on ends of transverse scle-
    rotic shield to form so-called spectacle or lie laterally either in
    shields or free in skin; palpi of normal size and much longer than
    rostrum   6

    Double eyes located laterally on more or less rodlike longitudinal
    sclerotic shield; palpi very small, only weakly surpassing rostrum;
    all legs richly haired but without true swimming hairs; body so
    soft that mite collapses when removed from water   Limnocharidae

6. Double eyes lie medially and are bound together by single trans-
    verse plates, or are lateral and are bound together by many-seg-
    mented plate; no true rostrum present but with large sucking
    mouth surrounded by "ruffles"; palpal segment III with group of
    setae on distal end; in the mites with eyes bound together by trans-
    verse plate genital suckers tiny and distributed over entire body
    skin; whereas in other group suckers are large and lie in shields on
    each side of genital opening   Eylaidae

    Double eyes lie laterally, free in the body skin, without sclerotic
    plate connecting them; rostrum present; mouth opening not
    sucker-like and without "ruffles"; no group of setae on distal end
    of palpal segment III; genital suckers often stalked and acorn-like
                                                              Protziidae

7. Genital organs possess more or less arched and movable genital
   plate which through its movement opens the genital lips   8

   Genital organs without movable plates   19

8. Many genital suckers, either small and porelike, or a few large,
   button-like ones on genital plates or connected with these plates;
   suckers isolated, occurring free between plates in genital lip region; palpal segment iv with or without clawlike or finger-like
   projection on distal end which forms short pincers with palpal
   segment v; frontal organ usually present; claws of legs usually
   simple, sickle-like, and without empodium   9

   Genital suckers, usually three on each side and seldom two, four,
   six or more, lie in a row, one after other, under or near inner edge
   of genital plates but not connected with plates; palpal segment iv
   without distal projection which forms shear with segment v;
   frontal organ lacking, with few exceptions; tarsal claws often
   double-pronged and with empodium   12

9. Palpal segment iv usually with robust spine or conelike appendage
   on distal end which is not equal in length to palpal segment v and
   does not form pincer; paired lateral eyes rarely found close together in sclerotic plate   10

   Palpal segment iv with narrow, finger-like projection on its distal
   end which opposes ultimate segment and forms shear with it; lateral eyes not in capsules, separated from each other; frontal organ
   not present; body skin weak and without sclerotic plates
                                                             Hydrodromidae

10. Legs without true swimming hairs   11

    Legs with swimming hairs; body usually soft-skinned and usually
    with sclerotic plate on anterior portion; seldom many plates
                                                             Hydryphantidae

11. Body covered with beautifully designed radiating sclerotic plates;
    with many genital suckers   Clathrosperchonidae

    Body simply armored; with many genital suckers; living in hot
    springs   Thermacaridae

    Body without armor but with skin papillae; with three pairs of
    large genital suckers   Ctenothyasidae

12. Palpal segments iv and v not dorso-ventrally flat and shovel-like 13

    Palpal segments iv and v medio-laterally broadened and dorso-
    ventrally strongly flattened, and with four medio-laterally end
    claws of segment v forming shovel-like organ   Rutripalpidae

13. Palpi in general narrow; palpal segment II seldom clublike, not longer than segment IV; segment IV as long or usually longer than segment II; dorsal length of palpal segment II never equals segments III plus IV, but III plus IV longer than segment II   14

Palpi short and clublike; palpal segment II especially thick and strong; palpal segment IV shorter than segment II; dorsal length of segment II same or longer than segments III plus IV; cheliceral claw proportionately small   Mamersopsidae

14. Palpal segment IV without sclerotic process on inner side; segment II usually with pegs or spines on inner side; skin without thick, spiny sclerotic plates   15

Palpal segment IV dorsally-distally elongated; segment II without appendage, peg, or spine on inner side; skin densely covered with thick-shafted, many-pointed, spiny sclerotic plates   Pseudohydryphantidae

15. Epimera in four groups of two each; these groups (at least second and third) separated from one another by skin areas   16

Epimera united into one group, often medianly united with one another; laterally epimera II and III completely united without suture or only partial suture present; genital plates fit snugly into epimera IV without free ventral skin being present   18

16. No gland on epimera IV   17
Large, glandular organ on anterior median corner of epimera IV   Teutoniidae

17. Lateral eyes united in eye capsules; palpal segment II with spine-covered projection on inner side; legs IV with claws   Sperchonidae

Lateral eyes not united in capsules but separated from each other by skin; palpal segment II only with spines on inner margin; legs IV without claws   Anisitsiellidae

18. Epimeral region not fused with ventral region and genital organ therefore not enclosed; ventral region behind genital organ unarmored and membranous; dorsum as a rule not sclerotized; dorsal-ventral suture lacking; with six (seldom four) large genital suckers   Lebertiidae

Epimeral region forming with venter (including genital organ) ventral armor which is closed behind genital organ; this extends laterally around body to dorsum where it is separated from dorsal shield by dorsal suture; genital organ with twelve small genital suckers under inner margin of genital flaps   Atractideidae

19. Genital suckers present; fresh-water mites   20

     Genital suckers not present: marine mites, on littoral of seas
                                          Pontarachnidae

20. No shears formed by palpal segments IV and V   21

     Clawlike palpal segment V so hinged to dorsal distal portion of segment IV that two segments form pincers; two fine sensory or grasping setae on inner margin of segment V; segment V usually with strong spine; body armored   30

21. Lateral eyes united (Astacocrotonidae with pair of eyes); leg IV as a rule with claws   22

     Lateral eyes separated from each other; leg IV usually without claw; palpal segment II often with sclerotic cone on inner edge; with three pairs of genital suckers   Limnesiidae

     As above but with many genital suckers   Neotorrenticolidae

22. Body as a rule membranous; seldom with more or less extensive dorsal plates; very seldom with completely hardened ventral and dorsal shields; epimera usually in four groups; sutures between them usually present but in several cases median suture between first epimera disappears or suture between third and fourth pair of plates not fully developed; genital organ of cutaneous or membranous form with distinct plates containing the more or less disklike, seldom porelike, suckers; palpal segments II, III, and IV frequently with cones or tubercles on inner margin   23

     Body almost entirely armored, dorsal and ventral armor generally separated by narrow dorsal suture; in a few cases genital organ in membranous area, or only ventral armor present; body usually flat, often discoidal; epimeral sutures lacking; genital organ between epimeral region and posterior end of body; the six, eight or more genital suckers lie upon more or less distinct plates, and ledgelike or roundish plates often united with ventral shield; if genital organ lies in vicinity of epimeral region then orifice usually in opening of ventral shield, and genital suckers lie on valvelike plates, or under or at inner edge of flaplike genital "rolls" which unite with ventral shield; the medial distal edge of palpal segment IV without sclerotic projection   27

23. Epimera I separated from one another behind rostral base by suture or skin area; rostrum, as a rule, lies free and is not united with epimeral region; legs generally have swimming hairs; palpal segment II without pegs or cones on inner margin (exception: *Pseu-*

dofeltria); palpal segment IV with many teeth or hair tubercles on inner margin   24

Epimera I usually united with one another and without median suture; posterior margin of rostrum frequently united with epimera I; legs without swimming hairs; genital organ usually with six suckers, in rare cases more, but not over twenty suckers on each side; genital suckers distinctly disklike; palpal segment II with peg or sclerotic tooth on inner side; palpal segment IV without inner tooth but perhaps with small tubercle bearing setae   Hygrobatidae

24. Without narrow rostrum, at best with short mouth cone   25

With narrow rostrum about one-third length of organ; genital plates possess many small, porelike suckers; legs with swimming hairs   Nautarachnidae

25. Usually found in stagnant waters and also in slow-moving water but seldom in cold streams; body usually weak-skinned, smooth, and seldom more or less entirely armored; palpal segment IV with conelike protuberance on inner margin; genital suckers usually disklike and distinct, seldom small and porelike; legs usually with swimming hairs; leg III of male without processes   26

Small mites usually living in streams; with flat body, dorsum with more or less extensive plate which covers anterior and median dorsal region and which is surrounded by small, paired plates in striated region; palpal segment IV without conelike projection on inner margin; epimera IV with large, linear expansion on lateral margin; legs without swimming hairs; leg III of male usually with processes; genital organ of male has many small, porelike suckers on large, medianly united plate and has small genital opening; genital opening of female large, lying between two genital plates and often cleftlike, extending around terminal part of body

Feltriidae

26. Body without plates; distal palpal segment with stout spines, some hooklike, for grasping gills of crab on which it is parasitic; no swimming hairs on legs; large gland on coxa IV; coxae arranged in two groups, lateral groups contiguous; four pairs of genital suckers on plates; genital opening on rear, far from epimeral region; no eyes in female; pair of eyes in immature male

Astacocrotonidae

Gland pores of skin often conelike, raised; basal segments of chelicerae usually united medianly with one another; palpal segment III often with very long, lateral spine; posterior part of epimera ɪ and ɪɪ often with common, rodlike, long process which often reaches subcutaneously far under epimera ɪɪɪ or even under ɪv; posterior margin of epimera ɪv usually transverse and as a rule without or only insignificant central process, and therefore without concave, medial region or genital indentation between coxae or epimera; genital organ usually back of epimeral region; legs ɪ and ɪɪ frequently thickened in proximal and middle segments and covered with paired, swordlike setae; tarsal claws as a rule simple, sickle-like, and without processes; legs ɪv of male not usually sexually differentiated   Unionicolidae

Gland pores of skin not conelike; chelicerae separated from each other; palpal segment ɪɪɪ without lateral spines; posterior process of anterior epimera short, with hooklike tips, and as a rule not reaching beneath posterior epimera; posterior end of epimera ɪv with median process, forming genital indentation; genital organ usually close to epimera and removed from posterior margin of body; legs ɪ and ɪɪ without conspicuous setae and not thickened; tarsal claws usually forked and with processes; legs ɪɪɪ and ɪv of male usually sexually differentiated   Pionidae

27. Genital suckers lie on more or less sickle-like plates in deep genital indentation, or the six, eight, or more suckers lie in "lipfields" (exception: ♀ of *Momonia* in which suckers are on flaplike plates in partially armored ventral skin) beside or under inner edge of genital rolls which are united with ventral plate; genital organ close to epimera ɪv, often in deep genital indentation; body in lateral view very round; palpal segment ɪɪ without protuberances on inner margin; segment ɪv often with processes on inner margin   28

Six, eight, or more genital suckers on more or less distinct, roundish, or ledgelike plate; plates on rear of body, more or less free in male, united with ventral plates; true genital indentation present; body, more or less flat, as a rule distinctly longer than broad; epimera often united medianly with one another; palpal segment ɪɪ at times with protuberance on inner margin; segment ɪv with tiny inner setae   Axonopsidae

28. Palpal segment ɪv shorter than segments ɪɪ plus ɪɪɪ; genital indentation does not reach to epimera ɪ and is either formed by margins of posterior epimeral plates or is entirely lacking; genital suckers lie in "lipfields" at inner margin of flaplike but solid, immovable genital folds which limit laterally genital opening in ventral armor (exception: ♀ of *Momonia* in which folds are narrow and not united with ventral shield); body usually disklike and flat   29

Palpal segment IV long, awl-like and longer than segments II plus III; genital organ almost completely within deep genital indentation which reaches to posterior end of united epimera I; numerous genital suckers on plates; body armored and highly arched; dorsal suture separates dorsal and ventral shields Mideidae

29. Body entirely armored; dorsal shield separated from ventral shield by suture; inner margin of palpal segment IV does not surpass proximal end of palpal segment V; segment IV not dorso-ventrally broadened or thickened; genital organ with six to ten suckers; epimera as a rule separated by suture in median line Mideopsidae

Body unarmored dorsally and without dorsal suture; palpal segment IV dorso-ventrally thickened distally; inner side of palpal segment IV surpasses proximal end of segment V and forms shearlike organ; genital organ with many suckers; epimera without median suture; posterior group medianly joined at angle

Acalyptonotidae

30. Four, six, eight or more usually disklike genital suckers are, as a rule, in "lipfields" which lie in opening in ventral shield near inner edge of the more or less valvelike, arched, but immovable genital "rolls" 31

Only genital lips, not many porelike genital suckers, lie in opening of ventral shield; genital suckers do not lie in opening of ventral armor but next to opening on more or less distinct, generally winglike plates in ventral armor; genital suckers usually numerous, small, and porelike; male often with appendage or petiole on rear of body Arrenuridae

31. Many small genital suckers A-Thienemanniidae

Three to eight pairs of large genital suckers arranged in longitudinal row Krendowskiidae

The paper on the family Stygomonidae Szalay, 1943, type *Stygomonia latipes* Szalay, 1943, has not been seen at this date.

Halacaridae Murray, 1876[1]

Figures 185, 186

Diagnosis: The halacarids are trombidoidea with a body typically flattened or, more rarely, circular in cross section and elliptical in outline. The mouthparts form a distinct capitulum which nearly always

[1] From Newell 1947.

projects well beyond the anterior margin of the body but in a few
forms is completely hidden in the dorsal view. The palpi have three
or four segments which are attached laterally, dorso-laterally, or dorsally to the base of the capitulum. The maxillary portions of the palpi
are completely fused. Lying in a dorsal groove in the rostrum the chelicerae are retractile; the ventral digit is large and movable while the
dorsal digit is reduced to a pointed membrane. The tracheal system is
very rudimentary and quite certainly is not functional in respiration.

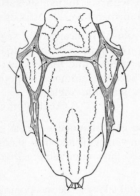

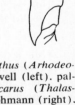

Figure 185 *Halacarus* (*Thalassarachna*) *subterraneus* (Schulz). Dorsum of
male. (After Newell 1947)

Figure 186 *Copidognathus* (*Arhodeoporus*) *submarinus* Newell (left). palpus of female; *Halacarus* (*Thalassarachna*) *capuzinus* Lohmann (right).
chelicera of female. (After Newell
1947)

Usually four plates dorsally (predorsal, postdorsal, and right and left
ocular plates) and four plates ventrally and laterally (anterior epimeral,
right and left posterior epimeral, genito-anal plates) reinforce the cuticle of the body wall. These plates show varying degrees of subdivisions
or fusion in different genera, in different species of a single genus, or
rarely in the two sexes of a single species. The legs are attached laterally: legs I and II are borne on anterior epimeral plate (or plates), and
project anteriorly; legs III and IV are borne on the right and left posterior epimeral plates and project posteriorly. In adults the legs have
six segments. The larvae have only three pairs of five-segmented legs.
Leg IV in the protonymph is also five-segmented but legs I, II, and III
are six-segmented. All legs in the deutonymph are six-segmented. The
tarsus always has two lateral claws while a median claw may be present or absent. The salivary glands are well developed. The mid-gut does

not open by way of the anus. The anus is present, but functions entirely as an opening for the single, dorsomedian, excretory tubule. The sexes are separate; sexual dimorphism is marked in the genito-anal plate and genitalia; other structures are usually (but not always) identical in form in both sexes. Three eye spots are apparently always present; the corneas number two, four, or six or may be absent. The median eye has no cornea. There are three pairs of genital suckers.

These mites are principally marine, but there are numerous freshwater forms ("Porohalacaridae" of Viets). They are not capable of swimming and are predominantly predaceous or herbivorous, although three parasitic genera are known. Newell 1947 gives keys to the subfamilies.

Rhombognathinae Viets, 1927

Genera:

1. *Rhombognathides* Viets, 1927
   Type. *Aletes pascens* Lohmann, 1889
2. *Isobactrus* Newell, 1947
   Type. *Aletes setosus* Lohmann, 1889
3. *Metarhombognathus* Newell, 1947
   Type. *Rhombognathus armatus* Lohmann, 1893
4. *Rhombognathus* Trouessart, 1888
   Type. *Pachygnathus notops* Gosse, 1855

Actacarinae Viets, 1939

Genus:

Actacarus Schulz, 1936
Type. *Actacarus pygmaeus* Schulz, 1936

Halacarinae Viets, 1927

Genera:

1. *Halacarus* Gosse, 1855
   a. *Halacarus* s. str.
      Type. *Halacarus ctenopus* Gosse, 1855
   b. *Thalassarachna* Packard, 1871
      Type. *Acarus basteri* Johnston, 1836
2. *Agaue* Lohmann, 1889
   Type. *Halacarus parvus* Chilton, 1883
3. *Agauopsis* Viets, 1927
   Type. *Agaue brevipalpus* Trouessart, 1889
4. *Coloboceras* Trouessart, 1889
   Type. *Coloboceras longiusculus* Trouessart, 1889

5. *Copidognathus* Trouessart, 1888
   a. *Copidognathus* s. str. (= *Copidognathopsis* Viets, 1927
      = *Werthella* Lohmann, 1907)
      Type. *Copidognathus glyptoderma* Trouessart, 1888
   b. *Arhodeoporus* Newell, 1947
      Type. *Copidognathus (Arhodeoporus) arenarius* Newell, 1947
6. *Pontacarus* Lohmann, 1901
   Type. *Halacarus basidentatus* Trouessart, 1900

Porohalacarinae Viets, 1933
Genera:

1. *Porohalacarus* Thor, 1923
   Type. *Halacarus alpinus* Thor, 1910
2. *Caspihalacarus* Viets, 1928
   Type. *Caspihalacarus hyrcanus* Viets, 1928
3. *Lohohalacarus* Viets, 1939 (= *Walterella* Romijn, 1924 *nom. praeocc.*)
   Type. *Walterella weberi* Romijn, 1924
4. *Troglohalacarus* Viets, 1937
   Type. *Troglohalacarus dentipes* Viets, 1937

Lohmannellinae Viets, 1927
Genera:

1. *Lohmannella* Trouessart, 1901
   Type. *Leptognathus falcatus* Hodge, 1863
2. *Porolohmannella* Viets, 1933
   Type. *Leptognathus violaceus* Kramer, 1879
3. *Scaptognathus* Trouessart, 1889
   Type. *Scaptognathus tridens* Trouessart, 1889

Simognathinae Viets, 1927
Genera:

1. *Simognathus* Trouessart, 1889
   Type. *Pachygnathus sculptus* Brady, 1875
2. *Acaromantis* Trouessart and Neumann, 1893
   Type. *Acaromantis squilla* Trouessart and Neumann, 1893
3. *Atelopsalis* Trouessart, 1896
   Type. *Atelopsalis tricuspis* Trouessart, 1896
4. *Ischyrognathus* Trouessart, 1900
   Type. *Simognathus coutieri* Trouessart, 1899

Limnohalacarinae Viets, 1927

Genera:

1. *Limnohalacarus* Walter, 1917
   a. *Limnohalacarus* s. str.
      Type. *Halacarus wackeri* Walter, 1914
   b. *Stygohalacarus* Viets, 1934
      Type. *Stygohalacarus scupiensis* Viets, 1934
2. *Hamohalacarus* Walter, 1931
   Type. *Hamohalacarus subterraneus* Walter, 1931
3. *Soldanellonyx* Walter, 1917
   a. *Soldanellonyx* s. str.
      Type. *Soldanellonyx chappuisi* Walter, 1917
   b. *Parasoldanellonyx* Viets, 1929
      Type. *Soldanellonyx parviscutatus* Walter, 1917

Halixodinae Viets, 1927

Genus:

Halixodes Brucker and Trouessart, 1900
Type. *Agaue chitonis* Brucker, 1897

Enterohalacarinae Viets, 1938

Genus:

Enterohalacarus Viets, 1938
Type. *Enterohalacarus minutipalpus* Viets, 1938

Astacopsiphaginae Viets, 1931

Genus:

Astacopsiphagus Viets, 1931
Type. *Astacopsiphagus parasiticus* Viets, 1931

Discussion: Newell 1947 has summarized the ecological zones of the mites by subfamilies as follows. The halacarids are either predaceous or lichen feeders, and in three genera are parasitic.

1. *Rhombognathinae* Viets, 1927, is principally intertidal, rarely if ever found in fresh water, and never lives under conditions which preclude algal growth. These mites are cosmopolitan.

2. *Actacarinae* Viets, 1939, is intertidal, arenicolous, and is never found under conditions which preclude algal growth. It is found in the North Sea.

3. *Lohmannellinae* Viets, 1927, is predaceous, either in marine or fresh water, and is probably cosmopolitan in distribution.

4. *Limnohalacarinae* Viets, 1927, is to be found in fresh water in Europe, Africa, and North and South America.

5. *Simognathinae* Viets, 1927, is marine and is to be found in the Adriatic, North Sea, Irish Sea, Caribbean, and Pacific-Antarctic Ocean. Predaceous forms are to be found in the Bay of Biscay and the western Indian Ocean.

6. *Enterohalacarinae* Viets, 1938, is parasitic in the gut of echinoderms, at least in the larval and nymphal stages, and is to be found in the western Pacific Ocean.

7. *Halixodinae* Viets, 1927, is parasitic, at least as nymphs, on gills of *Amphineura* in New Zealand.

8. *Astacopsiphaginae* Viets, 1931, is parasitic, at least as nymphs, on gills of fresh water decapod Crustacea in Australia.

9. *Halacarinae* Viets, 1927, is predaceous, principally marine, and rarely fresh water, and is cosmopolitan in distribution.

10. *Porohalacarinae* Viets, 1933, lives in fresh or brackish water, and is probably cosmopolitan in distribution except in the Arctic and Antarctic seas.

Reference:

Newell, Irwin M. 1947. A systematic and ecological study of the Halacaridae of eastern North America. Bull. of The Bingham Oceanographic Collection, Peabody Museum of Natural History, Yale Univ. 10 (3):1–232.

Hydrovolziidae Thor, 1905

Figures 187, 188

Diagnosis: Red watermites, the hydrovolziids measure from 0.80 to 0.95 mm. long. They have a small, predorsal shield and a large postdorsal shield. At the anterior, lateral margins of the postdorsal shield is a pair of large, lateral shields and surrounding the postdorsal shield is a series of small plates or shields. A double eye in a capsule is located in a lateral indentation of the predorsal shield (eyes are lacking in subterranean species). The coxae are divided into two distinct groups; the legs are placed laterally so that coxae III and IV stand out from the side of the body. There are no swimming hairs on the legs and the tarsal claws are smooth and sickle-like. No genital suckers are present. The palpi are five-segmented and simple with a clawlike end segment, somewhat as in Cunaxidae.

Genera and subgenera:

1. *Hydrovolzia* Thor, 1905
   a. *Hydrovolzia* s. str.
      Type. *Polyxo placophora* Monti, 1905
   b. *Hydrovolziella* Viets, 1935
      Type. *Hydrovolzia lata* Walter, 1935
2. *Acherontacarus* Viets, 1932
   Type. *Acherontacarus halacaroides* Viets, 1932

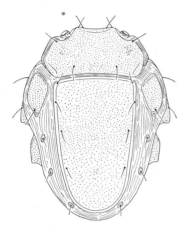 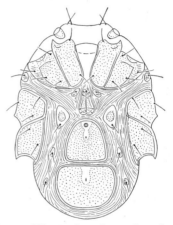

Figure 187 *Hydrovolzia placophora* (Monti). Dorsum. (After Viets 1936)

Figure 188 *Hydrovolzia placophora* (Monti). Venter. (After Viets 1936)

Discussion: These are nonswimming mites and can be found in springs and brooks of central Europe.

Rhynchohydracaridae Lundblad, 1936

Figures 189, 190

Diagnosis: The body of these mites is strongly armored dorsally and ventrally. The dorsal armor consists of a large central and many small marginal shields. Coxal plates I reach far past the anterior end of the body, closing together anteriorly to form a short sclerotized tube; coxal plates I and II are united. There are no swimming hairs on the legs. Two broad plates surround the genital opening but there are no genital suckers. The palpus does not have spines or protuberances and the chelicerae are long and slender.

Genus:

Rhynchohydracarus Lundblad, 1936
Type. *Rhynchohydracarus testudo* Lundblad, 1936

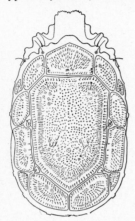 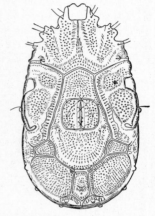

Figure 189 *Rhynchohydracarus testudo* Lundblad. Dorsum. (After Lundblad 1941)

Figure 190 *Rhynchohydracarus testudo* Lundblad. Venter. (After Lundblad 1941)

Hydrachnidae Leach, 1815

Figures 191, 192

Diagnosis: The hydrachnids are mostly red, large, globular swimming mites found in still water. Their skin has papillae and they possess paired eyes in capsules. The plates are of different sizes (excep-

 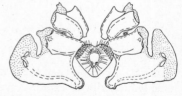

Figure 191 *Hydrachna kenyensis* Lundblad. Dorsal plate. (After Lundblad 1942)

Figure 192 *Hydrachna kenyensis* Lundblad. Coxal plates. (After Lundblad 1942)

tion: *Anohydrachna*) and shapes between the eyes. The coxal plates are usually united in four groups of two each. There are no swimming hairs on the legs and the tarsal claws are smooth and sickle-like. The chelicerae are unsegmented and stylet-like. Movably linked in front

the genital plates are fused medianly and have numerous small genital suckers.

Genera and subgenera:

1. *Hydrachna* Müller, 1776 (= *Atax* Fabricius, 1805)
   a. *Hydrachna* s. str. (= *Diplohydrachna* Thor, 1916)
      Type. *Hydrachna cruenta* Müller, 1776
   b. *Anohydrachna* Thor, 1916
      Type. *Hydrachna perniformis* Koenike, 1895
   c. *Chitohydrachna* Habeeb, 1950
      Type. *Hydrachna* (*Chitohydrachna*) *ennishonenses* Habeeb, 1950
   d. *Monohydrachna* Thor, 1916
      Type. *Hydrachna cruenta* Krendowsky, 1884
   e. *Rhabdohydrachna* Viets, 1913
      Type. *Hydrachna bisignifera* Viets, 1913
   f. *Schizohydrachna* Thor, 1916
      Type. *Hydrachna uniscutata* Thor, 1897
   g. *Scutohydrachna* Viets, 1933
      Type. *Hydrachna* (*Scutohydrachna*) *dorsoscutata* Viets, 1933
   h. *Tetrahydrachna* Lundblad, 1934
      Type. *Hydrachna globoso* var. *miliaria* Berlese, 1888
2. *Bargena* Koenike, 1893
   Type. *Bargena mirifica* Koenike, 1893

Limnocharidae Kramer, 1877

Figures 193–196

Diagnosis: Red, nonswimming mites found in standing and slow moving water, the limnocharids are weak-skinned. Eye capsules which

Figure 193 *Limnochares* (*Cyclothrix*) *natans* Lavers. Leg ɪv. (After Lavers 1941)

Figure 194 *Limnochares* (*Cyclothrix*) *natans* Lavers. Eye plate. (After Lavers 1941)

lie laterally on a median, rod-shaped, sclerotized plate are present. The rostrum is cylindrical, broad, and situated anteriorly with a mouth disk and fringe. The chelicerae are extensive, united with one another, and cover the maxillary organ. The genital suckers are small, numerous, and lie free in the skin.

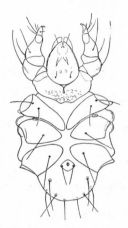
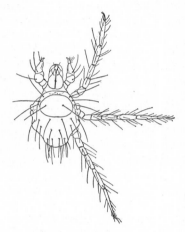

Figure 195 *Limnochares aquatica* (Linnaeus). Larva, venter. (After Viets 1936)

Figure 196 *Limnochares aquatica* (Linnaeus). Larva, dorsum. (After Viets 1936)

Limnocharinae Claus, 1880

Genera and subgenera:

1. *Limnochares* Latreille, 1796 (= *Hemitrombicula* Ewing, 1938)
   a. *Limnochares* s. str.
      Type. *Acarus aquaticus* Linnaeus, 1758
   b. *Cyclothrix* Wolcott, 1905
      Type. *Limnochares crinita* Koenike, 1898
2. *Neolimnochares* Lundblad, 1937
   Type. *Neolimnochares placophora* Lundblad, 1937

Rhyncholimnocharinae Lundblad, 1936

Genera:

1. *Rhyncholimnochares* Lundblad, 1936
   Type. *Rhyncholimnochares lamellipalpis* Lundblad, 1936
2. *Paralimnochares* Lundblad, 1937
   Type. *Paralimnochares sursumhians* Lundblad, 1937

Eylaidae Leach, 1815

Figures 197, 198

Diagnosis: These mites have a weak skin which usually lacks sclerotic shields. The maxillary organ has a large mouth disk surrounded by a fringe. The chelicerae are separated from one another, are large basally, tall dorso-ventrally, and have a small claw. The palpi are usually long and richly haired. The coxal plates are arranged in four groups of two each and the tarsal claws are simple. Placed in capsules the eyes are connected with one another by a sclerotized bridge and lie dorso-medianly

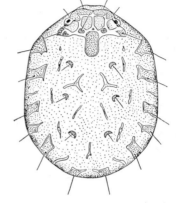

Figure 197 *Eylais desecta* Koenike. Eye plates of female. (After Marshall 1927)

Figure 198 *Piersigia koenikei* Viets. Dorsum. (After Viets 1936)

forming "spectacles," or if the eyes are lateral they are on the margin of a many-segmented plate.

Eylainae Claus, 1880

Genus and subgenera:

Eylais Latreille, 1796
a. *Eylais* s. str.
  Type. *Hydrachna extendens* Müller, 1776
b. *Capeulais* Thor, 1902
  Type. *Capeulais crassipalpis* Thor, 1902
c. *Meteylais* Szalay, 1934
  Type. *Eylais hamata* Koenike, 1897
d. *Pareylais* Szalay, 1934
  Type. *Eylais setosa* Koenike, 1897
e. *Proteylais* Szalay, 1933
  Type. *Eylais degenerata* Koenike, 1897

f. *Rhyncheylais* Lundblad, 1938
    Type. *Rhyncheylais connexa* Lundblad, 1938
g. *Syneylais* Lundblad, 1936
    Type. *Eylais infundibulifer* Koenike, 1897

Piersigiinae Oudemans, 1902

Genus:

  Piersigia Protz, 1896
  Type. *Piersigia limophila* Protz, 1896

Discussion: Lundblad 1941 lists this as a family.

Protziidae Viets, 1926

Figures 199, 200

Diagnosis: These mites are red in color, have a weak skin, are papillate or have striae, and usually lack true dorsal plates. Lateral eyes lie in capsules while a median eye may be present or lacking. The palptarsus located on the distal dorsal end of the tibia usually has a spine-

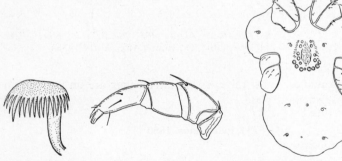

Figure 199   *Calonyx javanensis* Viets.
Tarsal claw (left), palpus (right).
(After Lundblad 1936)

Figure 200   *Calonyx javanensis*
Viets. Venter of male. (After
Lundblad 1936)

like elongation. Arranged in four groups, the coxal plates are about equal in size, the posterior group as a rule being far toward the rear. The legs lack swimming hairs while the tarsal claws are sickle-like, simple, or many-toothed. Between the anterior and posterior groups of coxal plates, far from the posterior margin of the body lies the genital organ. The usually numerous, more or less easily seen, often long-stalked genital suckers are in the skin, are variable in position, and have button-like or acorn-like suckers posteriorly. The genital plates are lacking or hair-bearing.

Genera:

1. *Protzia* Piersig, 1897
   Type. *Thyas eximia* Protz, 1896
2. *Calonyx* Walter, 1907
   Type. *Calonyx latus* Walter, 1907
3. *Neocalonyx* Walter, 1919
   Type. *Neocalonyx godeti* Walter, 1919
4. *Partnunia* Piersig, 1897
   Type. *Thyas angusta* Koenike, 1893
5. *Partnuniella* Viets, 1938
   Type. *Partnuniella thermalis* Viets, 1938
6. *Protziella* Lundblad, 1934
   Type. *Protziella hutchinsoni* Lundblad, 1934
7. *Wandesia* Schechtel, 1912
   Type. *Wandesia thori* Schechtel, 1912

Hydrodromidae Viets, 1936

Figures 201, 202

Diagnosis: The hydrodromids are red in color and have weak skin with papillae. No dorsal shield is present. Lateral eyes are separated from one another and are not contained in capsules while a median

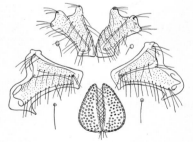
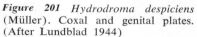
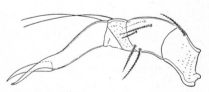

Figure 201 *Hydrodroma despiciens* (Müller). Coxal and genital plates. (After Lundblad 1944)

Figure 202 *Hydrodroma despiciens* (Müller). Palpus. (After Lundblad 1944)

eye is lacking. The coxal plates are divided in four groups of two each. The legs usually have swimming hairs and the tarsal claws have small outer accessory teeth. The palpal tibia has a long dorsal distal process above the palpal tarsus. Genital plates with many suckers are present.

Genera:

1. *Hydrodroma* Koch, 1837
   Type. *Hydrachna despiciens* Müller, 1776 (= *Hydrodroma umbrata* Koch, 1837)
2. *Oxopsis* Nordenskiöld, 1905
   Type. *Oxopsis diplodontoides* Nordenskiöld, 1905

Hydryphantidae Thor, 1900

Figures 203, 204

Diagnosis: The hydryphantids are red in color. Their skin has papillae and may or may not have a frontal plate but is seldom well armored. A median eye is present only when the frontal plate is present. The palpal tibia has a dorsal-distal process. The coxal plates are in

 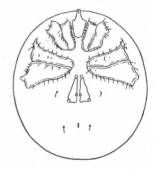

Figure 203 *Hydryphantes tenuabilis* Marshall. Anterior portion of body showing eyes and plate. (After Marshall 1946)

Figure 204 *Hydryphantes ruber* (De-Geer). Venter. (After Marshall 1944)

four groups. All legs have swimming hairs and the tarsal claws are simple, sickle-like. The genital organ has two movable plates and three or more pairs of genital suckers.

Hydryphantinae Piersig, 1896

Genera and subgenera:

1. *Hydryphantes* Koch, 1841
   a. *Hydryphantes* s. str.
      Type. *Acarus aquaticus ruber* DeGeer, 1778
   b. *Octohydryphantes* Lundblad, 1927
      Type. *Hydryphantes octoporus* Koenike, 1896

c. *Polyhydryphantes* Viets, 1926
  Type. *Hydrodroma flexuosa* Koenike, 1885
2. *Georgella* Koenike, 1907
  Type. *Hydrodroma helvetica* Haller, 1882
3. *Papilloporus* Walter, 1935
  Type. *Hydryphantes incertus* Koenike, 1893

Diplodontinae Vitzthum, 1942

Genus:

Diplodontus Dugès, 1833 (= *Eupatra* Koenike, 1896)
Type. *Diplodontus scapularis* Dugès, 1834

Mamersinae Viets, 1931

Genus:

Mamersa Koenike, 1898
Type. *Mamersa testudinata* Koenike, 1898

Thyasinae Viets, 1926

Genera and subgenera:

1. *Thyas* Koch, 1836
   Type. *Thyas venusta* Koch, 1836
2. *Javathyas* Viets, 1929 (=*Allothyas* Viets, 1929)
   Type. *Javathyas triumvirorum* Viets, 1929
3. *Kashmirothyas* Lundblad, 1934
   Type. *Kashmirothyas hutchinsoni* Lundblad, 1934
4. *Lundbladia* Viets, 1929
   a. *Lundbladia* s. str.
      Type. *Lundbladia feuerborni* Viets, 1929
   b. *Octolundbladia* Vitzthum, 1942
      Type. *Octolundbladia ladakiana* Vitzthum, 1942
5. *Octothyas* Lundblad, 1945
   Type. *Octothyas hewithi* Lundblad, 1945
6. *Panisellus* Viets, 1925
   Type. *Panisus thienemanni* Viets, 1820
7. *Panisoides* Lundblad, 1926
   Type. *Thyas setipes* Viets, 1911
8. *Panisus* Koenike, 1896
   Type. *Panisus michaeli* Koenike, 1896
9. *Parathyas* Lundblad, 1926
   Type. *Thyas thoracatus* Piersig, 1896
10. *Placothyas* Lundblad, 1926
    Type. *Thyas octopora* Viets, 1914

11. *Plesiothyas* Viets, 1935
    Type. *Trichothyas multipora* Walter, 1935
12. *Thyasella* Viets, 1926
    Type. *Thyas mandibularis* Lundblad, 1924
13. *Thyopsis* Piersig, 1898
    Type. *Thyas cancellata* Protz, 1896
14. *Trichothyas* Viets, 1926
    Type. *Thyas pennata* Viets, 1913
15. *Vietsia* Lundblad, 1926
    Type. *Thyas scutata* Protz, 1923

Euthyasinae Viets, 1931

Genera:

1. *Euthyas* Piersig, 1898 (= *Bradybates* Neuman, 1874 *nom. praeocc.*)
   Type. *Bradybates truncatus* Neuman, 1874
2. *Panisopsis* Viets, 1926
   Type. *Thyas vigilans* Piersig, 1896
3. *Thyasides* Lundblad, 1926
   Type. *Thyas dentata* Thor, 1897
4. *Zschokkea* Koenike, 1892
   Type. *Zschokkea oblonga* Koenike, 1892

Teratothyasinae Viets, 1929

Genus:

Teratothyas Viets, 1929
Type. *Teratothyas reticulata* Viets, 1929

Tartarothyasinae Viets, 1934

Genus:

Tartarothyas Viets, 1934
Type. *Tartarothyas micrommata* Viets, 1934

Clathrosperchonidae Lundblad, 1936

Figures 205, 206

Diagnosis: The body of these mites has a strong skin, which is covered with tiny spines and a radiating network pattern on the dorsal and ventral surface. Projecting only weakly above the skin surface the skin glands are strongly sclerotized and crater-like. The rostrum is either long and narrow, elongate and tubelike on the anterior end (*Clathrosperchon*), or not tubelike and relatively short (*Clathrosper-*

chonella). The chelicerae are slender in the preceding and strong in the latter genus; the palpus is not shearlike. No swimming hairs are to be found on the legs and the tarsal claws have accessory ventral teeth. Two genital plates with many genital suckers are present.

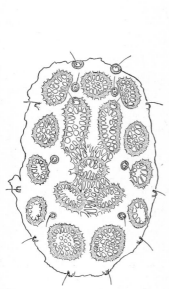 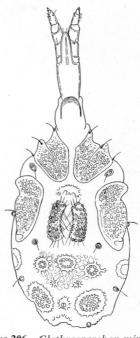

Figure 205 *Clathrosperchon minor* Lundblad. Dorsum of male. (After Lundblad 1941)

Figure 206 *Clathrosperchon minor* Lundblad. Venter of male. (After Lundblad 1941)

Genera:

1. *Clathrosperchon* Lundblad, 1936
   Type. *Clathrosperchon crassipalpis* Lundblad, 1936
2. *Clathrosperchonella* Lundblad, 1937
   Type. *Clathrosperchonella asterifera* Lundblad, 1937

Ctenothyasidae Lundblad, 1936

Figure 207

Diagnosis: The body of these mites is strongly skinned and has papillae but lacks armor. An apparently rudimentary median eye is present and the lateral eyes are single-capsuled. The skin gland areas are strongly raised and wartlike. The rostrum is *Thyas*-like; the palpal tibia lacks an end process. The coxal plates are divided in four groups;

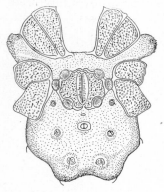

all tarsi have two simple claws and the legs lack swimming hairs. The outer genital organ of the female has two large, strongly sclerotized and porose plates with three large suckers on the lateral margins of each.

Figure 207 *Ctenothyas verrucosa* Lundblad. Venter of female. (After Lundblad 1936)

Genus:

Ctenothyas Lundblad, 1936
Type. *Ctenothyas verrucosa* Lundblad, 1936

Thermacaridae Sokolow, 1927

Figures 208, 209

Diagnosis: The body of these mites is entirely armored and the central dorsal shield is united with the ventral plate by a thin but strong suture. Two eyes lying in capsules are placed anteriorly on each side and a median eye is present. Coxal plates I are united medially without any suture, but sutures separate coxal plates I, II, III, and IV. The

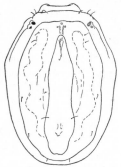

Figure 208 *Thermacarus nevadensis* Marshall. Ventral plates of female. (After Marshall 1928)

Figure 209 *Thermacarus nevadensis* Marshall. Dorsum of male. (After Marshall 1928)

coxal plates are contiguous. In the female the genital organ separates coxal plates III and IV; in the male coxal plates IV touch medianly and the genital organ is posterior to these. United plates I form a camerostome into which the gnathosoma can be withdrawn. Trochanters I, II, and III have a strong, cuplike cavity into which the basifemora articulate; the tarsal claws are strongly sickle-like and lack accessory claws but have a sharp tooth on the concave side. There are two movable genital plates which are divided into anterior and posterior parts, the posterior portion having many small genital suckers. These mites are to be found living in hot springs.

Genus:

> *Thermacarus* Sokolow, 1927
> Type. *Thermacarus thermobius* Sokolow, 1927

Discussion: These mites are to be found living in hot springs whose temperatures range from 42° to 46° C.

Reference:

Marshall, R. 1928. A new species of water mite from thermal springs. Psyche 35 (2): 92–96.

Rutripalpidae Sokolow, 1934

Figure 210

Diagnosis: The skin of these mites is weak, with a tendency to form sclerotized platelets or papillae. The coxal plates are divided into four groups of two each. There are no swimming hairs on the legs; the first three pairs of legs have well-developed tarsal claws provided with many narrow accessory spines (on leg IV these accessory spines are almost entirely reduced). From a lateral view the two end segments of the palps seem shovel-like and broadened. The fixed chela of the chelicera is reduced.

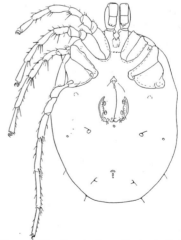

Figure 210 *Rutripalpus limicola* Sokolow. Venter. (After Sokolow 1934)

Genus:

    Rutripalpus Sokolow, 1934
    Type. *Rutripalpus limicola* Sokolow, 1934

Mamersopsidae Lundblad, 1930

Figures 211, 212

Diagnosis: Dorsal and ventral shields appear on the body of these mites and are separated from one another by a dorsal suture. The dorsal shield may consist of one plate or of many united plates; gland pore plates are located in the dorsal suture. The palpus is clublike,

Figure 211 *Mamersopsis thoracica* Nordenskiöld. Dorsum. (After Nordenskiöld 1905)

Figure 212 *Mamersopsis thoracica* Nordenskiöld. Venter. (After Nordenskiöld 1905)

especially the palpfemur which is strongly thickened dorsally and provided with spine or spine and protuberance on the inner margin. The palpal genu is shorter than the femur or tibia; the palpal tibia is strongly shortened and shorter than the femur and possesses a hair-bearing process on the inner margin; the palpal tarsus is spinelike distally. Forming one group, the coxal plates are united with the ventral plate and all plates are separated by weak sutures. The legs may or may not have swimming hairs; tarsus IV is often reduced and carries no claw or a simple one. The genital organ is more or less united or close to coxae IV and has two movable plates and three pairs of genital suckers.

Genera:

    1. *Mamersopsis* Nordenskiöld, 1905
       Type. *Mamersopsis thoracica* Nordenskiöld, 1905

2. *Bandakia* Thor, 1913
   Type. *Bandakia concreta* Thor, 1913
3. *Platymamersopsis* Viets, 1914
   Type. *Platymamersopsis nordenskiöldi* Viets, 1914

Pseudohydryphantidae Viets, 1926

Figure 213

Diagnosis: The skin is weak and has no sclerotized plate, although weakly sclerotized muscle insertions are present. The dorsum has short, robust, many-pointed papillae. Lateral eyes lie in capsules and

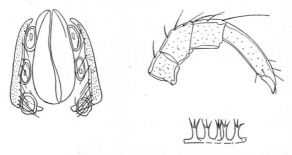

Figure 213 *Pseudohydryphantes parvulus* Viets. Female genital organ (left), palpus (upper right), skin papillae (lower right). (After Viets 1936)

a median eye is also present in a small, sclerotized ring. The coxal plates are divided into four groups of two each; legs III and IV have swimming hairs. The tarsal claws are simple and sickle-like while the palptibia has a dorsal distal process. The genital organ has two movable plates and three pairs of genital suckers.

Genus:

   Pseudohydryphantes Viets, 1907
   Type. *Pseudohydryphantes parvulus* Viets, 1907

Teutoniidae Lundblad, 1927

Figures 214, 215

Diagnosis: The body is weak-skinned and the lateral eyes are not in capsules but lie near each other. No median eye is present. The palpal femur has a cone on the inner margin. The coxal plates are divided into four groups of two each; coxal plates III and IV almost form a right angle; in the anterior median angle of coxal plates IV is a gland pore. Legs III and IV have swimming hairs and the tarsal claws of legs I, II, and III have accessory teeth; tarsus IV is constricted distally and lacks claws.

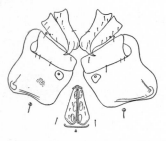

Figure 214 *Teutonia cometes* (Koch). Ventral plates of male. (After Viets 1936)

Figure 215 *Teutonia cometes* (Koch). Palpus (After Viets 1936)

Genus:

> *Teutonia* Koenike, 1889
> Type. *Teutonia primaria* Koenike, 1889

Sperchonidae Thor, 1900

Figures 216–218

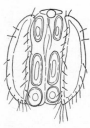

Figure 216 *Sperchon glandulosus* Koenike. Genital plates of female. (After Marshall 1943)

Diagnosis: The sperchonids have a weak or leather-like skin, which occasionlly has shields, with rugose or fine-pointed papillae in the striated area. Lateral eyes lie in capsules but a median eye is seldom present. The palpfemur has a spine-bearing peg on the inner side; the palpal tibia lacks distal-dorsal elongation and the inner side has two sensory spines. The coxal plates are arranged in four groups; coxal plates IV are three- or four-cornered; the legs have no swimming hairs and the tarsal claws as a rule have accessory teeth. With two lateral, movable plates and three pairs of genital suckers, the genital organ is situated more or less between the posterior coxal plates.

Genera and subgenera:

1. *Sperchon* Kramer, 1877
   a. *Sperchon* s. str.
   > Type. *Sperchon squamosa* Kramer, 1879

b. *Hispidosperchon* Thor, 1901
  Type. *Sperchon hispidus* Thor, 1898
c. *Mixosperchon* Viets, 1926
  Type. *Sperchon papillosus* Thor, 1901
d. *Scutosperchon* Viets, 1926
  Type. *Sperchon thori* Koenike, 1900
2. *Sperchonopsis* Piersig, 1896 (= *Pseudosperchon* Piersig, 1901)
  Type. *Sperchon verrucosus* Protz, 1896

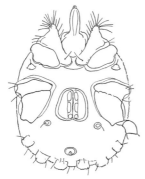

Figure 217 *Sperchonopsis verrucosa* (Protz). Venter of male. (After Marshall 1943)

Figure 218 *Sperchon cornutus* Viets. Palpus of male. (After Lundblad 1936)

Anisitsiellidae Viets, 1929

Figures 219, 220

Diagnosis: The body of these mites is weak-skinned or armored and has a dorsal suture. Lateral eyes are not placed in capsules, but are separated from each other. The inner side of the palpal femur has a process. Coxal plate IV does not have a large gland pore on the anterior median corner; tarsi IV are reduced distally and lack claws. The genital organ has two movable plates and three or four pairs of genital suckers.

Anisitsiellinae Koenike, 1910

Genera:

1. *Anisitsiella* Daday, 1905
  Type. *Anisitsiella aculeata* Daday, 1905
2. *Hydrobaumia* Halik, 1930
  Type.*Hydrobaumia malacensis* Halik, 1930

3. *Mamersella* Viets, 1929
   Type. *Mamersella thienemanni* Viets, 1929
4. *Mamersellides* Lundblad, 1937
   Type. *Mamersellides ventriperforatus* Lundblad, 1937
5. *Mamersides* Viets, 1935
   Type. *Mamersides saranganensis* Viets, 1935
6. *Mamersopides* Viets, 1916
   Type. *Mamersopides sigthori* Viets, 1916
7. *Rutacarus* Lundblad, 1937
   Type. *Rutacarus pyriformis* Lundblad, 1937
8. *Sigthoria* Koenike, 1907 (= *Amasis* Nordenskiöld, 1905 *nom. praeocc.*)
   Type. *Amasis niloticus* Nordenskiöld, 1905

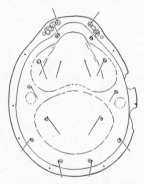 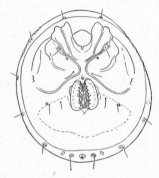

Figure 219 *Mamersellides ventriperforatus* Lundblad. Dorsum of female. (After Lundblad 1941)

Figure 220 *Mamersellides ventriperforatus* Lundblad. Venter of female. (After Lundblad 1941)

Nilotoniinae Viets, 1929

Genera and subgenera:

1. *Nilotonia* Thor, 1905
   Type. *Teutonia loricata* Nordenskiöld, 1905
2. *Dartia* Soar, 1917
   a. *Dartia* s. str.
      Type. *Dartia harrisi* Soar, 1917
   b. *Dartiella* Viets, 1929
      Type. *Dartia longipora* Walter, 1925
3. *Dartonia* Viets, 1929
   Type. *Dartonia caerulea* Viets, 1929
4. *Kawamuracarus* Uchida, 1937
   Type. *Kawamuracarus elongatus* Uchida, 1937

5. *Limnolegeria* Motas, 1928
   Type. *Limnolegeria longiseta* Motas, 1928
6. *Manotonia* Viets, 1935 (= *Mania* Walter, 1935 *nom. praeocc.*)
   Type. *Mania muscicola* Walter, 1935
7. *Ranautonia* Viets, 1929
   Type. *Ranautonia dentipalpis* Viets, 1929

Lebertiidae Thor, 1900

Figure 221

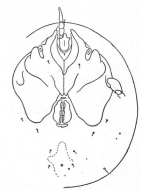

Diagnosis: The lebertiids are characterized by a weak to leather-like skin, a dorsum which as a rule has no shield, and a venter which often has extensive sclerotization. Lateral eyes are paired in a weak, sclerotized capsule. The palpus is more or less slender or narrow. All coxal plates are united in one group and a median suture is often lacking. The genital organ has two plates and three pairs of genital suckers, although in many cases only two pairs are present.

Figure 221 *Lebertia quinquemaculosa* Marshall. Venter. (After Marshall 1932)

Lebertiinae Wolcott, 1905

Genus and subgenera:

Lebertia Neumann, 1880
  a. *Lebertia* s. str. (= *Neolebertia* Thor, 1905)
     Type. *Pachygaster tau-insignatus* Lebert, 1879
  b. *Distolebertia* Husiatinschi, 1937
     Type. *Distolebertia bucovinensis* Husiatinschi, 1937
  c. *Hexalebertia* Thor, 1906
     Type. *Lebertia stigmatifera* Thor, 1900
  d. *Mixolebertia* Thor, 1906
     Type. *Lebertia brevipora* Thor, 1899
  e. *Pilolebertia* Thor, 1900
     Type. *Lebertia insignis* Neumann, 1880
  f. *Pseudolebertia* Thor, 1897
     Type. *Pseudolebertia glabra* Thor, 1897

Oxinae Viets, 1926

Genera and subgenera:

1. *Oxus* Kramer, 1877
   a. *Oxus* s. str.
      Type. *Oxus oblongus* Kramer, 1879
   b. *Pseudoxus* Thor, 1901
      Type. *Pseudoxus integer* Thor, 1901
2. *Frontipoda* Koenike, 1891
   Type. *Hydrachna musculus* Müller, 1776
3. *Gnaphiscus* Koenike, 1898
   a. *Gnaphiscus* s. str.
      Type. *Gnaphiscus setosus* Koenike, 1898
   b. *Gnaphoxus* Thor, 1913
      Type. *Gnaphiscus* (*Gnaphoxus*) *ekmani* Thor, 1913

Atractideidae Thor, 1902

Figures 222, 223

Diagnosis: In the atractideids the ventral shield is entire while the dorsal shield is divided into several plates by sutures. In general the palpi are small; the palpal femur and tibia frequently have spines or cones on

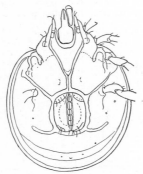 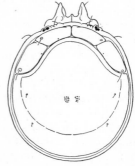

Figure 222 *Atractides sierrensis* Marshall. Venter of male. (After Marshall 1943)

Figure 223 *Atractides sierrensis* Marshall. Dorsum of male. (After Marshall 1943)

the inner margin. Coxal plates I lack a median suture and are united; a suture separating coxal plates II and III is more or less lacking and coxal plates IV posteriorly and outwardly are not well separated from the ventral shield. The legs have no swimming hairs and the tarsal claws have accessory teeth. The genital organ has two movable plates and with three or six pairs of genital suckers.

Genera and subgenera:

1. *Atractides Koch,* 1837
   a. *Atractides* s. str.
      Type. *Atractides anomalus* Koch, 1837
   b. *Monatractides* Viets, 1926
      Type. *Atractides uniscutatus* Viets, 1925
   c. *Rusetria* Thor, 1897
      Type. *Rusetria spinirostris* Thor, 1897
   d. *Rusetriella* Viets, 1931
      Type. *Atractides acutiscutatus* Viets, 1913
2. *Pseudotorrenticola* Walter, 1906
   Type. *Pseudotorrenticola rhynchota* Walter, 1906
3. *Testudacarus* Walter, 1928
   Type. *Testudacarus tripeltatus* Walter, 1928

Pontarachnidae Thor, 1929

Figure 224

Diagnosis: These mites are ocean livers and do not have any tracheal system. The coxal plates are divided into two groups of four each. The genital organ has no movable plates or genital suckers and the palpi are simple and lack inner protuberances.

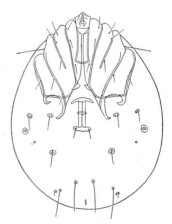

Figure 224 *Pontarachna punctulum* Philippi. Venter of female. (After Walter 1925)

Genera:

1. *Pontarachna* Philippi, 1840
   Type. *Pontarachna punctulum* Philippi, 1840
2. *Litarachna* Walter, 1925
   Type. *Litarachna incerta* Walter, 1925

Neotorrenticolidae Lundblad, 1936

Figures 225, 226

Diagnosis: These mites have a soft skin and eyes which are separated. The dorsum of the male is entirely armored while the dorsum of the female has many small, sclerotized plates. The palpus has hairbearing protuberances on the tibia and a spine-bearing tooth on the

Figure 225 *Neotorrenticola violacea* Lundblad. Venter of young female. (After Lundblad 1942)

Figure 226 *Neotorrenticola violacea* Lundblad. Palpus. (After Lundblad 1942)

femur. In the male the coxal plates are united but in the mature female they are separated into four groups. In the immature female the coxal plates are approximate. The legs are long and strong without swimming hairs but with strong and weak spines. The tarsal claws are large and have ventral accessory teeth. Many genital suckers surround the genital organ.

Genus:

Neotorrenticola Lundblad, 1936
Type. *Neotorrenticola violacea* Lundblad, 1936

References:

Lundblad, O. 1936. Dritte Mitteilung über Wassermilben aus Santa Catharina in Südbrasilien. Zool. Anz. 116:200–211.
——. 1942. Die Hydracarinenfauna Südbrasiliens und Paraguays—II. K. Svenska Vetensk Akad. Handl. 20(3):3–175.

Limnesiidae Thor, 1900

Figures 227, 228

Diagnosis: Usually weakly skinned, the body of these mites is smooth, has no papillae, and is seldom entirely armored. A small, unpaired

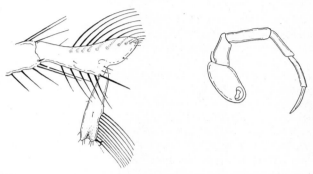

Figure 227 *Centrolimnesia bondi* Lundblad. Leg III (left), leg IV (right). (After Lundblad 1935)

shield, or two shields, is located posteriorly on the dorsum. Lateral eyes are separated from one another and lie singly. The palpal femur usually has a peg or small spine on the inner side while the palpal tibia has a small seta on the inner side. The coxal plates are arranged in four groups of two each and are seldom united into one group; coxal plates IV are large and triangular with the acetabula on the posterior lateral edge. The legs usually have swimming hairs and tarsi IV as a rule are reduced and lack claws. The genital organ is close to the coxal plates; the genital plates have three, but seldom four or more suckers. In the male the genital plates are united with one another.

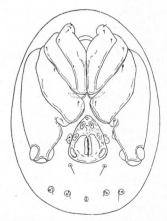

Figure 228 *Centrolimnesia bondi* Lundblad. Venter of male. (After Lundblad 1935)

Limnesiinae Koenike, 1909

Genera and subgenera:

1. *Limnesia* Koch, 1836
   a. *Limnesia* s. str.
      Type. *Limnesia fulgida* Koch, 1836
   b. *Allolimnesia* Viets, 1936
      Type. *Allolimnesia polypora* Viets, 1936
   c. *Limnesiopsides* Viets, 1938
      Type. *Limnesiopsides pectungulatus* Viets, 1938
   d. *Limnesiopsis* Piersig, 1897
      Type. *Limnesia anomala* Koenike, 1895
   e. *Neolimnesia* Lundblad, 1936
      Type. *Limnesia (Neolimnesia) plaumanni* Lundblad, 1936
   f. *Paralimnesia* Lundblad, 1938
      Type. *Limnesia (Paralimnesia) microdon* Lundblad, 1938
   g. *Tetralimnesia* Thor, 1923
      Type. *Limnesia aspera* Koenike, 1898
2. *Centrolimnesia* Lundblad, 1935
   Type. *Centrolimnesia bondi* Lundblad, 1935
3. *Duralimnesia* Viets, 1923
   Type. *Duralimnesia tenuipalpis* Viets, 1923
4. *Limnesiella* Daday, 1905
   a. *Limnesiella* s. str.
      Type. *Limnesiella pusilla* Daday, 1905
   b. *Limnesiellula* Viets, 1935
      Type. *Limnesiellula brasiliana* Viets, 1935
5. *Limnesicula* Viets, 1937
   Type. *Limnesicula verrucosa* Viets, 1937
6. *Pilolimnesia* Viets, 1938
   Type. *Pilolimnesia rostrata* Viets, 1938
7. *Tubophora* Walter, 1935
   Type. *Tubophora limnesioides* Walter, 1935

Protolimnesiinae Viets, 1940

Genera:

1. *Protolimnesia* Lundblad, 1927
   Type. *Limnesia unguiculata* Walter, 1919
2. *Crenolimnesia* Lundblad, 1938
   Type. *Crenolimnesia placophora* Lundblad, 1938
3. *Limnesides* Lundblad, 1936
   Type. *Limnesides epimerata* Lundblad, 1936

Tyrelliinae Koenike, 1910

Genera:

1. *Tyrellia* Koenike, 1895
   Type. *Tyrellia circularis* Koenike, 1895
2. *Neotyrellia* Lundblad, 1938
   Type. *Neotyrellia petricola* Lundblad, 1938

Hygrobatidae Koch, 1842

Figure 229

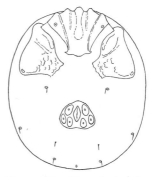

Diagnosis: As a rule the body of these mites is weak-skinned. The palpal femur often has processes on the inner side while the anterior inner margin of the palpal femur is often toothed. There are small setae on the inner side of the palpal tibia, and often a median, swordlike setae is present. The coxal plates usually lie in three groups (the coxal plates I are united behind the maxillary organ); the plates are seldom in four groups of two each or all united with one another. Coxal plates I, II, and III are usually narrow and elongated, while plate IV is large. The suture between plates III and IV usually does not reach the inner margin of the group. Usually the legs have no swimming hairs and seldom do they have separate, long hairs. The genital organs have plates and as a rule three pairs of suckers (they seldom have fewer or more suckers). The male has a roundish plate with a more or less splitlike sexual opening while the female has two (seldom four) separate plates.

Figure 229 *Hygrobates plebejus* Lundblad. Venter of male. (After Lundblad 1930)

Hygrobatinae Claus, 1880

Genera and subgenera:

1. *Hygrobates* Koch, 1837
   a. *Hygrobates* s. str.
      Type. *Hydrachna longipalpis* Hermann, 1804
   b. *Capobates* Thor, 1898
      Type. *Capobates sarsi* Thor, 1898

c. *Dekabates* Thor, 1923
   Type. *Hygrobates decaporus* Koenike, 1895
d. *Diktyobates* Thor, 1927
   Type. *Acarus fluviatilis* Ström, 1768
e. *Dodecabates* Viets, 1926
   Type. *Hygrobates dodecaporus* Koenike, 1895
f. *Monobates* Walter, 1935
   Type. *Hygrobates falcipalpis* Koenike, 1907
g. *Neohygrobates* Viets, 1935
   Type. *Neohygrobates puberulus* Viets, 1935
h. *Rhabdotobates* Thor, 1927
   Type. *Hygrobates calliger* Piersig, 1896
i. *Rivobates* Thor, 1897
   Type. *Rivobates norvegicus* Thor, 1897
j. *Tetrabates* Thor, 1923
   Type. *Hygrobates octoporus* Daday, 1913
2. *Corticacarellus* Lundblad, 1937
   Type. *Corticacarus labialis* Lundblad, 1936
3. *Corticacarus* Lundblad, 1936
   Type. *Corticacarus dentipalpis* Lundblad, 1936
4. *Crenohygrobates* Lundblad, 1938
   Type. *Crenohygrobates multiporus* Lundblad, 1938
5. *Hygrobatella* Viets, 1926 (= *Placobates* Lundblad, 1927)
   Type. *Hygrobates placophorus* Walter, 1919
6. *Hygrobatides* Lundblad, 1936
   Type. *Hygrobatides pachydermis* Lundblad, 1936
7. *Hygrobatopsis* Viets, 1924
   Type. *Hygrobatopsis levipalpis* Viets, 1924
8. *Kyphohygrobatella* Lundblad, 1936
   Type. *Kyphohygrobatella serratipalpis* Lundblad, 1936
9. *Kyphohygrobates* Viets, 1935
   Type. *Hygrobates verrucifer* Daday, 1905
10. *Megabates* Viets, 1924
    Type. *Megabates rectipes* Viets, 1924
11. *Paraschizobates* Lundblad, 1937
    Type. *Paraschizobates megapoides* Lundblad, 1937
12. *Schizobates* Thor, 1927
    Type. *Hygrobates disiunctus* Walter, 1924
13. *Schubartella* Viets, 1937
    Type. *Schubartella longipes* Viets, 1937
14. *Stylohygrobates* Viets, 1935
    Type. *Stylohygrobates longipalpis* Viets, 1935
15. *Subcorticacarus* Lundblad, 1937
    Type. *Subcorticacarus digitatus* Lundblad, 1937

16. *Thonia* Halik, 1941
    Type. *Thonia barbata* Halik, 1941
17. *Thoracohygrobates* Lundblad, 1936
    Type. *Thoracohygrobates cancellatus* Lundblad, 1936

Megapusinae Thor, 1927

Genera and subgenera:

1. *Megapus* Neumann, 1880
   a. *Megapus* s. str.
      Type. *Atractides spinipes* Koch, 1837
   b. *Octomegapus* Viets, 1926
      Type. *Megapus octoporus* Piersig, 1904
   c. *Polymegapus* Viets, 1926
      Type. *Megapus polyporus* Viets, 1922
   d. *Tetramegapus* Viets, 1926
      Type. *Megapus gabretae* Thon, 1901
   e. *Tympanomegapus* Thor, 1923
      Type. *Atractides pavesii* Maglio, 1905
2. *Hygrobatomegapus* Lundblad, 1927
   Type. *Hygrobatomegapus spathuliferus* Lundblad, 1927
3. *Megapella* Lundblad, 1936
   Type. *Megapella longimaxillaris* Lundblad, 1936
4. *Megapoides* Lundblad, 1936
   Type. *Megapoides porosus* Lundblad, 1936
5. *Mesobatella* Viets, 1931
   Type. *Megapus serratisetus* Viets, 1916
6. *Mesobates* Thor, 1901
   Type. *Mesobates forcipatus* Thor, 1901
7. *Mixobates* Thor, 1905
   Type. *Mixobates processifer* Thor, 1905

Atractidellidae Lundblad, 1936

Figures 230–233

Diagnosis: With shields on the anterior dorsum, the body of these mites is strongly skinned. The chelicerae are long and slender and the palpal femur and genu each have a ventral spine. The coxal plates lie in three groups; the two anterior pairs of plates are united behind the maxillary organ, coxal plate IV has a sclerotized posterior margin which is drawn out into a hooklike projection, and the anterior portion of coxal plates I surpasses the edge of the body. The legs are long and have no swimming hairs. The genital organ has two plates and three pairs of genital suckers.

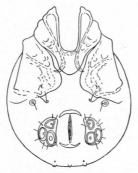

Figure 230   *Atractidella hamata* Lundblad. Venter of female. (After Lundblad 1942)

Figure 231   *Atractidella hamata* Lundblad. Palpus of female. (After Lundblad 1942)

Genera:

  1. *Atractidella* Lundblad, 1936
     Type. *Atractidella hamata* Lundblad, 1936
  2. *Atractidopsis* Lundblad, 1936
     Type. *Atractidopsis digitata* Lundblad, 1936

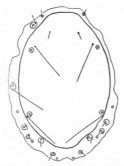

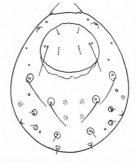

Figure 232   *Atractidella hamata* Lundblad. Dorsum of male. (After Lundblad 1942)

Figure 233   *Atractidella hamata* Lundblad. Dorsum of female. (After Lundblad 1942)

Reference:

Lundblad, O. 1936. Neue Wassermilben aus Santa Catharina in Südbrasilien. Zool. Anz. 115:29–51.

Nautarachnidae Viets, 1935

Figure 234

Diagnosis: These mites have a strong skin which has papillae. Lateral eyes lie in capsules. The chelicerae are two-segmented. The palpus has no peglike processes and the palpal tibia lacks sclerotized pegs distally. The coxal plates lie in four groups of two each; coxal plate IV has a posteriorly directed process on the median posterior margin. The legs have swimming hairs. The genital organ has two lateral, long, many-suckered plates.

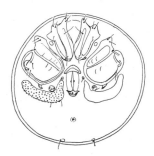

Figure 234 *Nautarachna crassa* (Koenike). Venter of female. (After Viets 1936)

Genus:

Nautarachna Moniez, 1888
Type. *Nautarachna asperrimum* Moniez, 1888

Feltriidae Thor, 1929

Figures 235–237

Diagnosis: The body skin of these mites is more or less plainly striated. In the male there are no large, sclerotized plates or shields while in the female there are small, sclerotized plates or shields. The coxal plates lie in four groups of two each. In the male the coxal plates are often very close to each other; coxal plates IV are laterally broadened and often lack a true medial margin; the posterior margin of coxal plate IV is transverse. No swimming hairs are present on the legs and tarsi III of the male is usually sexually differentiated. The genital organ is extensive or large, with many small, porelike suckers; the

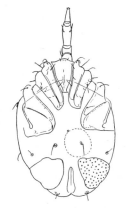

Figure 235 *Feltria zschokkei* Koenike. Venter of female. (After Viets 1936)

sucker plates of the male are united with one another and with the small sexual opening.

Genera and subgenera:

1. *Feltria* Koenike, 1892
    a. *Feltria* s. str.
       Type. *Feltria minuta* Koenike, 1892
    b. *Feltriella* Viets, 1930
       Type. *Feltria rubra* Piersig, 1898
    c. *Mesofeltria* Uchida, 1934
       Type. *Feltria* (*Mesofeltria*) *torrenticola* Uchida, 1934
2. *Kongsbergia* Thor, 1899
    Type. *Kongsbergia materna* Thor, 1899

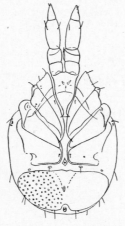
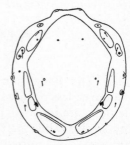

Figure 236 *Feltria minuta* Koenike. Venter of male. (After Viets 1936)

Figure 237 *Feltria minuta* Koenike. Dorsum of female. (After Viets 1936)

Unionicolidae Oudemans, 1909

Figure 238

Diagnosis: The skin is usually weak but at times may be solid, strong, and in some genera also more or less weakly armored. Usually the skin is smooth and has no roundish papillae; the skin glands are often cone-like. The palpal femur and genu as a rule lack inner processes. Frequently the genu has long, lateral spines while the palpal tibia has a spine on the distal, inner margin. The coxal plates lie in four groups of two each but are also united with one another and to the ventral shield. The anterior coxal plate group has a more or less long, posteriorly directed, subcutaneous process which often reaches to the posterior coxal plates. Posterior plates, especially IV, as a rule are rectangular and large. Legs I or legs I and II are often thickened and often have paired, swordlike setae on protuberances. Usually the legs have swimming hairs. The genital organ has a weak-skinned form with two genital plates; females of certain genera have four plates and have not under five or six pairs and often more genital suckers (the suckers seldom lie free in the skin). The genital organ of the armored forms has two or more weakly differentiated genital plates and many suckers.

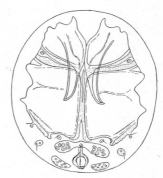

Figure 238 *Neumania curvipes* Lundblad. Venter. (After Lundblad 1930)

Unionicolinae Koenike, 1909

Genera and subgenera:

1. *Unionicola* Haldeman, 1842
   a. *Unionicola* s. str.
      Type. *Acarus ypsilophorus* Bonz, 1783
   b. *Atax* Koch, 1842 (= *Hexatax* Thor, 1926)
      Type. *Hydrachna crassipes* Müller, 1776
   c. *Pentatax* Thor, 1926
      Type. *Atax bonzi* Claparede, 1868
   d. *Polyatax* Viets, 1933
      Type. *Polyatax japonicus* Viets, 1933
   e. *Unionicolides* Lundblad, 1937
      Type. *Unionicola (Unionicolides) sica* Lundblad, 1937
2. *Atacella* Lundblad, 1937
   a. *Atacella* s. str.
      Type. *Atacella clathrata* Lundblad, 1937
   b. *Atacellides* Lundblad, 1941
      Type. *Atax rugosus* Koenike, 1890
3. *Polyatacides* Lundblad, 1941
   Type. *Unionicola prominens* Koenike, 1914

Encentridophorinae Viets, 1935

Genus:

Encentridophorus Piersig, 1897
Type. *Atax spinifer* Koenike, 1893

Huitfeldtiinae Viets, 1924

Genus:

Huitfeldtia Thor, 1898
Type. *Huitfeldtia rectipes* Thor, 1898

Najadicolinae Viets, 1935

Genus:

Najadicola Piersig, 1897
Type. *Atax ingens* Koenike, 1895

Neumaniinae Viets, 1931

Genera and subgenera:

1. *Neumania* Lebert, 1879
    a. *Neumania* s. str.
       Type. *Hydrachna spinipes* Müller, 1776
    b. *Lemienia* Koenike, 1910
       Type. *Atax multiporus* Daday, 1901
    c. *Tetraneumania* Lundblad, 1930
       Type. *Neumania (Tetraneumania) curvipes* Lundblad, 1930
2. *Amazonella* Lundblad, 1930
    Type. *Amazonella ribagai* Lundblad, 1930
3. *Ecpolus* Koenike, 1898
    a. *Ecpolus* s. str.
       Type. *Ecpolus tuberatus* Koenike, 1898
    b. *Subneumania* Viets, 1930
       Type. *Subneumania dura* Viets, 1930
4. *Koenikea* Wolcott, 1900
    a. *Koenikea* s. str.
       Type. *Koenikea concava* Wolcott, 1900
    b. *Diplokoenikea* Lundblad, 1936
       Type. *Koenikea (Diplokoenikea) pectinata* Lundblad, 1936
    c. *Ecpolopsis* Piersig, 1906
       Type. *Ecpolopsis multiscutata* Piersig, 1906
    d. *Koenikella* Lundblad, 1936
       Type. *Koenikea (Koenikella) crassipalpis* Lundblad, 1936

e. *Monokoenikea* Lundblad, 1941
   Type. *Koenikea melini* Lundblad, 1930
f. *Neokoenikea* Lundblad, 1936
   Type. *Koenikea (Neokoenikea) armipes* Lundblad, 1936
g. *Nyangalla* Viets, 1935
   Type. *Koenikea acanthophora* Viets, 1935
h. *Parakoenikea* Lundblad, 1936
   Type. *Koenikea (Parakoenikea) curvipalpis* Lundblad, 1936
i. *Pseudokoenikea* Lundblad, 1941
   Type. Koenikea rutae Lundblad, 1930
j. *Recifella* Viets, 1935
   Type. *Recifella laminipes* Viets, 1935
k. *Tanaognathella* Lundblad, 1941
   Type. *Koenikea marshallae* Viets, 1930
l. *Tanaognathus* Wolcott, 1900
   Type. *Tanaognathus spinipes* Wolcott, 1900
5. *Leptopterotrichophorus* Viets, 1914
   Type. *Leptopterotrichophorus verrucosus* Viets, 1914

Pionatacinae Viets, 1916

Genus:

Pionatax Viets, 1916
Type. *Pionatax uncipes* Viets, 1916

Pollicipalpinae Viets, 1925

Genus:

Pollicipalpus Viets, 1924
Type. *Pollicipalpus scutatus* Viets, 1924

Schadeellinae Lundblad, 1938

Genus:

Schadeella Lundblad, 1938
Type. *Schadeella crassipalpis* Lundblad, 1938

Pionidae Thor, 1900

Figures 239, 240

Diagnosis: The body as a rule is weak-skinned, has no papillae, and
seldom has shields. The chelicerae are not united with one another.
The palpal tibia has small setae and usually protuberances on the inner
margin and also a sclerotized peg on the distal-median end. The coxal
plates lie in four groups of two each; in the male the plates are often

close to one another or more or less united with one another. Coxal plate IV has a more or less long, subcutaneous process on the posterior margin while the concave posterior margins of coxal plates IV form the boundary of the genital indentation. The legs usually possess swimming

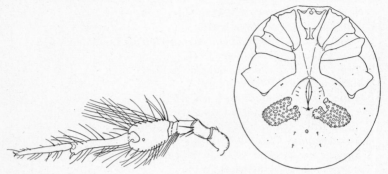

Figure 239 *Tiphys torris* var. *americanus* Marshall. Leg IV of male. (After Marshall 1937)

Figure 240 *Piona interrupta* Marshall. Venter of female. (After Marshall 1937)

hairs and the tarsal claws usually have accessory teeth. The genital organ has plates and six or more suckers. The suckers are seldom located in the skin. In the male the sucker plates are usually united with one another. The leg structure of the male usually shows sexual differentiation.

Pioninae Wolcott, 1905

Genus and subgenera:

> *Piona* Koch, 1836
> a. *Piona* s. str.
> > Type. *Hydrachna fuscata* Hermann, 1804
> b. *Dispersipiona* Viets, 1926
> > Type. *Hydrachna clavicornis* Müller, 1776
> c. *Tetrapiona* Viets, 1926
> > Type. *Nesaea variabilis* Koch, 1836

Foreliinae Viets, 1926

Genera:

> 1. *Forelia* Haller, 1882
> > Type. *Hydrachna liliacca* Müller, 1776
> 2. *Pseudofeltria* Soar, 1904
> > Type. *Pseudofeltria scourfieldi* Soar, 1904

Pionellinae Viets, 1937

Genus:

Pionella Viets, 1937
Type. *Pionella karamani* Viets, 1937

Tiphysinae Vitzthum, 1942

Genera and subgenera:

1. *Tiphys* Koch, 1836
    a. *Tiphys* s. str. (= *Acercus* Koch, 1842)
       Type. *Tiphys sagulatus* Koch, 1837
    b. *Acercopsis* Viets, 1926
       Type. *Acercus pistillifer* Koenike, 1908
    c. *Pionides* Thor, 1901
       Type. *Piona ensifera* Koenike, 1895
2. *Hydrochoreutes* Koch, 1837
    Type. *Spio ephippiata* Koch, 1836
3. *Pionacercus* Piersig, 1894
    a. *Pionacercus* s. str.
       Type. *Pionacercus leuckarti* Piersig, 1894
    b. *Pionacercopsis* Viets, 1936
       Type. *Tiphys yatrax* Koch, 1837
4. *Pionopsis* Piersig, 1894
    Type. *Hydrachna lutescens* Hermann, 1804
5. *Wettina* Piersig, 1892
    Type. *Tiphys podagricus* Koch, 1837 (= *Wettina macroplica* Piersig, 1892)

Astacocrotonidae Thor, 1927

Figure 241

Diagnosis: Astacocrotonids are parasitic in crab gills. Their skin is weak and has no dorsal plates. In all probability there are no skin pores, stigma, or trachea either. In the male eyes are present while there are none in the mature female. The gnathosoma lies free between the widely separated coxal plates I; all coxal plates are united on each side and are contiguous. On each coxal plate IV a large gland appears as shown in the figure. In the female the palpi are for grasping gill filaments; the palpi are very short and thick—thicker than the legs. No swimming hairs are on the legs and the tarsal claws are tridentated.

The female genital opening is on the rear, far from the coxal plates; on each side is a genital plate with a longitudinal row of four genital

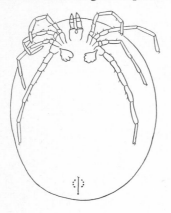

suckers. The male genital opening lies between the two coxal plate groups. These mites have also been reported on the gills of *Amia* (Pisces; Bowfin).

Figure 241 *Astacocroton molle* Haswell. Venter of female. (After Haswell 1922)

Genus:

> *Astacocroton* Haswell, 1922
> Type. *Astacocroton molle* Haswell, 1922

Axonopsidae Viets, 1929

Figures 242, 243

Diagnosis: The body is armored, porose, and has a dorsal suture. The coxal plates are united in one group; coxal plates I are united medianly with one another. The palpal tibia may or may not have inner

Figure 242 *Axonopsella spinigera* Lundblad. Dorsum of female. (After Lundblad 1930)

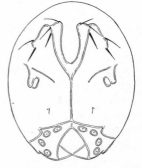

Figure 243 *Axonopsella spinigera* Lundblad. Venter of female. (After Lundblad 1930)

protuberances. There are usually three or four pairs of genital suckers. Swimming hairs may or may not be present on the legs.

Axonopsinae Viets, 1929

Genera and subgenera:

1. *Axonopsis* Piersig, 1893
   a. *Axonopsis* s. str.
      Type. *Hydrachna complanata* Müller, 1781
   b. *Hexaxonopsis* Viets, 1926
      Type. *Axonopsis violacea* Viets, 1911
2. *Axonopsalbia* Viets, 1913
   a. *Axonopsalbia* s. str.
      Type. *Axonopsalbia curvisetifera* Viets, 1913
   b. *Sumatralbia* Viets, 1929
      Type. *Sumatralbia rugosa* Viets, 1929
3. *Axonopsella* Lundblad, 1930
   a. *Axonopsella* s. str.
      Type. *Axonopsella spinigera* Lundblad, 1930
   b. *Neoaxonopsella* Lundblad, 1937
      Type. *Axonopsella* (*Neoaxonopsella*) *trifida* Lundblad, 1937
   c. *Paraxonopsella* Lundblad, 1937
      Type. *Axonopsella* (*Paraxonopsella*) *filunguis* Lundblad, 1937
4. *Barbaxona* Viets, 1924
   Type. *Barbaxona barbata* Viets, 1924
5. *Brachypoda* Lebert, 1879
   a. *Brachypoda* s. str.
      Type. *Hydrachna versicolor* Müller (= *Brachypoda paradoxa* Lebert, 1879)
   b. *Hemibrachypoda* Viets, 1937
      Type. *Brachypodella mutila* Walter, 1928
   c. *Parabrachypoda* Viets, 1929 (= *Brachypodella* Viets, 1926)
      Type. *Brachypoda montii* Maglio, 1924
6. *Kalobrachypoda* Viets, 1929
   Type. *Kalobrachypoda rhopalopoda* Viets, 1929
7. *Lethaxona* Viets, 1932
   Type. *Lethaxona pygmaea* Viets, 1932
8. *Ljania* Thor, 1898
   Type. *Ljania bipapillata* Thor, 1898
9. *Miraxona* Lundblad, 1936
   a. *Miraxona* s. str.
      Type. *Miraxona clavipes* Lundblad, 1936
   b. *Miraxonella* Lundblad, 1936
      Type. *Miraxona* (*Miraxonella*) *complicata* Lundblad, 1936

10. *Miraxonides* Lundblad, 1938
    Type. *Miraxonides alata* Lundblad, 1938
11. *Neoalbia* Lundblad, 1936
    a. *Neoalbia* s. str.
      Type. *Neoalbia violacea* Lundblad, 1936
    b. *Pentalbia* Lundblad, 1937
      Type. *Neoalbia (Pentalbia) walteri* Lundblad, 1936
12. *Neoaxona* Lundblad, 1936
    a. *Neoaxona* s. str.
      Type. *Neoaxona oblonga* Lundblad, 1936
    b. *Lamellaxona* Lundblad, 1937
      Type. *Neoaxona (Lamellaxona) abnormipes* Lundblad, 1937
13. *Neoaxonopsis* Lundblad, 1938
    Type. *Neoaxonopsis odontogaster* Lundblad, 1938
14. *Neobrachypoda* Koenike, 1914
    Type. *Axonopsis (?) ekmani* Walter, 1911
15. *Submiraxona* Lundblad, 1937
    Type. *Submiraxona crassipes* Lundblad, 1937

Albiinae Viets, 1925

Genera:

1. *Albia* Thon, 1899
    Type. *Albia stationis* Thon, 1899
2. *Parasitalbia* Viets, 1935
    Type. *Parasitalbia sumatrensis* Viets, 1935
3. *Subalbia* Viets, 1913
    Type. *Subalbia proceripalpis* Viets, 1913

Aturinae Wolcott, 1905

Genera and subgenera:

1. *Aturus* Kramer, 1875
    a. *Aturus* s. str.
      Type. *Aturus scaber* Kramer, 1875
    b. *Crinaturus* Thor, 1930
      Type. *Aturus mirabilis* Piersig, 1897
    c. *Subaturus* Viets, 1916
      Type. *Subaturus sulcatus* Viets, 1916
2. *Aturides* Lundblad, 1937
    Type. *Subaturus dentatus* Lundblad, 1936
3. *Hjartdalia* Thor, 1901
    Type. *Hjartdalia runcinata* Thor, 1901
4. *Pseudokongsbergia* Walter, 1935
    Type. *Pseudokongsbergia longipalpis* Walter, 1935

Frontipodopsinae Viets, 1931

Genus:

Frontipodopsis Walter, 1919
Type. *Frontipodopsis staheli* Walter, 1919

Mideidae Viets, 1929

Figures 244, 245

Diagnosis: The mideids have a highly arched body which is armored and has a dorsal suture. The palpal femur and genu are strong while the tibia is thin, narrow, longer than the femur and genu combined, and lacks inner protuberances. The coxal plates are combined in one group; coxal plates I are united medianly and coxal plates IV are tri-

Figure 244 *Midea expansa* Marshall. Ventral plates. (After Marshall 1940)

Figure 245 *Midea expansa* Marshall. Dorsum. (After Marshall 1940)

angular in shape. Legs II, III, and IV have swimming hairs. Tarsi III of the male are clasping organs. The genital indentation is large, reaching to the rear of coxae I; the genital organ is located between coxal plates IV. In the female the genital organ has sickle-like, sucker-bearing plates each with from five to seven pairs of suckers. In the male each plate has five to six pairs of suckers. The genital plates of the male have a three-cornered, movable, sclerotized wing.

Genus:

Midea Bruzel., 1854
Type. *Hydrachna orbiculata* Müller, 1776

Mideopsidae Thor, 1928

Figure 246

Figure 246 *Mideopsella forficicalpis* Lundblad. Venter of female. (After Lundblad 1943)

Diagnosis: The body of these mites is more or less flattened, armored, and has a dorsal suture. Usually the dorsal shield is in one piece. The palpal tibia is shorter than the femur and genu combined and usually has a process on the inner margin, or only spines or small hairs may be present distally. The coxal plates are more or less united into one group. The genital indentation reaches to the posterior end of coxal plates I. Swimming hairs may or may not be present on the legs. Usually found in the indentation formed by coxal plates IV the genital organ has three to five pairs of genital suckers.

Mideopsinae Koenike, 1910

Genera and subgenera:

1. *Mideopsis* Neumann, 1880
   a. *Mideopsis* s. str.
      Type. *Hydrachna orbicularis* Müller, 1776 (= *Mideopsis depressa* Neumann, 1880)
   b. *Neoxystonotus* Lundblad, 1927
      Type. *Mideopsis torrei* Marshall, 1927
   c. *Octomideopsis* Viets, 1931
      Type. *Mideopsis minutus* Soar, 1910
   d. *Paraxystonotus* Lundblad, 1936
      Type. *Xystonotus willmanni* Viets, 1920
   e. *Xystonotus* Wolcott, 1900
      Type. *Xystonotus asper* Wolcott, 1900
2. *Notomideopsis* Wolcott, 1905
   Type. *Mideopsis spinipes* Nordenskiöld, 1904

Djeboinae Viets, 1935

Genus and subgenera:

   Djeboa Viets, 1911
   a. *Djeboa* s. str.
      Type. *Djeboa multidentata* Viets, 1911

b. *Djeboella* Viets, 1935

Type. *Djeboella elongata* Viets, 1935

Momoniinae Viets, 1926

Genera:

1. *Momonia* Halbert, 1906 (= *Kondia* Sokolow, 1926)
    Type. *Momonia falcipalpis* Halbert, 1906
2. *Momoniella* Viets, 1929
    Type. *Momoniella sumatrensis* Viets, 1929

Mideopsellinae Lundblad, 1937

Genus:

Mideopsella Lundblad, 1937

Type. *Mideopsella forcipalpis* Lundblad, 1937

Acalyptonotidae Walter, 1911

Figure 247

Diagnosis: The body of these mites is unarmored dorsally and has no dorsal suture. The palpal tibia is distally, dorso-ventrally broadened; the distal inner edge is elongated and forms a shear with the palpal tarsus. The median suture of the anterior coxal plate group is lacking; the rear group of coxae forms an indentation into which the genital organ fits. There are many suckers on the genital organ.

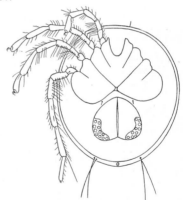

Figure 247 *Acalyptonotus violaceus* Walter. Venter of female. (After Walter 1911)

Genus:

Acalyptonotus Walter, 1911

Type. *Acalyptonotus violaceus* Walter, 1911

A-Thienemanniidae Lundblad, 1930

Figure 248

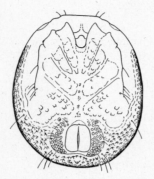

Diagnosis: These mites have an armored body and a dorsal suture. The maxillary organ usually has a short rostrum and the palpal tibia projects ventrally and distally to form a weak shear with the palpal tarsus. The coxal plates have a tendency to grow together. Usually the genital organ lies in the opening in the ventral armor. As a rule genital pads are covered with setae and many genital suckers are present.

Figure 248 *Plaumannia crenophila* Lundblad. Venter of female. (After Lundblad 1936)

A-Thienemanniinae Viets, 1923

Genus:

A-Thienemannia Viets, 1923
Type. *A-Thienemannia schermeri* Viets, 1923

Harpagopalpinae Viets, 1924

Genus:

Harpagopalpus octoporus Viets, 1924

Mundamellinae Viets, 1931

Genera:

1. *Mundamella* Viets, 1913
   Type. *Mundamella germanica* Viets, 1913
2. *Hungarohydracarus* Motas and Tanaschi, 1947
   Type. *Hungarohydracarus subterraneus* Motas and Tanaschi, 1947
3. *Stygohydracarus* Viets, 1931
   Type. *Stygohydracarus troglobius* Viets, 1931

Plaumanniinae Lundblad, 1936

Genus:

Plaumannia Lundblad, 1936
Type. *Plaumannia arrenuripalpis* Lundblad, 1936

Eupatrellidae Viets, 1935

Figures 249, 250

Diagnosis: This family is based on a nymphal form and no diagnosis is given here.

 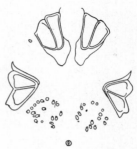

Figure 249 *Eupatrella reticulata* Walter. Palpus of nymph. (After Walter 1935)

Figure 250 *Eupatrella reticulata* Walter. Nymph. (After Walter 1935)

Genus:

Eupatrella Walter, 1935

Type. *Eupatrella reticulata* Walter, 1935 (probably = *Hydryphantes incertus* Koenike, 1893)

Arrenuridae Thor, 1900

Figure 251

Diagnosis: The body is armored and usually has a dorsal suture. On the palpus is a shear formed by the tibia and tarsus. The coxal plates are united with the ventral shield. The genital organ is in the opening in the ventral shield. Genital suckers are numerous, small and pore-like, and more or less growing out of plates. Often the male has an extension on the posterior of the body. Also the genu of leg IV is sexually differentiated.

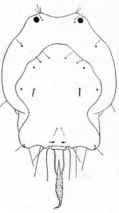

Figure 251 *Arrenurus valencius* Marshall. Dorsum of male. (After Lundblad 1935)

Genera and subgenera:

1. *Arrenurus* Dugès, 1833
   a. *Arrenurus* s. str. (= *Petiolurus* Thon, 1900)
      Type. *Arrenurus viridis* Dugès, 1834
   b. *Megaluracarus* Viets, 1911
      Type. *Hydrachna globator* Müller, 1776
   c. *Micruracarus* Viets, 1911
      Type. *Arrhenurus forpicatus* Neumann, 1880
   d. *Micruracaropsis* Viets, 1939
      Type. *Micruracaropsis phytotelmaticola* Viets, 1939
   e. *Truncaturus* Thor, 1900
      Type. *Arrenurus knauthei* Koenike, 1895
2. *Africasia* Viets, 1931
   Type. *Mundamella arrhenuripalpis* Viets, 1913
3. *Dadayella* Koenike, 1907
   Type. *Arrhenurella minima* Daday, 1905
4. *Rhinophoracarus* Viets, 1916
   Type. *Rhinophoracarus praeacutus* Viets, 1916
5. *Thoracophoracarus* Viets, 1914
   Type. *Thoracophoracarus arrhenuroides* Viets, 1914
6. *Wuria* Viets, 1916
   Type. *Wuria falciseta* Viets, 1916
7. *Wuriella* Viets, 1935
   Type. *Wuriella sumatrensis* Viets, 1935

Krendowskiidae Lundblad, 1930

Figures 252, 253

Diagnosis: Body armored, with dorsal suture, paired lateral eyes in capsules, skin with papillae; short rostrum; palpal tarsus forms a shear. Coxal plates with a tendency to fuse. With immovable genital plates and three to eight pairs of inner genital suckers the genital organ lies in the indentation formed by coxae IV.

Genera and subgenera:

1. *Krendowskia* Piersig, 1895
   a. *Krendowskia* s. str. (= *Arrhenurella* Ribaga, 1902)
      Type. *Krendowskia latissima* Piersig, 1895
   b. *Krendowskiella* Viets, 1931
      Type. *Krendowskia megalopsis* Lundblad, 1930
   c. *Neokrendowskia* Lundblad, 1941
      Type. *Krendowskia* (*Neokrendowskia*) *quadripustulata* Lundblad, 1941

2. *Allokrendowskia* Lundblad, 1941
    Type. *Allokrendowskia dentipes* Lundblad, 1941
3. *Geayia* Thor, 1897
    a. *Geayia* s. str.
        Type. *Geayia venezuelae* Thor, 1897
    b. *Geayella* Lundblad, 1936
        Type. *Geayia (Geayella) catharinensis* Lundblad, 1936
    c. *Geayidea* Lundblad, 1941
        Type. *Geayia coeruleocruciata* Lundblad, 1936
    d. *Pirapama* Viets, 1935
        Type. *Pirapama schubarti* Viets, 1935

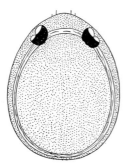 

Figure 252 *Krendowskia megalopsis* Lundblad. Dorsum of female. (After Lundblad 1930)

Figure 253 *Krendowskia megalopsis* Lundblad. Venter of female. (After Lundblad 1930)

4. *Roqueella* Lundblad, 1930
    a. *Roqueella* s. str.
        Type. *Roqueella flabellifera* Lundblad, 1930
    b. *Neoroqueella* Lundblad, 1937
        Type. *Roqueella (Neoroqueella) maculata* Lundblad, 1937
    c. *Pararoqueella* Lundblad, 1937
        Type. *Roqueella (Pararoqueella) striata* Lundblad, 1937

CHAPTER VII

The Suborder Sarcoptiformes Reuter, 1909

STIGMATA are not present but some possess a tracheal system opening through porose areas on various parts of the body. The coxae form apodemes beneath the skin on the venter of the body. The chelicerae are usually scissors-like, for chewing, with strong chelae; a few have specialized or modified chelicerae. The palpi are simple. Pseudostigmatic organs may or may not be present. Anal suckers are often present in the male. ·

The Sarcoptiformes are divided into the Acaridiae and the Oribatei, the former containing the cheese mites, itch mites, and feather mites, and the latter the oribatid mites. Although the two groups can be separated rather easily, their relationship is close and they possess many characters in common, such as body shape in many of the genera, mouth parts for chewing, arrangement of coxal plates, and the Claparède organ which is to be found in larvae of both groups.

Key to the Sarcoptiformes

1. Weak skinned, nonarmored; without pseudostigmata and prominent clublike pseudostigmatic organs (exception: Pediculochelidae); tarsi with caruncles; sexual dimorphism at times strongly marked; many males with copulatory suckers on tarsi or anal region   Acaridiae

   Leather-like or strongly sclerotized; usually, with only a few exceptions, with prominent clublike pseudostigmatic organs; tarsi without caruncles; sexual dimorphism not marked   Oribatei

ACARIDIAE LATREILLE, 1802

The gnathosoma is usually visible from above, rarely being concealed within a camerostome. No stigmata or tracheae are to be found.

320

Pseudostigmatic organs are not present. The body is, as a rule, soft skinned but usually has a dorsal plate or plates. The coxae form characteristic plates. The tarsi usually have a stalked or sessile empodial claw and caruncle, and when without claws the caruncle is bell-like. The palpi are simple, usually with two free, seldom four, movable segments. Sexual dimorphism is marked in some cases. Two pairs of genital suckers are usually present, and the males generally have prominent adanal suckers.

The *Acaridiae* can be divided into the free-living type (Acaridae or cheese mites), the parasitic type (*Sarcoptes* or itch mites), and the feather- or hair-inhabiting type (feather mites) and by certain morphological structures such as skin sclerotization and striations, but actually there are not clear-cut morphological differences to be found here as in the other suborders.

Key to the Acaridiae

1. Body without plates, or with single, lightly sclerotized propodosomal shield (occasionally hysterosomal shield present); legs not modified for clasping hairs; as a whole, free-living mites or skin parasites   2

   Body plates strongly sclerotized, usually with more than one well-defined shield; or legs or maxillae modified for clasping hairs; feather or hair mites   27

2. Hysterosoma not segmented   3

   Hysterosoma divided into four sections by transverse sutures; propodosoma with pair of bladder-like sensory setae; tarsi with caruncles but no claws   Pediculochelidae

3. Chelicerae with opposed chelae, although sometimes minute   4

   Fixed chela reduced, movable chela normally developed   17

4. Caruncle with claws, sometimes very minute (Ensliniellidae and Canestriniidae [1])   5

   Caruncle without claws   19

5. Caruncle sessile and with claw   6

   Caruncle more or less pedunculate, on distal part of which is claw, often minute   8

---

[1] After Vitzthum; Canestriniidae fits in very close to Sarcoptidae; in some cases the claws seem to have disappeared; with different type of caruncles on tarsi.

6. Males with copulatory suckers on tarsi IV and near anal plate (exception: *Caloglyphus anomalus* Nesbitt)   7

   Males without copulatory suckers on tarsi or near anal plate; larvae without "urstigma"; genital opening between coxae IV   Saproglyphidae

7. Body setae of adults long, loose, whiplike; in young stages often stiff, rodlike   Acaridae

   Body setae of adults feathered, pectinate, clublike   Forcelliniidae

8. Skin smooth, fine, not sclerotized   9

   Skin sclerotized, leathery, scaly, not smooth   15

9. Caruncles terminal on all legs   10

   Caruncles of legs I and II which bear terminal claws long, cylindrical, and flexible and placed laterally on clawlike tarsus; tarsi III and IV normal   Hyadesidae

10. Body with suture between propodosoma and hysterosoma   11

    Body without suture; no propodosomal shield; dorsal body setae simple, with two pairs of long posterior setae; epimera of legs I and II united and partially encompassing female genital opening which lies between legs II and III   Carpoglyphidae

11. Without cervical setae; without suckers on tarsus IV or near anal opening in male   12

    With cervical setae; males with suckers on tarsi IV or near anal opening   14

12. No lenslike eyes present in place of cervical setae   13

    Lenslike eye in place of each cervical seta; no propodosomal shield; body with four pairs of long, whiplike setae, two pairs on rear, one on shoulders of hysterosoma and one pair in posterior row of propodosomal setae; genital opening of female between coxae III and IV; male not known   Oulenziidae

13. Female genital opening between coxae III; male genital opening between coxae IV; dorsal setae simple, of medium length; with propodosomal shield   Ensliniellidae

    Female genital opening between coxae III and IV; with propodosomal shield; dorsal body setae as a whole, short; dorsal surface of body very finely wrinkled   Czenspinskiidae

    Female genital opening between coxae IV; with propodosomal shield; dorsal setae simple, of medium length   Winterschmidtiidae

14. Cervical setae marginal, long, pilose; female genital opening between coxae III; male genital opening between coxae IV; tarsal claws in larvae and nymphs single, normal; in adults claws double, Y-shaped or forked on tarsi I and II   Lardoglyphidae

    Cervical setae marginal, minute, almost a curved spine; tarsi I-III each with three spoon-shaped or lanceolate setae; tarsus IV with one such seta; tarsal claws with a ventral knob; body with three pairs of long setae; adults not known, described from nymph

    Olafseniidae

15. Male genital opening between coxae III-IV   16

    Male genital opening between coxae I-II; male with tarsal IV and anal suckers; body acarid-like, but skin well sclerotized; dorsal setae simple, very short; female genital opening between coxae III-IV   Chortoglyphidae

16. Skin dull, or roughened by numerous fine distinct points or scales; body variously shaped; tarsi gradually tapering towards tip, with caruncle, on distal half of which is claw, often minute; clublike sensory setae on tarsi I and II; dorsal setae usually pilose, feathered, or fanlike   Glycyphagidae

    Skin leathery or scaly; body depressed, round or oval, lozenge-shaped or almost quadrangular; tarsi with pedunculate caruncle; claw, which is often minute (and apparently absent at times), wholly involuted in caruncle; tarsi I and II without clublike sensory sestae; dorsal setae simple   Canestriniidae

17. Movable chela sawlike; all legs of more or less equal size and equally developed   18

    Movable chela not sawlike, enclosed in tube formed by palpi; legs I and II with claws but no lobes; legs III and IV enormously developed into clasping organs without claws but with tarsi adapted as claws; found on gills of crab   Ewingidae

18. Distal segment of palpus with two flagella; caruncle with sessile claw   Anoetidae

    Palpus with normal setae; tarsi with caruncles without claws; distal portion of tarsus clawlike   Linobiidae

19. With pair of anterior vertical propodosomal setae   20

    Without vertical setae on propodosoma   21

20. Skin smooth; body segmented between propodosoma and hysterosoma; few long, simple setae; tarsi with sessile caruncles; free-living mites   Nanacaridae

Skin smooth, body segmented between propodosoma and hysterosoma; propodosomal shield present; body setae few, tiny; tarsi with bell-like caruncles on long stalks; free-living mites

Hemisarcoptidae

Skin with strong transverse striations; body without suture between propodosoma and hysterosoma; caruncles stalked, on short legs; skin parasites

Sarcoptidae

21. Mouth parts well developed, chelicerae chelate for chewing   22

Mouth parts reduced, specialized into sucking tube; small, hairless mite; tarsi with caruncles but without claws; in air sacks of chickens and lung tissue of squirrels

Cytoditidae

22. Legs ɪ and ɪɪ with caruncles   23

Legs ɪ and ɪɪ without caruncles but tarsi divided into clawlike points; tarsi ɪɪɪ and ɪᴠ with caruncles; elongated mite; in subcutaneous tissues of fowl

Laminosioptidae

23. Caruncle or adhesive lobes on short or long stalks; caruncle of normal size or even smaller, never greatly enlarged   24

Caruncle not stalked, of monstrous size; tarsi ɪɪɪ and ɪᴠ with three ventral, clawlike spines pointing to rear; on skin of small birds

Heteropsoridae

24. Tarsi ɪ with caruncles   25

Tarsi ɪ without caruncles and shaped like anchor; with propodosomal shield; no suture between propodosoma and hysterosoma; legs on anterior portion of body; tarsi ɪɪ, ɪɪɪ, and ɪᴠ without claw but with adhesive lobe

Myialgesidae

25. Caruncles on all legs of females   26

Tarsi ɪɪɪ of females ending in long whiplike setae; posterior margin of male bilobate; usually skin parasites of mammals   Psoroptidae

26. Small mites with propodosomal shield; female rounded; male bilobate on rear; larvae and nymphs with caruncles on all legs (?)

Epidermoptidae

Small mites with propodosomal shield; female rounded; male bilobate on rear; larvae and nymphs with caruncles on legs ɪ and ɪɪ only   Psoralgidae

27. Maxillae and legs normal, not modified for clasping hair   28

Maxillae or one or more pairs of legs modified into clasping organs for grasping hairs of host   Listrophoridae

28. Legs ı and ıı normal, segments cylindrical, without spinelike projections 29

   Legs ı and ıı with sharp latero-ventral projections on segments
   Analgesidae

29. Rear of hysterosoma of both sexes rounded or slightly bilobate
   Dermoglyphidae

   Rear of hysterosoma of female and often of male tapering, strongly bilobate
   Proctophyllodidae

Pediculochelidae Lavoipierre, 1946

Figure 254

Diagnosis: The pediculochelids are tiny, whitish mites measuring from 0.184 to 0.24 mm. in length. Their skin is soft, striated, and without plates. Separated from the propodosoma by a distinct suture, the hysterosoma is divided by three dorsal, transverse sutures. The

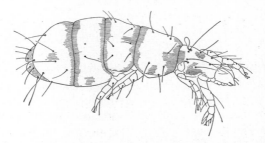

Figure 254 *Pediculochelus raulti* Lavoipierre. Dorsal view of female.

propodosoma lacks eyes, but has several long, whiplike setae and a pair of dorsal clavate sensory setae. A pair of vertical setae is also present. The chelicerae are large and have strong, opposed chelae for chewing or crushing as in the oribatid mites. The palpus is four-segmented, simple, and has few setae. The legs are relatively weak and the tarsi lack claws but have a sucker-like caruncle on a pedicle. The anal opening is on the rear and there are two pairs of genital suckers.

Genus:

   Pediculochelus Lavoipierre, 1946
   Type. *Pediculochelus raulti* Lavoipierre, 1946

Discussion: Lavoipierre 1946 found the only known species, *Pediculochelus raulti* Lavoipierre, associated with bees at Durban, Natal, South Africa; a single specimen was collected on a rat in Florida during an ectoparasitic survey of rats in that region, and specimens have been found on *Gallus gallus* on the island of Samar in the Philippines. The body is segmented and the general appearance is that of a primitive type of acarid-like mite which is perhaps an intermediate form between these and the oribatids. This would indicate a more or less general acarid habitat. Because of their minute size the mites have probably been overlooked up to the present time.

Reference:

Lavoipierre, M. 1946. A new acarine parasite of bees. Nature 158 (4004):
    130, 131.

Saproglyphidae Oudemans, 1924

Figure 255

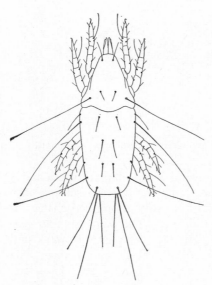

Diagnosis: It is possible that these mites do not have any propodosomal shield. Their skin is smooth. The propodosoma and hysterosoma are separated by a suture. A transverse row of four setae is situated on the rear of the propodosoma, the inner pair being considerably shorter than the outer. A pair of vertical setae are also present and the marginal setae of the body are very long and whiplike. All tarsi have a claw and caruncle. The female genital opening lies between coxae III and IV while the male genital opening is between coxae IV. In the male there are no adanal copulatory suckers and no suckers on tarsi IV.

Figure 255 *Saproglyphus neglectus*
Berlese. Dorsal view of female.
(After Berlese 1890)

Genus:

Saproglyphus Berlese, 1890
Type. *Saproglyphus neglectus* Berlese, 1890

Discussion: *Saproglyphus neglectus* Berlese was collected on rotting shelf fungus, *Polyporus hispidus,* in Italy; *S. cocciphagus* Womersley, 1941 was found in gall on tree-lucerne in New South Wales, Australia.

References:

Berlese, A. 1890. Acari, Myriopoda et Scorpiones Crypt. Fasc. LXXXIX, No. 11; Fasc. LVII, No. 6.
Womersley, H. 1941. Studies in Australian acarina (2) Tyroglyphidae (s.l.) Rec. South Austral. Mus. VI(4): 451–488.

Acaridae Ewing and Nesbitt, 1942
(= Tyroglyphidae Donnadieu, 1868)

Figures 256–262

Diagnosis: [1]   The body of these mites is distinctly divided into a proterosoma and hysterosoma by a transverse groove. The body is stout, white, or fawn and the integument is usually smooth and shiny, rarely rough. The chelicerae are chelate. Five pairs of setae are found on the propodosoma: (i) rostral setae; (ii) Grandjean's organ in Acarinae = nuchal setae in Rhizoglyphinae; (iii) cervical bristles; (iv) outer propodosomatic setae; (v) inner propodosomatic setae (a reduction in the number of these setae is to be found in the genera *Thyreophagus* and *Histiogaster*). Usually the anterior part of the propodosoma is covered by a shield. In all genera a pseudostigmatic organ is present. The male and female genital opening is between

Figure 256 *Rhizoglyphus echinopus* (Fumouze and Robin). Ventral view of larva. Note Claparède's organ or urstigma on coxa I.

coxae III and IV. Two distinct copulatory suckers are located on either side of the male anus. Epimera I is united to the sternum but all others are free. All coxae except IV bear a spine on the ventral surface. The tarsi may be longer than the tibia plus the genu. Tarsus I bears: (i) macrosense seta with a microsense seta before it at its base; (ii) sub-

1 After Nesbitt 1945.

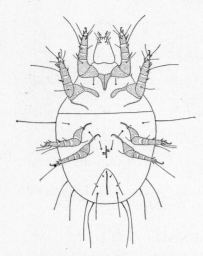

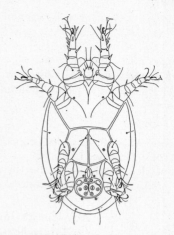

Figure 257 *Rhizoglyphus echinopus*
(Fumouze and Robin). Ventral view
of protonymph.

Figure 258 *Rhizoglyphus echinopus*
(Fumouze and Robin). Ventral view
of hypopus.

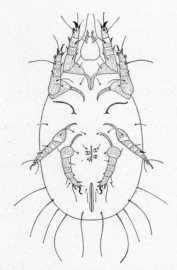

Figure 259 *Rhizoglyphus echinopus*
(Fumouze and Robin). Ventral view
of deutonymph.

Figure 260 *Rhizoglyphus echinopus*
(Fumouze and Robin). Ventral view
of male.

328

basal seta with the occasional addition of a parasub-basal seta; (iii) a group of four median setae; (iv) a ventral-terminal group of three to five spines; (v) a dorsal-terminal group of four long setae that may be modified; (vi) a claw surrounded by a caruncle that is never pedunculate. Tarsus II bears a macrosense seta but does not have either a microsense seta or a parasub-basal seta. Tarsus III in heteromorphic

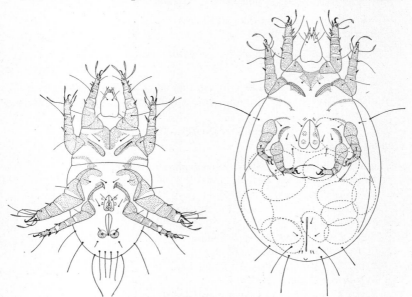

Figure 261 *Rhizoglyphus echinopus* (Fumouze and Robin). Ventral view of heteromorphic male.

Figure 262 *Rhizoglyphus echinopus* (Fumouze and Robin). Ventral view of gravid female.

males is modified as a large claw. Tarsus IV in the female bears two lateral spines; in the male these are replaced by two suckers, except in the genus *Thyreophagus* where there is only one. In the more primitive members of the group the tarsal setae are thin, slight hairs; in the more advanced members they become modified as large spines. Larvae have a well-developed, cylindrical, or pin-shaped "Bruststiele" (urstigmata).

Key to the Acaridae

1. Without sexual dimorphism; inner propodosomal setae as long as or longer than outer; legs slender with hairlike setae, lateral and mesial median setae of tarsi unmodified; microsense and macrosense setae not arising from same base   Acarinae

Frequently with well-developed sexual dimorphism; inner propodosomal setae shorter than outer; legs stout, the setae in many
cases being modified as stout spines; microsense and macrosense
setae arising from same base   Rhizoglyphinae

Nesbitt 1950 has placed the Pontoppidanidae as a subfamily of the
Acaridae and separates them thus:

Nuchal setae thin, rootlike structures adhering closely against the
lateral wall of the body   Acarinae

Nuchal setae distinct hornlike processes standing free of body
                                                 Rhizoglyphinae

Nuchal setae distinct, heavily pectinated processes standing free
of body and readily visible in dorsal mounts   Pontoppidaniinae

Acarinae Nesbitt, 1945
Genera and subgenera:

1. *Acarus* Linnaeus, 1758 (= *Tyroglyphus* Latreille, 1796)
   Type. *Acarus siro* Linnaeus, 1758
2. *Aleuroglyphus* Zakhvatkin, 1940
   Type. *Tyroglyphus ovatus* Troupeau, 1879
3. *Ebertia* Oudemans, 1924
   Type. *Tyroglyphus australis* Oudemans, 1917
4. *Podoglyphus* Oudemans, 1937
   Type. *Glyciphagus buski* Murray, 1877
5. *Tyrolichus* Oudemans, 1924
   Type. *Tyrolichus casei* Oudemans, 1910
6. *Tyrophagus* Oudemans, 1924 (= *Coelognathus* v. Heffling, 1852)
   a. *Tyrophagus* s. str.
      Type. *Acarus putrescentiae* Schrank, 1781
   b. *Tyroborus* Oudemans, 1924
      Type. *Tyroborus lini* Oudemans, 1924
   c. *Povelsenia* Oudemans, 1924
      Type. *Tyroglyphus neotropicus* Oudemans, 1917

Rhizoglyphinae Zakhvatkin, 1941
Genera and subgenera:

1. *Rhizoglyphus* Claparede, 1869
   Type. *Tyroglyphus echinopus* Fumouze and Robin, 1868
2. *Caloglyphus* Berlese, 1923 (? = *Achropodophorus* Rosas Costa,
   1927)
   Subgenera of *Caloglyphus* after Vitzthum

a. *Caloglyphus* s. str.
   Type. *Tyroglyphus berlesei* Michael, 1903 (= *Tyroglyphus myco-phagus* Berlese, 1891, *sed non* Mégnin, 1874)
b. *Pachyglyphus* Berlese, 1923
   Type. *Tyroglyphus pergandis* Berlese, 1920
c. *Lagenoglyphus* Berlese, 1923
   Type. *Tyroglyphus lamermanni* Berlese, 1923?
d. *Isoglyphus* Zakhvatkin, 1937
   Type. *Isoglyphus sphaerogaster* Zakhvatkin, 1937
3. *Ceroglyphus* Vitzthum, 1919 (= *Petzschia* Oudemans, 1923)
   Type. *Ceroglyphus monstruosus* Vitzthum, 1919
4. *Eberhardia* Oudemans, 1924 (= *Acotyledon* Oudemans, 1903)
   a. *Eberhardia* s. str.
      Type. *Eberhardia michaeli* Oudemans, 1924 (= *Rhizoglyphus agilis* Michael, 1903)
   b. *Cosmoglyphus* Oudemans, 1932
      Type. *Tyroglyphus kramerii* Berlese, 1881
5. *Froriepia* Vitzthum, 1919—deutonymph
   Type. *Froriepia vimariensis* Vitzthum, 1919
6. *Garsaultia* Oudemans, 1916—deutonymph
   Type. *Garsaultia testudo* Oudemans, 1916
7. *Histiogaster* Berlese, 1883
   Type. *Tyroglyphus carpio* Kramer, 1882
8. *Megninietta* Jacot, 1936
   Type. *Megninietta ulmi* Jacot, 1936
9. *Mycetoglyphus* Oudemans, 1932
   Type. *Mycetoglyphus fungivorus* Oudemans, 1932
10. *Myrmoglyphus* Vitzthum, 1935—deutonymph
    Type. *Myrmoglyphus bipilis* Vitzthum, 1935
11. *Sancassania* Oudemans, 1916—deutonymph
    Type. *Sancassania chelone* Oudemans, 1916
12. *Schwiebea* Oudemans, 1916
    Type. *Schwiebea talpa* Oudemans, 1916
13. *Stereoglyphus* Berlese, 1923
    Type. *Stereoglyphus haemisphaericus* Berlese, 1923
14. *Suidasia* Oudemans, 1905 (= *Aphelenia* Oudemans, 1923)
    Type. *Suidasia pontifica* Oudemans, 1905
    (Nesbitt did not place this genus in with the Acaridae but left it dangling; however, it is placed here following Vitzthum's list.)
15. *Thyreophagus* Rondani, 1874 (= *Monieziella* Berlese, 1897)
    Type. *Acarus entomophagus* Laboulbéne, 1852
16. *Tyroglyphopsis* Vitzthum, 1926—deutonymph
    Type. *Tyroglyphopsis ocellata* Vitzthum, 1926

17. *Valmontia* Oudemans, 1923
     Type. *Valmontia mira* Oudemans, 1923
18. *Viedebanttia* Oudemans, 1929—deutonymph
     Type. *Viedebanttia schmitzi* Oudemans, 1929

Pontoppidaniinae Oudemans, 1925

Genera:

1. *Pontoppidania* Oudemans, 1923
    Type. *Tyroglyphus littoralis* Halbert, 1920
2. *Calvolia* Oudemans, 1911
    Type. *Calvolia hagensis* Oudemans, 1911 (= *Tyroglyphus heterocomus* Michael, 1913, hypopus)
3. *Diphtheroglyphus* Nesbitt, 1950
    Type. *Diphtheroglyphus maculata* Nesbitt, 1950

Discussion:

The members of the family Acaridae are notable for the extent of their distribution. They are found in all types of habitat from Arctic tundra to tropical rain forests and wherever man in his wanderings has taken mites in his food and produce. Living on all kinds of organic substances, these creatures are commonly found infesting such materials as preserved meats, cured and raw hides, organic powders, seeds, and farinaceous products. In stored grains they cause great economic loss not so much by what they eat (although populations of astronomical figures are found at times) as by the damage that they cause by changing the moisture content of the medium and initiating the growth of moulds. In the state of nature they are usually found on rotting leaves and plant debris, on the bark of trees, on decaying bulbs and tubers, on fresh and putrid mushrooms, and in the nests of mammals and birds, where presumably they live on organic wastes and bits of hair and feathers. In speaking of ecological niches it is interesting to note that, even as the family may be divided taxonomically into two quite distinct subfamilies on morphological grounds, it may also be separated into the same two subfamilies on the basis of the type of habitat preferred. Almost without exception the members of the one group prefer to live in substances having a low moisture content (20 to 30 per cent), viz., wheat, seeds, and stored farinaceous products, whereas the members of the other group can exist only in a very humid habitat, many seeming to prefer a place where they are wading in a film of water. As a result of these studies, I am persuaded that the members of the former group can, and do, eat the more solid organic substances such as the germ and endosperm of seeds, whilst those of the latter group live fairly exclusively on the fungi and moulds growing on the excessively damp substratum that they prefer. Furthermore, many eat dead and decaying insects, the caloglyphids being the most notable example. Apart from a few species of the genus *Thyreophagus,* which live on oyster-shell scale and kindred insects, none of the family appears to be either a predator or a parasite. As yet no fossil records have been found of either the Acaridae or their immediate progenitors, but this is not to be wondered at, as they are extremely small creatures, which do not lend themselves to easy fossilization.[1]

The life cycle of the mite may be summarized briefly as follows, *Rhizoglyphus echinopus* (Fumouze and Robin) being used as an example. Garman 1937 found that at a room temperature of 60°-75° F. (68° average) the mite went through its life cycle in seventeen to twenty-seven days; and that at 70°-80° F. its life cycle was completed in nine to thirteen days. The mite becomes torpid at 55°-50° in the lower temperature range and at about 95° in the upper extreme. The mite needs a rather high humidity. Garman lists the stages as follows (between each stage, except egg and larva, the mite becomes quiescent).

A. Cycle in which the hypopial stage (second nymph) is omitted
    Egg—larva—first nymph—third nymph
            adult female
            normal male
            heteromorphic male

B. Cycle with hypopial stage (second nymph)
    Egg—larva—first nymph—hypopus—third nymph
            adult female
            normal male
            heteromorphic male

Many of the Acaridae have a hypopial or "wandernymph" stage in which the mite changes into a small creature with suckers or claspers for grasping insects for dispersal, and at times they have been mistaken for parasites. Apparently the mites can withstand dryness best in this stage. The hypopus of one species has even been taken from the gill chambers of a mollusk and another from the gonads of a millipede. Whereas the length of the hypopal stage is from five to thirteen days, the other stages are from three to eight days or less. The hypopi then develop into nymphs which may produce any type of adult. Michael 1901 found hypopi of various acarids produced under several conditions and could describe no reason for their development. Garman

[1] From Nesbitt 1945.

1937, on the other hand, found that *Rhizoglyphus echinopus* (Fumouze and Robin) produced most hypopi under wet, sticky conditions. This has also been observed in species of *Histiostoma* and *Caloglyphus*.

The heteromorphic male is to be found in various genera of the Acaridae, and that of *Rhizoglyphus echinopus* is shown in Figure 261. With some species it is rarely found, but with *R. echinopus* as high as 20 per cent of the males may be heteromorphic. They may be easily distinguished by the enlarged third pair of legs. These males breed with the females and produce both types of males as well as females. The normal male, mated with a female, will also produce the same type of offspring.

Rhizoglyphus echinopus (Fumouze and Robin), the well-known bulb mite, is cosmopolitan in distribution and may be found in bulbs of amaryllis, crocus, Easter lily, gladiola, hyacinth, narcissus, and tulip. It can probably feed on most tubers, especially those which have loose scales permitting the entry of the mite. Shipments are usually infested with this mite, which may destroy as high as 15 to 20 per cent of the bulbs. However, the rotted area is not always due to the mite but can be caused by other factors. In the field the mite apparently does little damage to healthy plants, affecting only rotted bulbs, but if the mites become established in stored bulbs they appear to hasten decay. Although it usually feeds on rotted or decayed tissue the mite can infest healthy tissue if in contact with it. This indicates the necessity of eliminating rotten, infested bulbs to prevent the spread of the mite in storehouses. The mites probably carry fungus and bacterial diseases with them externally.

Tyrophagus lintneri (Osborne)[1] is a widely distributed pest, serious in stored foods, and at one time on cultivated mushrooms. The mites eat the spawn and make holes in the stems and caps of the mushrooms and can seriously hinder mushroom culture if not controlled (Davis 1944). It is to be found in greasy soda fountains and in cupboards wherever food is available.

Thyreophagus entomophagus Laboulbène has been found associated with dried insects in collections and with scale insects in the field. Although occasionally reported as being predaceous on the scale insects they actually live on the cast skins and dead scales, which must be slightly moist. In brief, it can be said that this mite lives on dried ani-

---

1 *Caloglyphus* sp. has displaced *Tyrophagus lintneri* in mushroom houses in Maryland and Pennsylvania within the last few years.

mal and vegetable matter. It appears to be cosmopolitan in distribution.

Acarus siro Linneaus is a destructive cosmopolitan species found in grain and flour, as well as in cheese, dried fruits, and vegetables. The mite actually eats the grain, leaving only the husk. The male is easily distinguished by a large, toothlike projection on femur i.

Tyrophagus longior (Gervais) is another well-known European species and has been taken occasionally in America. Michael 1903 says that an entire haystack in Ireland was practically destroyed by these mites, and at times countless millions of them may be on hay and fodder. It also infests foodstuffs. This mite has been found in human feces, and their presence in the intestinal tract causes pain, nausea, vomiting, and diarrhea. The mites are finally passed. The patient must have a constant supply of mites on food or the symptoms disappear. Oviposition and hatching take place in the intestine but the completion of the life cycle is doubtful. Hinman and Kampmeier 1934 also report cases from literature of infestation of the urogenital system, probably from contaminated catheters.

Van den Bruel 1940 reports *Tyrophagus dimidiatus* (Hermann) injuring spinach in unheated greenhouses in Belgium. The value of the crop was reduced 80 per cent. Blades of the inner leaves were very short, crumpled, and deformed. The petioles were normal. The epidermis was at times perforated with small holes surrounded by a corky tissue. The leaves finally turned black. The damage was attributed to this mite which was present in large numbers and was brought in on manure. Similar damage has been reported from spinach fields in the eastern United States, the same mite species being present.

Tyrophagus castellanii (Hirst) causes the "copra itch" of handlers of that product. Sigrianskii 1940 also reports *Tyrophagus castellanii* (Hirst) as feeding on spores of *Tilletia tritici* and transmitting these spores to healthy wheat on their body and hairs. Mites that fed on onions infected with *Botrytis allii* transmitted the spores to healthy onions. They were also able to transmit a virus disease from infected to healthy potatoes.

A mite, *Caloglyphus julidicolus* Lawrence (hypopus), was taken on the gonads of a South African millipede and is found only on the males. Lawrence 1939 states that it must have entered through "the narrow opening between the apices of the gonopods and their surrounding membranous sheath, passing upward and slightly forward for a distance of about 5 mm. before arriving at the final place of attachment to the bases of the gonopods. The mites appear to have sought out the most sheltered parts of the sex organs of the host."

Halbert 1920 gives the following information on *Pontoppidania littoralis* (Halbert): "Two females and a male found in moist decaying seaweed amongst shingle close to the harbour at Howth, Co. Dublin. The locality is slightly above high-water mark, and evidently within reach of high tides, September, 1918." *Calvolia hagensis* Oudemans hypopus is peculiar in that it possesses a pair of large, lenslike eyes near the anterior end of the body. *Diphtheroglyphus maculata* Nesbitt were taken from salted steer hides, Buenos Aires, Argentina.

References:

André, M. 1931. Acariens nuisables aux produits pharmaceutiques. Assoc. Franç pour l'Avanc. des Sci., pp. 395–399.

——. 1935. Acariens infestant les milieux de culture dans les laboratoires. Assoc. Franç pour l'Avanc. des Sci., pp. 469–471.

Davis, A. C. 1944. The mushroom mite [*Tyrophagus lintneri* (Osborne)] as a pest of cultivated mushrooms. U. S. Dept. Agr. Tech. Bull. 879.

Ewing, H. E., and H. H. J. Nesbitt. 1942. Some notes on the taxonomy of grain mites (Acarina: Acaridae, formerly Tyroglyphidae). Proc. Biol. Soc. Wash. 55: 121–124.

Grandjean, F. 1937. Sur quelques caracteres des Acaridiae libres. Bull. Soc. Zool. France. 62 (6): 388–398.

Halbert, J. N. 1920. The Acarina of the seashore. Proc. Roy. Irish Acad., 35, Sect. B, No. 7: 106–152, Pls. 21–23.

Hinman, E. H., and R. H. Kampmeier. 1934. Intestinal Acariasis due to *Tyroglyphus longior* Gervais. Amer. J. Trop. Med. 14 (4): 355–362.

Hughes, A. M. 1948. The mites associated with stored food products. Ministry of Agriculture and Fisheries, London, pp. 1–168.

Nesbitt, H. H. J. 1945. A revision of the family Acaridae (Tyroglyphidae), order Acari, based on comparative morphological studies. Canad. J. Res., D, 23: 139–188.

——. 1950. On a new Argentinian mite, *Diphtheroglyphus maculata* n. sp., n. gen., and the taxonomic position of the family Pontoppidanidae Oudms. 1925. Can. Ent. 82 (10): 211–216.

Snyder, W. C., and H. N. Hansen. 1946. Control of culture mites by cigarette paper barriers. Mycologia 38 (4): 455–462.

Solomon, M. E. 1943. Tyroglyphid mites in stored products. 1. A survey of published information. Dept. of Scientific and Industrial Research. London. pp. 1–36.

——. 1944. Tyroglyphid mites in stored products. 1. A survey of published information. Supplement, 1944. Dept. of Scientific and Industrial Research. London, pp. 1–7.

——. 1945. Tyroglyphid mites in stored products. Methods for the study of population density. Ann. Appl. Biol. 32 (1):71–75.

——. 1946. Tyroglyphid mites in stored products. Nature and amount of damage to wheat. Ann. Appl. Biol. 33 (3): 280–289.

——. 1946. Tyroglyphid mites in stored products. Ecological Studies. Ann. Appl. Biol. 33 (1): 82–97.

Van den Bruel, W. E. 1940. Un ravageur de l'epinard d'hiver: *Tyroglyphus dimidiatus* Herm. (*longior* Gerv.). Bull. Inst. Agron. Gembloux 9 (1–4): 81–99.

Zakhvatkin, A. A. 1940. Key to mites injuring stores of agricultural products in U.S.S.R. (in Russian). Uchenye Zapiski Mosk. Godudarst Univ. No. 42, 2 Vol., pp. 7–68.

Forcelliniidae Oudemans, 1927

Figures 263, 264

Diagnosis: These mites have a propodosomal shield and a shiny, smooth (?) skin. On the posterior part of the propodosoma is a transverse row of four setae, the inner pair being somewhat shorter than the outer. The body setae are mostly rodlike or narrow, clublike, and feathered. Cervical setae are dorsal, feathered, comblike, and placed in a line with trochanter I. A pair of vertical setae are also present. The female genital opening lies between coxae III and IV while the male genital opening is between coxae IV. The male has adanal copulatory suckers and two suckers on tarsi IV. They have not been found since the original descriptions and consequently detailed knowledge of their structure is not known.

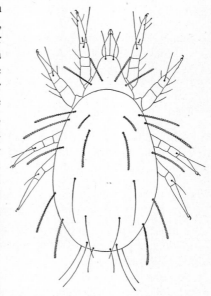

Figure 263 *Forcellinia wasmanni* (Moniez). Dorsal view of female. (After Michael 1903)

Acarology

Genera:

1. *Forcellinia* Oudemans, 1924
   Type. *Tyroglyphus wasmanni* Moniez, 1892
2. *Scatoglyphus* Berlese, 1913
   Type. *Scatoglyphus polytrematus* Berlese, 1913

Discussion: Forcellinia wasmanni (Moniez) was described from ants' nests and is European in distribution. All stages of the mite are to be found in the nests. According to information from Michael 1903 the mites often appear to increase in great numbers in nests and the hypopi adhere to the ants in such quantities that they cause the death of the ant. Fifty to a thousand mites may be found attached to one ant. They

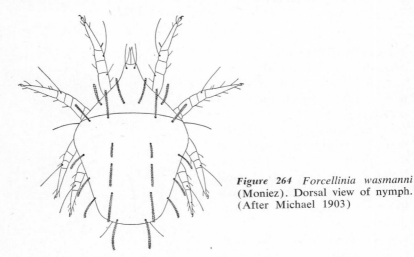

Figure 264 *Forcellinia wasmanni* (Moniez). Dorsal view of nymph. (After Michael 1903)

are most numerous on the head, abdomen, and legs; only a few are found on the thorax. The hypopi are supposed to attach themselves in the direction of the long axis of the segment they are on, their anterior end being directed toward the point of the segment.

Scatoglyphus polytrematus Berlese was found in fowl excrement with other acarids.

References:

Berlese, A. 1913. Acari Nuovi. Redia 9: 77–105.
Michael, A. D. 1903. British Tyroglyphidae 2: 131–136.

Hyadesidae Halbert, 1915
Figures 265, 266

Diagnosis: Strongly arched dorsally the body of these mites is plump. The propodosoma and hysterosoma are separated by a suture. A pair of vertical setae are present and a delicate propodosomal shield may also be present. The skin is otherwise soft, with very fine striae. The chelicerae are normal. Tarsi I and II in both sexes are in shape of a large claw, with an accessory claw on the inside; the extremely long

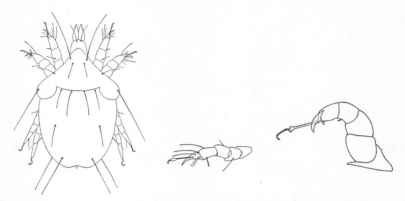

Figure 265 *Hyadesia algivorans* (Michael). Dorsal view of female. (After Michael 1901)

Figure 266 Left, leg I of *Hyadesia algivorans* (Michael). (After Michael 1901); right, leg I of *Hyadesia fusca* Lohman. (After André 1931)

stalk of the small caruncle, which carries distally the very small, true claw, is attached at the base of the accessory claw. Tarsi III and IV of the female have one large claw on a short stalk; in the male the large claw sits on a longer stalk. There is slight sexual dimorphism. Both male and female genital openings are at a considerable distance behind coxae IV. There are no genital suckers nor does the male have adanal copulatory suckers.

Genus:

Hyadesia Mégnin, 1889 (= *Lentungula* Michael, 1893)
Type. *Hyadesia uncinifer* Mégnin, 1889

Discussion: These mites are found in the tidal zone, on sea algae. Michael 1901 reports finding large numbers of *Hyadesia algivorans*

(Michael) in a patch of green alga "growing where the fresh water of a small stream trickled over the face of the granite cliffs within reach of the spray of the sea, near Lands' End, Cornwall." Michael says these mites are not swimmers but "crawlers, frequenting algae and stones in shallow water, or even left dry between tides, or living in places where fresh water trickling over rock becomes mixed with salt spray, and the growth of green algae takes place; but they are evidently capable of living comfortably under water." Halbert 1920 found *Hyadesia fusca* (Lohmann) "in numbers at edges of rock crevices in the Pelvetia and Spiralis zones at Malahide, June 1916. In the same locality it was found fairly common in rock-pools containing much *Enteromopha,* in the Orange Lichen zone, July and September. First recorded as a British species from Clare Island, where it is abundant amongst coralline seaweeds in rock-pools. Lohmann gives its distribution as the North Sea and the Baltic." *Hyadesia uncinifer* Mégnin has been reported as being semiaquatic in Tierra del Fuego, South America. The four known species are: *uncinifer* Mégnin, *algivorans* (*Michael*), *fusca* (Lohmann), and *kerguelenensis* Lohmann.

References:

André, M. 1931. Sur le genre *Hyadesia* Mégnin 1889 (Sarcoptides hydrophiles). Bull. Paris, Mus. d'Hist. Nat., Ser. 2, 3 (6): 496–506.

Halbert, J. N. 1915. Acarinida: II. Terrestrial and Marine Acarina. Clare Island Survey, 31 (39), Section II, pp. 45–136, Pls. 4–8.

———. 1920. The Acarina of the sea-shore. Proc. Roy. Irish Acad. 35, Sect. B, pp. 106–152.

Michael, A. D. 1901. British Tyroglyphidae 1: 200.

Carpoglyphidae Oudemans, 1923

Figure 267

Diagnosis: These mites have a skin which is smooth but not shiny. They may have a propodosomal shield (*Carpoglyphus*) or be armored and lack a specially circumscribed propodosomal shield (*Ferminia*). A pair of vertical setae is present and the propodosoma and hysterosoma are not separated by a suture. All tarsi have stalked claws and caruncles. The female genital opening reaches anteriorly to the medianly united apodemes of coxae II; the male genital opening lies between coxae IV (*Carpoglyphus*), or behind coxae IV (*Ferminia*). The male lacks adanal genital suckers and suckers on tarsi IV.

Genera:

1. *Carpoglyphus* Robin, 1869
   Type. *Acarus lactis* Linnaeus, 1758 (= *Carpoglyphus anonymus*
   Haller, 1882 = *C. passulorum* Robin, 1869)
2. *Ferminia* Oudemans, 1928
   Type. *Glycyphagus fuscus* Oudemans, 1902

Discussion: Carpoglyphus lactis (Linnaeus) is a widely distributed species to be found on dried fruits, milk products, glucose, decaying potatoes, flour, and many other food products. It has been recorded as breeding in large numbers inside bottles of wine in Paris, maintaining itself on floating pieces of cork and drawing nourishment from the wine. *Carpoglyphus alienus* Banks, 1904 was found in urine of a patient with a kidney disease. Each time the patient passed urine these mites were found surrounded by purulent matter. The location of the type of the mite is not known and consequently the exact taxonomic status of the species cannot be determined but the figure indicates a true *Carpoglyphus*. The habitat suggests that of *Dermatophagoides takeuchii* Sasa.

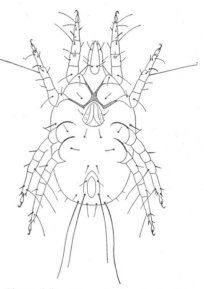

Figure 267 *Carpoglyphus lactis* (Linnaeus). Venter of female.

References:

André, M. 1931. Presence d'Acariens dans les vins sucres. Bull. Soc. Zool.
de France 56: 335–340.

Banks, N. 1904. An alleged parasitic Tyroglyphid. Proc. Ent. Soc. Wash.
8 (1): 40–42.

Michael, A. D. 1903. British Tyroglyphidae, Vol. 2.

Oudemans, A. C. 1926. Krit. hist. Overz. Acarol., I. Tijdschr. v. Entom.,
LXIX, Suppl., pp. 218, 225.

Oulenziidae Oudemans, 1928

Figure 268

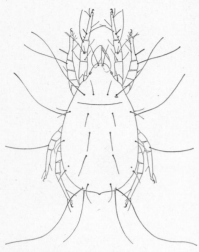

Diagnosis: The oulenziids have a propodosomal shield which is not strongly sclerotized as in some groups. Their skin is wrinkled. On the rear of the propodosoma lies a transverse row of four setae, the inner pair being much shorter than the outer. In place of the cervical seta on each side of propodosoma is a lenslike eye. A pair of vertical setae are present. The female genital opening is situated between coxae III and IV. All tarsi are slender, with stalked claws and caruncles and with minute spines. Males are not known.

Figure 268   *Oulenzia arboricola* (Oudemans). Dorsum of female. Note eyes on lateral margins of propodosoma.

Genus:

Oulenzia Radford, 1950 (= *Lenzia* Oudemans, 1928, *nom. praeocc.*)
Type. *Lenzia arboricola* Oudemans, 1928

Discussion: This mite, the only known species, was found on leaves of *Hevea* in Sumatra; specimens were also collected on jute in India. Like *Czenspinskia* it is probably a vegetable feeder.

References:

Oudemans, A. C. 1928. Acarologische aanteekeningen XCI. Lenziidae, n. fam. Ent. Ber. 7(161): 327, 328.
Radford, C. D. 1950. Systematic check list of mite genera and type species. Union Internat. des Sci. Biol., Ser. C (Sec. Ent.) 1: 152.

Ensliniellidae Vitzthum, 1924

Figures 269–271

Diagnosis: These mites have a propodosomal shield, and a shiny, smooth skin. On the rear of the propodosoma is a transverse row of four setae, the inner pair being either of the same length as the outer (*Ensliniella*) or much shorter (*Riemia*). There are no cervical setae but a pair of vertical setae is present. The tarsi have stalked claws and caruncles. The female genital opening is found between coxae III and IV while the male genital opening is between coxae IV. Males do not have adanal copulatory suckers or suckers on tarsi IV.

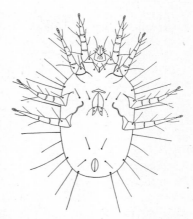

Figure 269 *Ensliniella parasitica* Vitzthum. Venter of female. (After Vitzthum 1925)

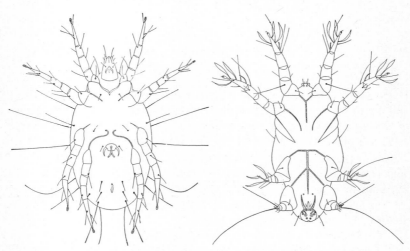

Figure 270 *Ensliniella parasitica* Vitzthum. Venter of male. (After Vitzthum 1925)

Figure 271 *Ensliniella parasitica* Vitzthum. Venter of hypopial nymph. (After Vitzthum 1925)

Genera:
1. *Ensliniella* Vitzthum, 1925
    Type. *Ensliniella parasitica* Vitzthum, 1925
2. *Horstia* Oudemans, 1905
    Type. *Trichotarsus ornatus* Oudemans, 1899
3. *Mantidoglyphus* Vitzthum, 1940
    Type. *Mantidoglyphus anastati* Vitzthum, 1940
4. *Riemia* Oudemans, 1925
    Type. *Riemia hesperidum* Oudemans, 1925
5. *Tortonia* Oudemans, 1911
    Type. *Trichotarsus intermedius* Oudemans, 1901
6. *Vidia* Oudemans, 1905
    Type. *Vidia undulata* Oudemans, 1905

Discussion: This is another little-known family. *Ensliniella parasitica* Vitzthum was collected on the resting larvae (Ruhelarve) of *Odynerus* (*Lionotus*) *delphinalis* Giraud, family Vespidae, Hymenoptera, in Germany; and *Vidia undulata* Oudemans was taken from *Prosopis conformis* Foerst., family Colletidae, Hymenoptera, in Italy.

Reference:

Vitzthum, H. 1925. Eine neue Milbengattung und-art als Parasit von *Odynerus* (*Lionotus*) *delphinalis* Giraud 1866. Deut. Ent. Ztschr., Heft IV: 289–305.

Czenspinskiidae Oudemans, 1927

Figure 272

Diagnosis: A propodosomal shield is present, and the skin is shiny and finely striated. On the rear of the propodosoma is a transverse row of four setae, the inner pair much shorter than the outer. No cervical setae are present but a pair of vertical setae is present. All tarsi have stalked claws and caruncles are long, slender, and have minute spines. The female genital opening lies between coxae III and IV. Males are not known.

Genus:

Czenspinskia Oudemans, 1927 (= *Donndorfia* Oudemans, 1931)
Type. *Tyroglyphus heterocomus* Michael, 1903 (adults)

Discussion: *Czenspinskia heterocomus* (Michael) was beaten off oak trees in Hampshire, England, and was also taken in considerable numbers in the moss of a squirrel's summer nest. Michael 1903 reared a great many by feeding them pieces of fungus. *Czenspinskia lordi* Nesbitt 1946 was found on apple trees in Nova Scotia. They live in colonies near the midribs of the leaves, feeding on vegetable matter and apparently overwintering beneath lichens and old oyster-shell scales. No males have been found and the mite apparently reproduces parthenogenetically.

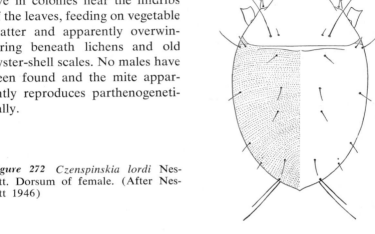

Figure 272 *Czenspinskia lordi* Nesbitt. Dorsum of female. (After Nesbitt 1946)

References:

Michael, A. D. 1903. British Tyroglyphidae 2: 106–109, Pl. 33.
Nesbitt, H. H. 1946. Three new mites from Nova Scotian apple trees. Canad. Ent. 78: 15–22.

Winterschmidtiidae Oudemans, 1923

Figures 273, 274

Diagnosis: These mites have a propodosomal shield and a shiny skin. On the posterior part of the propodosoma is a transverse row of four setae of equal length. No cervical setae are present, but a pair of vertical setae is present. The legs are short and robust. All tarsi have stalked claws and caruncles. Ventro-distally the tarsi have one, and terminally two very strong spines (especially on tarsi I and II). Male and female genital openings are between coxae IV. The male does not have adanal suckers or suckers on tarsi IV but does have a latero-ventral sucker on tarsus I.

Genus:

Winterschmidtia Oudemans, 1923
Type. *Suidasia* (?) *hamadryas* Vitzthum, 1923

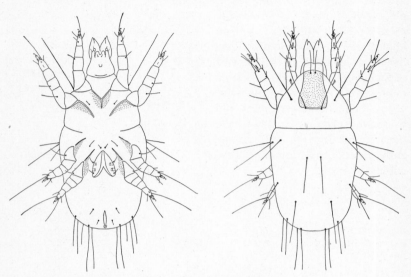

Figure 273 *Winterschmidtia hamadryas* (Vitzthum). Venter of female. (After Vitzthum 1923)

Figure 274 *Winterschmidtia hamadryas* (Vitzthum). Dorsum of female. (After Vitzthum 1923)

Discussion: *Winterschmidtia hamadryas* (Vitzthum) was found in the passageways of *Eccoptogaster rugulosus* Ratz. in *Prunus insititia,* Germany. *W. crassisetosa* Willmann was taken from larvae and pupae of a scolytid, *Phloeotribus scarabaeoides,* Italy. This suggests that related species and genera should be found in bark beetle tunnels. To date very little has been done on the study of mites in such habitats.

References:

Vitzthum, H. 1923. Acarologische Beobachtungen 7. Reihe. Arch. f. Naturgesch., Abt. A, Hft. 2: 97–181.
Willmann, C. 1939. *Winterschmidtia crassisetosa* spec. nov. (Winterschmidtiidae, Acari). Boll. Lab. Zool. Generale e Agraria della Facolta Agraria in Portici, 31: 65–68.

Lardoglyphidae Oudemans, 1927

Figures 275, 276 [1]

Diagnosis: These mites have propodosomal shield and a shiny skin. The body setae are smooth, a pair of vertical setae is present and the cervical setae are feathered. The tarsi have stalked claws and suckers. In the immature stages the claws are normal. Claws of the male on tarsi I and II and those of the female on all tarsi are Y-shaped and

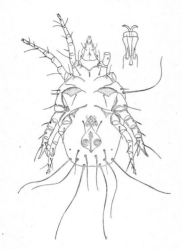 

Figure 275 *Lardoglyphus zacheri* Oudemans. Ventral view of male and of tarsus I. (After Oudemans unpublished)

Figure 276 *Lardoglyphus zacheri* Oudemans. Ventral view of female and tarsus I. (After Oudemans unpublished)

forked. Tarsus III of the male is forked but does not have a claw. The female genital opening lies between coxae III while the male genital opening is between coxae IV. Males have adanal copulatory suckers and two suckers on tarsi IV.

Genus:

    Lardoglyphus Oudemans, 1927
    Type. *Lardoglyphus zacheri* Oudemans, 1927

[1] Our sincere thanks to D. Boschna and Mr. Hammen of the Rijksmuseum van Natuurlijke Historie, Leiden, Holland, for permission to use these unpublished figures of Oudemans.

Acarology

Discussion: Oudemans published very little on this group, apparently giving just enough information to include the mite in his key.

Reference:

Oudemans, A. C. 1927. Acarologische aanteekeningen LXXXVI. Ent. Ber. 7: 242–248.

Olafseniidae Oudemans, 1927

Figure 277

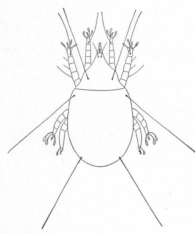

Diagnosis: This family is known only from the homeomorphic nymph. It (according to Vitzthum) is probably without a propodosomatic shield and has a smooth skin. On the posterior part of the propodosoma is a transverse row of two very long setae. There is also a pair of long setae on the shoulder and posterior of the hysterosoma. A pair of vertical setae is present as are marginal cervical setae which are weak and in the form of a bent spine. All tarsi have lancelike or spoonlike "adhesive" setae. The tarsi have unsegmented claws and caruncles and the claws have a knoblike swelling on the venter. Epimera I form a Y.

Figure 277   *Olafsenia trifolium* (Oudemans). Dorsum of nymph. (After Oudemans 1901)

Genus:

Olafsenia Oudemans, 1924
Type. *Tyroglyphus trifolium* Oudemans, 1901

Discussion: The single species, *Olafsenia trifolium* (Oudemans), a nymph, was collected from *Heliocopris bucephalus* from Java.

Reference:

Oudemans, A. C. 1901. Notes on Acari. Third series. Tijd. Dierkundige Ver., Ser. 2, 50–88.

Chortoglyphidae Berlese, 1897

Figures 278–280

Diagnosis: The body of these mites is oval and there is no suture between the propodosoma and the hysterosoma. The skin is hard, smooth, and shiny. The dorsal setae are smooth and short (with the exception of the setae scapulares internae in *Fusacarus*). A pair of vertical setae are present. The chelicerae are normal, scissor-shaped, or chelate. All tarsi have caruncles and tarsal claws are inserted into the anterior or distal portions of the caruncles. The female genital opening lies between coxae III and IV while the male genital opening is between coxae I and II.

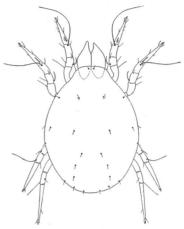

Figure 278 *Chortoglyphus arcuatus* (Troupeau). Dorsum of female. (After Zakhvatkin 1940)

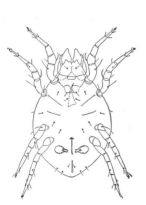

Figure 279 *Chortoglyphus arcuatus* (Troupeau). Venter of male. (After Zakhvatkin 1940)

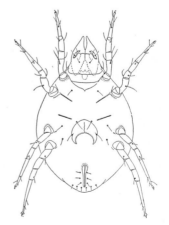

Figure 280 *Chortoglyphus arcuatus* (Troupeau). Venter of female. (After Zakhvatkin 1940)

Genera:

1. *Chortoglyphus* Berlese, 1884
   Type. *Tyroglyphus arcuatus* Troupeau, 1879
   (= *Chortoglyphus nudus* Berlese, 1884)
2. *Fusacarus* Michael, 1903
   Type. *Fusacarus laminipes* Michael, 1903

Discussion: *Chortoglyphus arcuatus* (Troupeau) has been recorded by Michael 1903 as being found on the floors and beams of an old barn and from an old stable in England, from stables and hay in Italy, as well as on rabbit excrement, on flour in France, in debris in freighters, and in a poultry house in Massachusetts. *Fusacarus laminipes* Michael has been taken from moles' nests (but not upon the mole) by Michael in England.

References:

Michael, A. D. 1903. British Tyroglyphidae 2: 1–12, Pls. XX, XXI.
Zakhvatkin, A. A. 1940. Key to mites injuring stores of agricultural products in U.S.S.R. (In Russian). Uchenye Zapiski Mosk. Godudarst Univ. No. 42 Zool.: 7–68.

Glycyphagidae Berlese, 1887

Figures 281–284

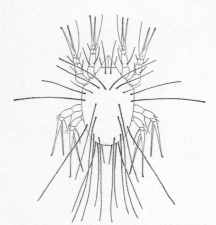

Diagnosis: Rather broad in body, these mites usually do not have a suture between the propodosoma and the hysterosoma. A pair of vertical setae are present. The

Figure 281 *Glycyphagus geniculatus* Vitzthum. Dorsum of female. (After Vitzthum 1931)

Figure 282 *Glycyphagus domesticus* (DeGeer). Hypopial stage. (After Hughes and Hughes 1938)

skin is smooth but not shiny or rough because of fine granulations or punctures. Dorsal setae are usually pilose, feathered, or fan-shaped. The chelicerae are normal and scissor-like. All tarsi are uniformly pointed distally and have caruncles. On the anterior or distal part of the caruncle is a tiny claw or sometimes a very large empodial claw.

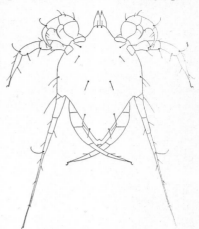

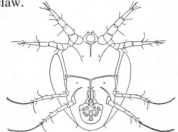

Figure 283 *Fusohericia incredibilis* Vitzthum. Hypopial stage. (After Vitzthum 1931)

Figure 284 *Fusohericia incredibilis* Vitzthum. Dorsum of female. (After Vitzthum 1931)

Genera and subgenera:

1. *Glycyphagus* Hering, 1838
    a. *Glycyphagus* s. str.
        Type. *Glycyphagus prunorum* Hering, 1838
    b. *Oudemansium* Zakhvatkin, 1936
        Type. *Acarus domesticus* DeGeer, 1771
2. *Blomia* Oudemans, 1928
    Type. *Glycyphagus tjibodas* Oudemans, 1910
3. *Cerophagus* Oudemans, 1902
    Type. *Cerophagus bomborum* Oudemans, 1902
4. *Chaetodactylus* Rondani, 1866 (= *Trichotarsus* Canestrini, 1888)
    Type. *Trichodactylus osmiae* Dufour, 1839
5. *Cometacarus* Zakhvatkin, 1936
    Type. *Cometacarus smirnovi* Zakhvatkin, 1936 (deutonymph)
6. *Crastidoglyphus* Oudemans, 1937
    Type. *Acarus hyalinus* Koch, 1841
7. *Ctenoglyphus* Berlese, 1928
    Type. *Glycyphagus canestrinii* Armanelli, 1887 (= *Acarus plumiger* Koch, 1835)
8. *Dermacarus* Haller, 1878
    Type. *Homopus sciurinus* Koch, 1842

9. *Fusohericia* Vitzthum, 1931
   Type. *Fusohericia incredibilis* Vitzthum, 1931
10. *Gohiera* Oudemans, 1938
    Type. *Glycyphagus fuscus* Oudemans, 1903
11. *Hericia* Canestrini, 1888
    Type. *Glycyphagus hericius* Robin, 1868
12. *Labidophorus* Kramer, 1877
    Type. *Labidophorus talpae* Kramer, 1877
13. *Lepidoglyphus* Zakhvatkin, 1936
    Type. *Acarus destructor* Schrank, 1781 (= *A. cadaverum* Schrank, 1781)
14. *Melisia* Lombardini, 1944
    Type. *Melisia melisii* Lombardini, 1944
15. *Sennertia* Oudemans, 1905
    Type. *Pediculus cerambycinus* Scopoli, 1763
16. *Stroemia* Oudemans, 1923
    Type. *Dermacarus cantharobius* Oudemans, 1905

Discussion: The genus *Glycyphagus* is best known. *G. domesticus* (DeGeer) is found in dried fruits and organic matter such as skin and feathers, and is often found in enormous numbers in homes and stores. *G. domesticus* causes the "grocers' itch" when highly infested material is handled. *Lepidoglyphus destructor* (Schrank) (known in literature as *Glycyphagus destructor* or *cadaverum*) damages certain seeds in storage, lowering the germination of the seed. The seeds of Italian rye grass and Kentucky blue grass are susceptible to mite injury. In other seeds, damage is done to the already broken kernels, and as quoted from Prescott 1933 "the mites live essentially on broken grains, glumes, and other inert matter in the sample, and only, in certain cases, are they capable of attacking sound germinable grains to such an extent as to have any injurious effects on these grains." Joyeux and Baer 1945 report *Glycyphagus domesticus* (DeGeer) as the intermediate host of *Catenotaemia pusilla* (Goeze), a cestode parasite of rodents. This is an interesting observation in view of the role the related oribatid mites play to the sheep tapeworm, *Moniezia expansa* (Rudolphi).

Hughes and Hughes (1938) 1939, have published on the anatomy and post-embryonic development of *Glycyphagus domesticus* (DeGeer). There is an egg, a larval, and a protonymphal stage; at the end of the protonymphal stage the nymph may pass into the resting stage to give rise to an active deutonymph, or it may pass into an hypopial stage, remaining surrounded by the cast skin of the protonymph. This hypopial stage may rest as long as six months before giving rise to the active deutonymph. Michael 1901 states that the hypopus of *G. spinipes* (Koch), however, is fully formed and capable of moving its legs but is not able to walk. In the Acaridae, for example, the hypopi are active and usually attach themselves on some insect or large mite and are carried about. In no case, however, does the hypopus feed. The deutonymph is very similar to the adult into which it changes after a short resting period.

References:

André, M. 1941. Invasions de Glycyphages (Acariens). Bull. Soc. Zool. de France 66:142–148.

Hughes, T. E., and A. M. Hughes. 1939 (1938). The internal anatomy and post-embryonic development of *Glycyphagus domesticus* (DeGeer). Proc. Zool. Soc. London, Ser. B, 108(4):714–733.

Joyeux, Ch., and G. Baer. 1945. Morphologie, évolution et position systématique de *Catenotaenia pusilla* (Goeze, 1782), Cestode parasite de Rongeurs. Rev. Suisse de Zool. 52(2):13–51.

Prescott, R. T. M. 1933. Mites in seeds. J. Victoria Dept. Agr. (10):519–523.

Canestriniidae Berlese, 1884

Figure 285

Diagnosis: The body of these mites is hardly longer than it is wide and may be flattened, round or oval, pentagonal or diamond-shaped. The skin is either leathery or scaly. A pair of vertical setae is present, and the chelicerae are normal and scissor-shaped. The tarsal claws are frequently tiny and are completely wrapped up with the stalked caruncles. No olfactory, rodlike sensory setae are found on tarsi ɪ and ɪɪ. There are two pairs of genital suckers. Males may or may not have adanal copulatory suckers.

Genera:

1. *Canestrinia* Berlese, 1881
   Type. *Canestrinia dorcicola* Berlese, 1881
2. *Acrotacarus* Banks, 1915
   Type. *Acrotacarus mirabilis* Banks, 1915
3. *Amansia* Oudemans, 1937
   Type. *Dermaleichus chrysomelinus* Koch, 1841
4. *Canestriniella* Berlese, 1910
   Type. *Canestriniella amplexans* Berlese, 1910

5. *Caraboecius* Cooreman, 1950
   Type. *Caraboecius coriacei* Cooreman, 1950
6. *Coleoglyphus* Berlese, 1910
   Type. *Coleoglyphus fuscipes* Berlese, 1910
7. *Coleopterophagus* Berlese, 1882
   Type. *Dermoglyphus megninii* Berlese, 1881
8. *Dicanestrinia* Berlese, 1911
   Type. *Dermaleichus cerambycis* G. Canestrini, 1878
9. *Grandiella* Lombardini, 1938
   Type. *Grandiella tetracaudata* Lombardini, 1938
10. *Megacanestrinia* Trägårdh, 1906
    Type. *Megacanestrinia mucronata* Trägårdh, 1906
11. *Paramansia* Cooreman, 1950
    Type. *Paramansia menthastri* Cooreman, 1950
12. *Percanestrinia* Berlese, 1911
    Type. *Alloptes blaptis* Canestrini and Berlese, 1880
13. *Photia* Oudemans, 1904 (= *Eucanestrinia* Berlese, 1911)
    Type. *Canestrinia procrustidis* Berlese, 1881
14. *Procericola* Cooreman, 1950
    Type. *Procericola ichthyoides* Cooreman, 1950
15. *Pseudamansia* Cooreman, 1950
    Type. *Dermaleichus chrysomelinus* Koch, 1841
16. *Rosensteinia* Oudemans, 1923
    Type. *Rosensteinia sieversi* Oudemans, 1923

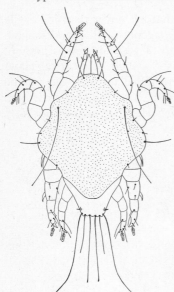

Discussion: Canestrinia dorcicola Berlese was taken from *Dorcus parallelepipedus* (L.), family Lucanidae, Coleoptera, Italy; *Coleopterophagus megninii* (Berlese) has been collected from under elytra of various species of *Cetonia,* Italy; *Photia procrustidis* (Berlese) was collected from under the elytra of *Procrustes coriacei* (L.), family Passalidae, Coleoptera; and *Grandiella tetracaudata* Lombardini was found on *Phanaeus* species, family Scarabaeidae, Coleoptera, Brazil.

Figure 285 Grandiella escaudata Lombardini. Dorsum of female. (After Lombardini 1938)

References:

Cooreman, J. 1950. Étude de quelques Canestriniidae (Acari) vivant sur des Chrysomelidae et sur des Carabidae (Insecta Coleoptera). Bull. Inst. Roy. Sci. Nat. de Belgique 26(33):1–54.

Lombardini, G. 1938. Acari Novi II. Mem. Soc. Ent. Ital. 17:118–120.

———. (1943) 1944. Acari. Un Nuovo Genere della famiglia "Tyroglyphidae." Redia 30:1–24.

———. 1950. Canestriniidae dell'America del Sud (Acarina). Arthropoda 1(2/4):279–290.

Hemisarcoptidae Oudemans, 1908

Figure 286

Diagnosis: Measuring about 0.23 to 0.34 mm. in length, these mites have an egg-shaped body. Their skin is smooth, shiny, and they have a propodosomal shield. Vertical setae are present. The chelicerae are normal, scissor-shaped, but not denticulate. The legs are short and robust. All tarsi lack claws, but the tip of the tarsus has two strong clawlike spines, with the long stalk of the bell-shaped caruncle attached between them. There is no sexual dimorphism. Male and female genital openings are far behind coxae IV. Two pairs of genital suckers are present. Males lack adanal copulatory suckers. Tarsi III and IV each have a long whiplike seta.

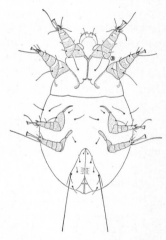

Figure 286 *Hemisarcoptes malus* (Shimer). Venter of female.

Genus:

Hemisarcoptes Ligniéres, 1893
Type. *Acarus malus* Shimer, 1868 (= *Hemisarcoptes coccisugus* Ligniéres, 1893)

Discussion: Hemisarcoptes malus (Shimer), the only species in the family, is widely distributed and is to be found associated with scale insects. It feeds upon the eggs or the scale itself and at times is nu-

merous enough to be of material importance in reducing the population. It has been found preying on many species, among which are the
following:

Lepidosaphes ficus (Sign.), on fig, California
L. ulmi L., in France, Germany, Pennsylvania, and eastern Canada
L. becki (Newman), on citrus, California
Parlatoria oleae, on olive, California
Aspidiotus latanae, in insectaries, California
Diaspis carueli Targ., on cypress, Bermuda
Aonidiella perniciosa Comstock, in France
Chionaspis salicis L., in Germany

The eggs of *Lepidosaphes* appear to be the favorite food. Tothill 1918
studied the mite and found it "perhaps even more useful than has been
supposed." In certain areas of eastern Canada he found the oyster-
shell scale controlled by the mite. He states: "It at least seems certain
that when the scale is abundant this mite is the most important single
factor operating toward control in eastern Canada. In places where
the host is less abundant, the mite becomes proportionately less efficient." *Hemisarcoptes malus* (Shimer) was found attacking the latana
scale, *Aspidiotus latanae* being reared in the insectary of the Citrus
Experiment Station, Riverside, California, for parasite studies. Correspondence from B. Bartlett and P. DeBach stated that the work on
rearing was being disrupted by this mite.

References:

André, M. 1942. Sur l'Hemisarcoptes malus Shimer (= coccisugus
    Lignières) (Acariens). Bull. Paris Mus. d'Hist. Nat., Ser. 2, 14(3):
    173–180.
Ewing, H. E., and R. L. Webster. 1912. Mites associated with the oyster-
    shell scale (*Lepidosaphes ulmi* Linne) Psyche 19:121.
Lord, F. T. 1947. The influence of spray programs on the fauna of apple
    orchards in Nova Scotia: II. Oyster-shell scale. Canad. Ent. 79(11,
    12):196–209.
Shimer, H. 1868. Notes on the apple bark-louse (*Lepidosaphes conchi-
    formis,* Gmelin sp.), with a description of a supposed new *Acarus.*
    Trans. Amer. Ent. Soc. 1:368.
Tothill, J. D. 1918. The predaceous mite, *Hemisarcoptes malus* Shimer,
    and its relation to the natural control of the oyster-shell scale, *Lepi-
    dosaphes ulmi* L. Agr. Gaz. Canada 5(3):234–239.

Ewingidae Pearse, 1929

Figure 287

Diagnosis: The body of the ewingids is egg-shaped and has a few setae. Vertical setae are present. On the rear of the pro-podosoma is a transverse row of two long setae. No suture separates the propodo-soma and the hysterosoma. There is one pair of long setae on the anterior portion of the hysterosoma; few other minute body setae are present. The two-segmented palpi appear to form a tube enclosing the deformed chelicerae, which are not chelate but have only the movable chela remain-ing. Tarsi I and II have claws but lack caruncles; legs III and IV are enormously thickened and transformed into clasping organs without tarsal claws but with tarsi adapted as claws. The genital opening lies between coxae III and IV and has (?) two pairs of genital suckers.

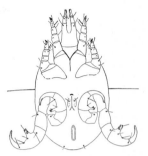

Figure 287 *Ewingia cenobitae* Pearse. Venter of female. (After Pearse 1929)

Genus:

> *Ewingia* Pearse, 1929
> Type. *Ewingia cenobitae* Pearse, 1929

Discussion: *Ewingia cenobitae* Pearse is to be found in the gills of the land hermit crab, *Cenobita diogenes* (Latreille), at Loggerhead, Dry Tortugas, Florida. The mites cling near the outside of the gills by means of the clasping adaptations of legs III and IV and the body lies between the gill lamellae. Eggs containing fully developed larvae apparently ready to hatch have been seen within several of the females. The larvae possess six legs and are similar to the adults. Pearse also examined the ghost crab, *Ocypoda albicans* (Bosc.), but found no mites. This may be due to the fact that these crabs often visit the ocean to bathe their gills, whereas the hosts of the mite visit the ocean only once each year to hatch their young.

Reference:

Pearse, A. S. 1929. Two new mites from the gills of land crabs. Carnegie Inst. Wash. Publ. 391:225–230.

Anoetidae Oudemans, 1904

Figures 288, 289

Diagnosis: The shape of the body is often distorted by large protuberances. A suture may or may not be found between the propodosoma and the hysterosoma. Also a propodosomal shield may or may

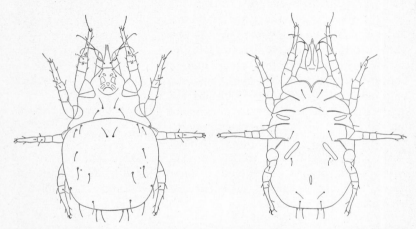

Figure 288 *Histiostoma humidiatus* (Vitzthum). Dorsum of female. (After Vitzthum 1927)

Figure 289 *Histiostoma humidiatus* (Vitzthum). Venter of female. (After Vitzthum 1927)

not be present. Both vertical and cervical setae are found. The skin is usually smooth, but occasionally it may be strewn with tiny points. The chelicerae have only one sawlike chela (an exception is *Cederhjelmia* which has the two sawlike chelae), and the palpal tarsus has two conspicuous, laterally projecting structures. All tarsi have slightly curved, unstalked claws but lack caruncles. Adults usually have four large organs in the shape of a ring or shoe located in the region of the coxae. Only the deutonymph possesses two pairs of genital suckers.

Genera:

1. *Anoetus* Dujardin, 1842 (= *Nodipalpus* Karpelles, 1893)
   Type. *Hypopus alicola* Dujardin, 1849 (= *Anoetus discrepans* Oudemans, 1903)
2. *Anoetoglyphus* Vitzthum, 1927
   Type. *Anoetoglyphus ateuchi* Vitzthum, 1927

3. *Cederhjelmia* Oudemans, 1931
   Type. *Cederhjelmia quadriuncinata* Oudemans, 1931
4. *Chiropteranoetus* Womersley, 1942
   Type. *Chiropteranoetus chalinolobus* Womersley, 1942
5. *Creutzeria* Oudemans, 1932
   Type. *Creutzeria tobaica* Oudemans, 1932
6. *Glyphanoetus* Oudemans, 1929
   Type. *Glyphanoetus fulmeki* Oudemans, 1929
7. *Histiostoma* Kramer, 1876 (= *Zschachia* Oudemans, 1929)
   Type. *Hypopus feroniarum* Dufour, 1839 (= *Tyroglyphus rostroser-ratus* Mégnin = *Histiostoma pectineum* Kramer, 1876)
8. *Mauduytia* Oudemans, 1929
   Type. *Anoetus tropicus* Oudemans, 1911
9. *Myianoetus* Oudemans, 1929
   Type. *Acarus muscarum* Linnaeus, 1758
10. *Prowichmannia* Radford, 1950 (= *Wichmannia* Oudemans, 1929, *nom. praeocc.*)
    Type. *Histiostoma spiniferum* Michael, 1901
11. *Sellea* Oudemans, 1929
    Type. *Histiostoma pulchrum* Kramer, 1886
12. *Zwickia* Oudemans, 1924
    Type. *Anoetus guentheri* Oudemans, 1915

Discussion: The Anoetidae are usually to be found in damp places such as in the sap of trees around wounds, in rotten damp fungi, in *Drosophila* cultures, in rotting potatoes, and in similar habitats. The deutonymphs, hypopial forms, or travelers are to be found on insects. One of our most common species is *Histiostoma feroniarum* (Dufour). Michael 1901 gives the following information under habitat. "Mégnin found the species originally wading in great quantities in the thin film of liquid which covers decaying mushrooms. It is hardly an exaggeration to say that it may be found on all kinds of damp, decaying, soft vegetation which has substantial thickness; it is perhaps most abundant on fungi and roots, but it is very generally distributed; it is extremely abundant. The species has been recorded in France, Germany, Italy, and Switzerland; it is found in all parts of England. It is, I think, a follower, not an initiator of decay." The life cycle of *Zwickia guentheri* Oudemans is well illustrated in Vitzthum 1931; the larval, protonymphal, deutonymphal (hypopial or traveling stage), tritonymphal, and adult (male and female) stages are represented. Womersley 1941 gives a key to the genera of the Anoetidae based upon the deutonymphs.

References:

Cooreman, J. 1941. Études Biospéologiques. XXVIII (1). Note sur *Myianoetus diadematus* Willmann, 1937 (Acariens, Sarcoptiformes) Pseudoparasite des Helomyzidae (Diptères) de Transylvanie. Bull. Musée Royal d'Hist. Nat. Brussels 17(42):1–16.

——. 1947. Le stade adulte de *Myianoetus muscarum* (Linne). Bull. et Ann. Soc. Ent. de Belg. 73:141–149.

Hughes, R. D. 1950. The genetics laboratory mite *Histiostoma laboratorium*, n. sp. (Anoetidae). J. Wash. Acad. Sci. 40(6):177–182.

Michael, A. D. 1901. British Tyroglyphidae 1.

Vitzthum, H. 1931. Terrestrische Acarinen der Deutschen Limnologischen Sunda-Expedition. Suppl. Bd. IX "Tropische Binnengewässer. Arch. f. Hydrobiol. Band II: 59–134.

Womersley, H. 1941. Studies in Australian Acarina (2) Tyroglyphidae (s.l.). Rec. South Austral. Mus. 6(4):451–488.

Linobiidae Oudemans, 1908

Figures 290, 291

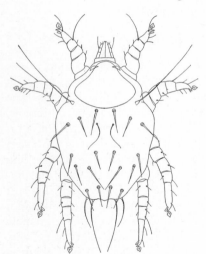

Diagnosis: The body of these mites is broadly oval or pentagonal and there are no vertical setae and no propodosomal shield. The skin is otherwise smooth. The chelicerae have only a sawlike, movable chela. All tarsi are clawlike but lack claws and have stalked caruncles. There are no rodlike sensory setae on tarsi I and II. Two pairs of genital suckers are present. The males lack copulatory suckers.

Figure 290 *Linobia coccinellae* (Scopoli). Dorsum of female. (After Berlese 1887)

Figure 291 *Linobia coccinellae* (Scopoli). Chelicera. (After Berlese 1887)

Genus:

    Linobia Berlese, 1884 (= *Linocoptes* Berlese, 1887)
    Type. *Acarus coccinellae* Scopoli, 1763

Discussion: The only known species, *Linobia coccinellae* (Scopoli), has been taken from under the elytra of *Melasoma populi* in Italy.

Reference:

Berlese, A. 1887. Acari, Myriopoda et Scorpiones, Crypt. Fasc. XXXIX, No. 7.

Nanacaridae Oudemans, 1923

Figures 292, 293

Diagnosis: These mites have a shiny skin and possibly no propodosomal shield. On the posterior part of the propodosoma is a cross row of four setae, the inner pair being much shorter than the outer.

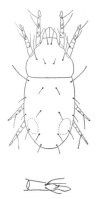
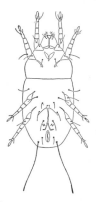

Figure 292 *Nanacarus minutus* (Oudemans). Dorsum of female; tarsus II of female. (After Oudemans 1928)

Figure 293 *Nanacarus minutus* (Oudemans). Venter of female. (After Oudemans 1928)

There are no cervical setae, but a pair of vertical setae is present. Male and female genital openings are behind coxae IV. The males have adanal copulatory suckers but do not have suckers on tarsi IV. All tarsi have only a caruncle and no claws (in the immature stage there is a weakly developed claw). The tarsal tip is pointed, clawlike, and curved; legs without long, whiplike setae.

Genera:

1. *Nanacarus* Oudemans, 1902 (= *Froweinia* Oudemans, 1923)
   Type. *Hypopus minutus* Oudemans, 1902
2. *Giardius* Perraud, 1896
   Type. *Giardius vitis* Perraud, 1896

Discussion: *Nanacarus minutus* (Oudemans) has been taken on *Megapodius buruensis,* Buru Islands; on *Koptorthosoma tenuiscapa,* Java; and on *Vesperugo serotinus, Vespertilio pipistrellus,* and *Sorex vulgaris, Germany.* This species and *Giardius vitis* Perraud are the only two known in this family.

Sarcoptidae Trouessart, 1892

(= Acaridae Oudemans, 1904 of European workers)

Figures 294, 295

Diagnosis: The sarcoptids are skin parasites of warm-blooded animals. Their body shape is globose and there is no distinct suture be-

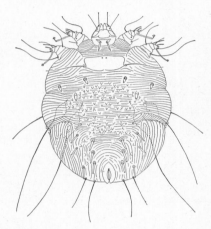

Figure 294 *Notoedres cati* (Hering). Tarsus I. (After Grandjean 1938)

Figure 295 *Sarcoptes scabiei* var. *equi* (Gerlach). Dorsum of female. (After Hirst 1922)

tween the propodosoma and hysterosoma. A propodosomal shield may or may not be present. There is a pair of vertical setae on the propodosoma. In other areas the skin has fine striae which are often interrupted by scaly areas or by areas strewn with small points or spines. The legs are very short and may or may not have caruncles· or claws. No genital suckers are present.

Genera:

   1. *Sarcoptes* Latreille, 1802 (= *Acarus* of Vitzthum)
      Type. *Acarus scabiei* DeGeer, 1778

2. *Knemidokoptes* Fürstenburg, 1870 (= our *Cnemidocoptes*)
   Type. *Sarcoptes mutans* Robin and Lanquetin, 1859
3. *Notoedres* Railliet. 1893
   Type. *Sarcoptes cati* Hering, 1838 (= *Sarcoptes minor* var. *cati* Railliet, 1893)
4. *Nycteridocoptes* Oudemans, 1897
   Type. *Nycteridocoptes poppei* Oudemans, 1897
5. *Prosopodectes* Canestrini, 1897
   Type. *Sarcoptes chiropteralis* Trouessart, 1896
6. *Teincoptes* Rodheim, 1923
   Type. *Teinocoptes epomorphi* Rodheim, 1923
7. *Trixacarus* Sellnick, 1944
   Type. *Trixacarus diversus* Sellnick, 1944

Discussion: The *Sarcoptes scabiei* of man and other animals such as dogs, cattle, pigs, sheep, goats, camels, rabbits, and horses are morphologically alike but probably consist of biological races. The species from horse, for example, can attack man but will not usually produce a permanent infestation.

Mellanby 1943 has presented an excellent review of the scabies mite in England from which most of the following account is taken.[1] The life cycle is very simple, consisting of egg, larva, nymph, male adult, immature, and mature female. The transformation of the immature female to the ovigerous female probably takes place after fertilization. A new victim is successfully infected in all probability by newly fertilized females which can move rapidly on warm skin. The mite takes about one hour to bury itself into the horny layer of skin and goes no deeper. The burrowing is accomplished by the suckers adhering to the skin and the legs and mouth parts cutting into the host. The mature female usually stays in the burrow her entire life. She may remain in the burrow for three weeks and then leave, apparently of her own accord. The mite begins egg-laying within a few hours after starting her burrow, laying eggs at two- to three-day intervals for about two months, stringing the eggs out behind her as she lengthens her burrow. In the thick, horny layer the mite does not raise a lump but in the thinner skin the mite raises a tiny lump. Eggs may hatch in three to eight days at 35° C., although usually it takes about five days. The larvae leave the burrows and move about on the skin looking for shelter and probably food. Larvae and nymphs are to be

---

[1] I am indebted to G. W. Eddy for reviewing this section and adding his own observations made on "self-infection" with gravid female mites.

found in the skin follicles. The adult male or immature female emerges within four to six days after the egg hatches. The male, which is rare, is found in a short burrow where it remains for a brief period, since it spends a considerable time on the skin surface searching for unfertilized females. Although the unfertilized female makes a small burrow it stays in it for only a day or so. Mating probably takes place on the skin. The cycle from egg to ovigerous female takes from ten to fourteen days. Less than 10 per cent of the eggs give rise to adults. Movement or burrowing usually follows egg deposition.

The mites cause severe itching which keeps the patient awake at night. Itching is associated directly with burrowing; each time the mites irritated the skin or caused itching they were found to be moving on. There is a characteristic rash, due both to the mite and to scratching. Erythematous patches and follicular papules appear in areas under the arms, around the waist, on the wrists, between the legs, on the thighs, and on the ankles. Most of the skin symptoms are due to secondary infections which follow scabies. It is believed that the first case of scabies causes no itching. After a month or so, when the rash appears in the area of the burrows, the itching begins since the patient has now become sensitized to the mite. Once having had scabies and acquiring another infection, the area around the burrow becomes inflamed within a few hours. A sensitized person begins to scratch immediately and often is able to dislodge the *Sarcoptes* and automatically stops the infection, whereas in the nonsensitized person the infection builds up over a period of about a month before the patient is aware of harboring the mites.

Scabies is common in the history of man and appears to come in waves. Sensitization forms a so-called immunity and the mites can be located easily and dislodged. The next group of people have not been infected and are not sensitized and the mite population builds up as in diseases. The real causes of the rise and fall may not yet be known. The highest incidence is in winter when people sleep together to keep warm and there is less washing. Scabies is not acquired through ordinary social contacts but through sleeping in the same bed with an infected person.

Secondary infections due to scratching are often more serious than the actual scabies. Reaction to different sulfur compounds used to control the mite may also set up a serious skin condition.

Sarcoptes mange of the dog is caused by *Sarcoptes scabiei* var. *canis*. It is to be found on any part of the animal but usually first on the head.

It spreads rapidly. Hirst 1922 lists the symptoms as follows: "There are reddish spots rather like flea bites, and the scratching of the animal causes reddish places and papules to appear. The infected part often becomes dry and covered with yellowish crusts. The hair falls out and the skin becomes thickened, wrinkled and creased. Pruritus is intense. The presence of the parasite is the chief distinctive feature." Human beings may become infected with the dog *Sarcoptes*. The mite is apparently cosmopolitan. Sarcoptic mange of pigs, caused by *S. scabiei* var. *suis*, is common in the United States as well as in other countries. The general symptoms are as in the scabies of the dog. This species can also be transferred to man. *Sarcoptes scabiei* var. *ovis* Mégnin is parasitic on sheep, where it is to be found around the head although in more serious cases the limbs and rarely the body become affected. It is not to be found on the wooly parts of the body. This mite can be transmitted to goats. *Sarcoptes scabiei* var. *caprae* Fürstenburg can frequently cause the death of goats. This mite has been transmitted to man, horses, sheep, cattle, and pigs.

The genus *Notoedres* contains mites causing mange in various animals. *N. cati* Hering is the cause of mange in cats, which usually starts around the head, forming crusts until the skin becomes hard, thickened, and creased like leather. It is usually restricted to the head and neck. The mite has caused mange in dogs. Essig 1929 has recorded it as a pest of the wild gray squirrels in California, sometimes even causing their death. *Notoedres cati* var. *cuniculi* Gerlach attacks the rabbit, especially around the head, although in serious cases it may extend to the legs and genital regions. *Notoedres muris* Mégnin is parasitic on the common brown rat and may be fatal. Both tame and wild rats are attacked by this mite.

Knemidokoptes mutans Robin and Lanquetin causes the scaly-leg of fowl and small domestic birds. Hirst describes it thus: "The large scales of the tarsus of the feet are first affected, becoming raised at the edges by whitish floury powder, which is sometimes mixed with exuded serum. In advance cases the disease assumes a characteristic form, the feet becoming greatly distorted and covered with thick nodular spongy crusts. The comb and neck may also be attacked." Scaly-leg is highly contagious. The depluming itch of poultry is caused by *Knemidokoptes laevis* var. *gallinae* (Railliet). The mites, which are embedded in the tissue or scales at the base of the quills, cause a falling out of feathers over more or less extended areas of the body. It is to be found both in North America and Europe. *K. laevis* Railliet was described from pigeons. Other birds such as pheasants and geese suffer from a depluming itch in France.

References:

Baker, D. W. 1946. Barn Itch. N.Y. State Vet. Col., Vet. Expt. Sta., Parasit. Lab., 36 pp.

Friedman, R. 1942. Biology of Acarus scabiei, 183 pp. Froben Press, N.Y.

Grandjean, F. 1938. Observations sur les acaridiae (1 serie) Bull. Soc. Zool. France 63(4–5):214–224.

Hirst, S. 1922. Mites injurious to domestic animals. Brit. Mus. (Nat. Hist.) Econ. Ser., No. 13.

Imes, Marion. 1918. Cattle Scab. U.S. Dept. Agr. Farmers' Bull. 1017 (revised 1935).

——. 1924. Sheep Scab. U.S. Dept. Agr. Farmers' Bull. 713 (revised 1927, 1935).

Mellanby, K. 1943. Scabies. Oxford Univ. Press. London. 81 pp. illus.

van Eyndhoven, G. L. 1947 (1945). Beschrijving van een nieuwen vleermuisparasiet Notoedres vanschaiki v. Eyndh. 1946 (Acar.). Tijdschrift v. Ent. 88:132–154.

Cytoditidae Oudemans, 1908

Figure 296

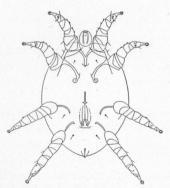

Diagnosis: The cytoditids are medium-sized mites measuring from 0.45 to 0.60 mm. long and shaped like an egg. Their skin is smooth dorsally but has fine striae in all other regions. There are no vertical setae and only a few tiny, dorsal setae. The gnathosoma is terminal and the chelicerae and pedipalps are fused into a sucking tube. All tarsi have caruncles on long stalks without claws. No genital suckers are present. Males do not have adanal copulatory suckers.

Figure 296 *Cytodites nudus* (Vizioli). Venter of female. (After Hirst 1922)

Genus:

Cytodites Mégnin, 1877 (= *Cytoleichus* Mégnin, 1880)

Type. *Sarcoptes nudus* Vizioli, 1870 (= *Cytodites glaber* Mégnin, 1877)

Discussion: *Cytodites nudus* (Vizioli) is to be found in chickens in the air sacks and respiratory system, in the body cavity in general, among and on the surface of the hepatic lobes and similar places. The presence of small numbers does not appear to damage the host, but large numbers may be of some importance. They have been accused of causing enteritis and peritonitis in fowl and can produce suffocation by being present in large numbers in the air passages and sacks. Myers 1923 states that *C. nudus* brings forth living young with three pairs of legs.

Reference:

Myers, J. G. 1923. The internal mite of the domestic fowl. New Zealand J. Sci. and Tech. 6(1):59–61.

Laminosioptidae Vitzthum, 1931

Figure 297

Diagnosis: Very small mites measuring from 0.20 to 0.26 mm. in length, the laminosioptids have an elongated, slightly flattened figure. Dorsally smooth, their skin has fine striae in other regions. No vertical setae appear on the propodosoma. The body has a few long setae. The gnathosoma is normal and not visible from above. The legs are short, especially I and II. Tarsi I and II lack both claws and caruncles; tarsi III and IV have minute caruncles on long stalks or pedicles. There are no genital suckers, and the males do not have adanal copulatory suckers.

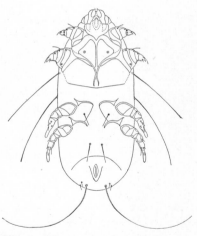

Figure 297 *Laminosioptes cysticola* (Vizioli). Venter of female. (After Hirst 1922)

Genus:

Laminosioptes Mégnin, 1880 (= *Symplectoptes* Railliet, 1885)
Type. *Sarcoptes cysticola* Vizioli, 1870

Discussion: *Laminosioptes cysticola* (Vizioli) is an internal parasite of the fowl. In Europe it is to be found by the millions in the cellular tissue of turkeys. It destroys the fibers. The mite may be detected by the occurrence of calcareous cysts in the subcutaneous tissues, but the mites are to be found alive in the tissues and not in the cysts which form around the dead mites. Deaths of birds have been reported due to heavy infestations. This species has also been reported from domestic fowl in this country.

References:

Hirst, S. 1922. Mites injurious to domestic animals. Brit. Mus. (Nat. Hist.) Eco. Ser., No. 13.

Taylor, T. 1884. Microscopic observations. Internal parasites in domestic fowls. U.S. Dept. Agr., Dept. Rpt. 34:1–5.

Heteropsoridae Oudemans, 1908

Figure 298

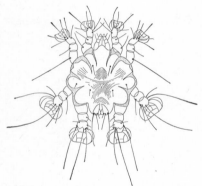

Diagnosis: These mites are very small (about 0.22 mm. in length). The body is very plump and almost circular in shape. No vertical setae are present. The apodemes of all coxae end free. All legs are very thick, of equal length, and are arranged radially. All tarsi have monstrous, broadly leaf-shaped caruncles; tarsi III and IV have ventral, clawlike spines pointing posteriorly.

Figure 298 *Heteropsorus pteroptopus* Trouessart and Neumann. Dorsum of female. (After Vitzthum 1929)

Genus:

> *Heteropsorus* Trouessart and Neumann, 1887
> Type. *Heteropsorus pteroptopus* Trouessart and Neumann, 1887

Discussion: The single species is to be found on the skins of birds and has been collected on *Acrocephalus arundinaceus, Erithacus cyanecula, Emberiza cirlus* and *E. schoeniclus* in Italy and France. It apparently has not been found since its original discovery.

Reference:

Berlese, A. 1897. Acari Myriopoda et Scorpiones. Ordo Crytpostigmata (Sarcoptidae). Fasc. LXXVIII, No. 4.

Myialgesidae Trouessart, 1907

Figures 299, 300

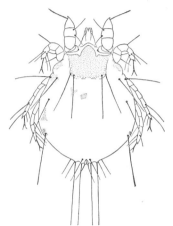

Diagnosis: These mites are parasitic on the Hippoboscidae, Diptera, and occasionally on Mallophaga. The body of the female is broadly oval (broadly pear-shaped when pregnant). Males are not known. No suture separates the propodosoma from the hysterosoma. There are no vertical setae, but there is propodosomal shield. The skin other-

Figure 299 *Myialges caulotoon* Spieser. Dorsum of female. (After Ferris 1928)

Figure 300 Left, *Myialges anchora* Sergent and Trouessart. Tarsus I; right, *Myialges caulotoon* Spieser. Tarsus I. (After Ferris 1928)

wise is soft with fine striae. The median side of the palpi has groove-excavations with the ends of the deformed chelicerae almost surrounded by a tube. Tarsi II, III, and IV lack claws but have a stalked caruncle; tarsi I have no claw or lobe and are shaped like an anchor. The legs are located on the anterior portion of the body. The genital opening of the female lies between coxae IV. No genital suckers are present.

Genera:

1. *Myialges* Sergent and Trouessart, 1907
   Type. *Myialges anchora* Sergent and Trouessart, 1907
2. *Myialgopsis* Cooreman, 1944
   Type. *Myialgopsis trinotoni* Cooreman, 1944

Discussion: There are three species, *Myialges anchora* Sergent and Trouessart, *M. caulotoon* Spieser, and *Myialgopsis trinotoni* Cooreman. Ferris 1928 has found *M. anchora* "attached by their beaks to the body of the fly host," usually to the abdomen although one specimen was found on the thorax; Sergent and Trouessart found them on both thorax and abdomen. The mites are true parasites of flies, and scars are formed at the point of attachment by the deposition of additional chitin, an indication of long periods of attachment. Males are not known and it has been suggested by some that they may be found on the bird hosts of flies.

References:

Cooreman, J. 1944. Un nouveau cas d'hyperparasitism parmi les Acaridiae: *Myialgopsis trinotoni* n. gen. n. sp. parasite d'un Mallophage. Bull. Mus. Roy. d'Hist. Nat. de Belgique 20(26):1–12.

Ferris, G. F. 1928. The genus *Myialges* (Acarina: Sarcoptidae). Ent. News 39(5):137–140.

Oudemans, A. C. 1935. Description du *Myialges anchora* Sergent et Trouessart 1907 (Acarien). Ann. de Parasitol. Humaine et Compar. 13(1):5–11.

Psoroptidae Canestrini, 1892

Figures 301, 302

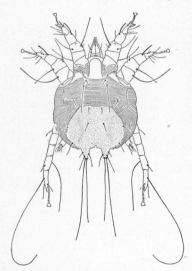

Diagnosis: With few exceptions the psoroptids are parasites of mammals. No vertical setae are present but there are dorsal shields. Bell-shaped caruncles are found on long, segmented stalks (*Psoroptes*), or short, unsegmented stalks appear on all tarsi in the male (except on tarsi IV of *Psoroptes*) and on tarsi I, II, and IV in the female (except in *Oto-*

Figure 301 *Psoroptes equi* var. *ovis* (Hering). Dorsum of male. (After Hirst 1922)

Figure 302 *Otodectes cynotis* (Hering). Tip of leg I. (After Grandjean 1937)

dectes and *Caparinae* where they are on tarsi ɪ and ɪɪ). In the male legs ɪᴠ are considerably shorter than ɪɪɪ. Tarsi ɪɪɪ of the females end in long, whiplike setae. The males have adanal copulatory suckers. The posterior margin of the abdomen of the male is bibolate or slightly emarginate.

Genera:

1. *Psoroptes* Gervais, 1841 (= *Dermatodectes* Gerlach, 1857 = *Dermatokoptes* Fürstenburg, 1861)
   Type. *Sarcoptes equi* Hering, 1838
2. *Caparinia* Canestrini, 1894
   Type. *Chorioptes setiferus* Mégnin, 1880
3. *Chorioptes* Gervais, 1859 (= *Symbiotes* Gerlach, 1857 *nom praeocc.* = *Dermatophagus* Fürstenburg, 1861)
   Type. *Sarcoptes caprae* Delafond, 1854
4. *Otodectes* Canestrini, 1894
   Type. *Sarcoptes cynotis* Hering, 1838

Discussion: The genus *Psoroptes* can be considered as consisting of one species with the varieties existing upon the various hosts. These varieties are only slightly differentiated morphologically (Hirst 1922) and it is difficult or impossible to transfer the mites from one host to another of a different species.

Psoroptes equi var. *ovis* causes the disease known as sheep-scab which damages the wool and at times causes the loss of the animals. The psoroptic mange differs from the sarcoptic mange in being found on the body wherever there is wool. The mites pierce the skin with their chelicerae, causing the characteristic irritation, scabs, and exudation of serum. The wool may become matted and even detached in some cases. The mites live under the scabs formed by the exudation of the serum at the site of the punctures and their activity continually adds to the thickness of the scab. Van Es 1904 states that "weak animals or such as are not well cared for show the physical effects of the disease in the form of loss of flesh, anaemia, and an increased weakness which may be the forerunner of a fatal termination." They are readily transmittable through direct contact or through infected materials. It is world-wide in distribution.

Psoroptes equi var. *caprae* is to be found on goats but is confined to the ears. Usually the mite is not a serious pest but at times can cause deafness, loss of appetite, and, in extreme cases, death of the animal.

Psoroptes equi var. *cuniculi* is to be found in the ear of rabbits and apparently attacks only the concha. Marine 1924 gives the following description of the symptoms: "The earliest manifestations of infection are indicated by hyperemia and the formation of reddish brown crusts near the bottom of the concha. The hyperemia and crust formation extend and after months may involve nearly all the inner surface of the ear. The most serious complication of the disease is pyogenic infection of the middle ear which may extend to the internal ear and meninges. The parasite spreads more rapidly during the warm months. The disease is widespread, and few, if any, laboratories escape its occasional introduction."

Psoroptic mange is to be encountered on horses and cows. That of the horse is common in France and is also present in England. It is probably widespread.

Psoroptes equi var. *bovis* causes the common cattle scab. As is the case with the other members of the genus the entire life cycle of the mite is passed upon the host. Imes 1918 reports: "The first lesions on cattle appear on the withers, on top of the neck or just in front of the withers, or around the root of the tail. From these points it spreads over the back and sides and unless checked it may involve practically the entire body. When a scab mite finds lodgment on the body it pricks the skin to obtain food and in so doing probably introduces a poisonous secretion into the wound. A slight inflammation is caused, but this early stage of the disease is rarely, if ever, detected by casual observation. As the mites multiply, large numbers of small wounds are made in the skin and are followed by intense itching, formation of papules, inflammation, and exudation of serum. The serum which oozes to the surface becomes mixed with particles of dirt and more or less infected with microorganisms. This mass soon hardens into yellowish or gray-colored scabs which frequently are stained with blood. In the early stages of the disease the scab may be about the size of a pea, but as the mites seek the healthy skin around the edges of the wound the scab or lesion gradually increases in size."

The genus *Chorioptes* consists of several species which may actually be nothing but physiological varieties as in *Psoroptes*. They are to be found on horses, cattle, sheep, goats and a few other animals. *Chorioptes bovis* (Gerlach) is usually restricted to the feet or to the base of the tail and anal fossa in cattle. In some cases it spreads on to the neck and back, or to the belly and perineum. This mange is usually of a mild type, remaining localized and spreading slowly. Other species are *C. equi* (Hering) on horse, *C. caprae* (Delafond) on goat,

C. ovis (Railliet) on sheep, and *C. cuniculi* (Zurn) on rabbit.

Mites belonging to the genus *Otodectes* live in the ears of dogs, cats, ferrets, and fox. As with the above species they are structurally similar but are considered as varieties of *Otodectes cynotis* Hering. The mites cause a canker in the ears of cats in England and the presence of the mites in dogs' ears causes the animal to shake its head constantly.

References:

Good, E. S. 1909. Sheep scab. Kentucky Agr. Expt. Sta. Bull. 1437, 219–246.

Grandjean, F. 1937. *Otodectes cynotis* (Hering) et les prétendues trachées des acaridiae. Bull. Soc. Zool. France (4):280–290.

Hirst, S. 1922. Mites injurious to domestic animals. Brit. Mus. (Nat. Hist.) Econ. Ser., No. 13.

Imes, M. 1918. Cattle scab and methods of control and eradication. U.S. Dept. Agr. Farmers' Bull. 1017, pp. 1–29 (revised 1935).

——. 1924. Sheep scab. U.S. Dept. Agr. Farmers' Bull. 7–13 (revised 1935).

Marine, D. 1924. The cure and prevention of ear canker in rabbits. Science 60(1546):158.

Van Es, L. 1904. Scabies in sheep and cattle and mange in horses. N. Dak. Agr. Col. Expt. Sta. Bull. 61:399–435.

Epidermoptidae Trouessart, 1892

(= Mealiidae Oudemans, 1923)

Figures 303, 304

Diagnosis: Very small mites measuring from 0.17 mm. to 0.39 mm. in length, the epidermoptids are rather flat, usually very short, and approximately circular. A shield is present but is found only on the propodosoma in the females. There are no vertical setae on the propodosoma. The skin is soft and striated. The posterior of the male is often notched or bilobate while that of the female is rounded. The male possesses copulatory suckers. All tarsi end in caruncles.

Genera:

1. *Epidermoptes* Rivolta, 1876
   Type. *Epidermoptes bilobatus* Rivolta, 1876
2. *Dermation* Trouessart and Neumann, 1887
   Type. *Epidermoptes bihamatus* Trouessart and Neumann, 1887

3. *Dermatophagoides* Bogdanow, 1864 (= *Pachylichus* G. Canestrini, 1894 = *Mealia* Berlese, 1897)
   Type. *Dermatophagoides scheremetewskyi* Bogdanow, 1864
4. *Microlichus* Trouessart and Neumann, 1887
   Type. *Symbiotes avus* Trouessart and Neumann, 1887
5. *Rivoltasia* G. Canestrini, 1894
   Type. *Epidermoptes bifurcatus* Rivolta, 1876
6. *Turbinoptes* Boyd, 1949
   Type. *Turbinoptes strandtmanni* Boyd, 1949

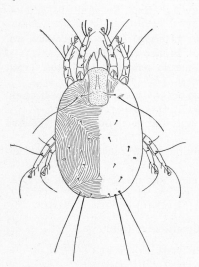
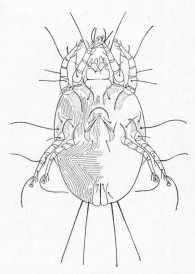

Figure 303   *Dermatophagoides schere-metewskyi* Bogdanow. Dorsum of female.

Figure 304   *Dermatophagoides schere-metewskyi* Bogdanow. Venter of female.

Discussion: These mites are usually to be found on the skin of birds. *Epidermoptes bilobatus* Rivolta lives on the skin of chicken and has been found in great numbers associated with pityriasis (scaly skin disease) in some cases and has been accused of being the cause of the disease. *Dermatophagoides scheremetewskyi* Bogdanow 1864 was described from mites causing dermatitis in man. Traver 1951 reports on *D. scheremetewskyi* infesting the human scalp for a period of sixteen years. The first symptoms were small itching red papules accompanied by the sensation of something crawling and scratching. The epidermis over the infested areas thickened and these regions became swollen and painful. The mites did not remain upon the scalp, but on irritation caused by chemicals applied for control moved down from the head, invading the eyes, ears, and nostrils. The eyes became badly swollen and movement of the eyeballs was impossible. Invasion of the nostrils was accompanied by irritation of the throat, trachea, and bronchi. The mites were apparently confined to the pina region of the ears, forming itching papules. Small incrustations frequently covered infested areas. Possible sources of the infestation were pet cats and dogs suffering from "mange." Fisher *et al.* 1951 report on this same mite infesting the foot of a patient in conjunction with a fungus and causing a dermatitis. From the few case histories he suggests the possibility that a dermatitis must first be present before the mite can establish itself. Sasa 1950 reviews the genus *Dermatophagoides* in Japan and reports finding *D. takeuchii* Sasa in urine, and *D. saitoi* Sasa in sputum from a patient with Loeffler's syndrome, and *Dermatophagoides* sp. from sputum of a patient with chronic bronchial asthma.

References:

Boyd, E. 1949. A new genus and species of mite from the nasal cavity of the ring-billed gull (Acarina, Epidermoptidae). J. Parasitol. 35 (3):295–300.

Cooreman, J. 1950. Sur un acarien nouveau, préjudiciable aux matières alimentaires entreposées: *Mealia maynéi* n. sp. Bull. et Ann. Soc. Ent. Belg. 86:164–168.

Fisher, A. A., A. G. Franks, M. Wolf, and M. Leider. 1951. Concurrent infestation with a rare mite and infection with a common dermatophyte. Archiv. of Dermatology and Syphilology 63(3):336–342.

Sasa, M. 1950. Mites of the genus *Dermatophagoides* Bogdanoff, 1864 found from three cases of human acariasis. Japanese J. Expt. Medicine 20:519–525.

Traver, J. R. 1951. Unusual scalp dermatitis in humans caused by the mite *Dermatophagoides*. Proc. Ent. Soc. Wash. 53(1):1–25.

Psoralgidae Oudemans, 1908

Diagnosis: These mites are rather flat and short bodied. The male has a deep posterior-median abdominal incision (bilobate). The skin is soft, wrinkled. A median dorsal shield is always present, but there are no other shields (?) nor are there any vertical setae. The chelicerae are chelate and the maxillae have two-segmented palpi. The legs are almost equal in size except in the male where legs III and IV are thicker (legs III are even much longer). Both sexes have a bell-shaped caruncle on a short, unsegmented stalk. The male has adanal copulatory suckers.

Genus:

> *Psoralges* Trouessart, 1896
> Type. *Psoralges libertus* Trouessart, 1896

Discussion: These mites were found in the fur of *Tamandua* sp., a mammal. The larvae and nymphs live in colonies in subcutaneous bladders, causing a kind of itch; the adults live free among the hairs of the host. No figure is known.

Listrophoridae Canestrini, 1892

Figure 305

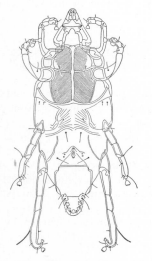

Diagnosis: The dorsal shields vary in number and shape. Parts of the skin are smooth, wrinkled, have transverse striations, or are scaly. A pair of vertical setae is present. The maxillae, parts of the legs, or the entire leg or sternal formation are transformed into clasping organs that enclose a single hair of the mammalian host. The body is oblong (except *Myocoptes*) and often strongly compressed laterally, and has vertical setae. There are genital suckers (some exceptions) and the males have adanal copulatory suckers that may be very inconspicuous or even lacking.

Figure 305 Chirodiscoides caviae Hirst. Venter of male. (After Hirst 1922)

Genera:

1. *Listrophorus* Pagenstecher, 1861
   Type. *Listrophorus leucharti* Pagenstecher, 1861
2. *Alabidocarpus* Ewing, 1929
   Type. *Labidocarpus megalonyx* Trouessart, 1895

3. *Atopomelus* Trouessart, 1918
   Type. *Atopomelus locusta* Trouessart, 1918
4. *Austrochirus* Womersley, 1943
   Type. *Austrochirus queenslandicus* Womersley, 1943
5. *Campylochirus* Trouessart, 1893
   Type. *Campylochirus chelopus* Trouessart, 1893
6. *Chirodiscoides* Hirst, 1917 (Womersley 1943 synonymizes this with *Campylochirus* Trouessart)
   Type. *Chirodiscoides caviae* Hirst, 1917
7. *Chirodiscus* Trouessart and Neumann, 1890
   Type. *Chirodiscus amplexans* Trouessart and Neumann, 1890
8. *Eulabidocarpus* Lawrence, 1948
   Type. *Labidocarpus compressus* Ewing, 1910
9. *Eurychiroides* Womersley, 1943 (= *Euryzonus* Trouessart, 1918 *nom. praeocc.*)
   Type. *Euryzonus ventricosus* Trouessart, 1918
10. *Labidocarpus* Trouessart, 1895
    Type. *Labidocarpus rollinati* Trouessart, 1895
11. *Listrophoroides* Hirst, 1923
    Type. *Listrophoroides aethiopicus* Hirst, 1923
12. *Marquesania* Womersley, 1943 (= *Listrophoroides* Ferris, 1932 *nom. praeocc.*)
    Type. *Listrophoroides expansus* Ferris, 1932
13. *Myocoptes* Claparède, 1869 (= *Criniscansor* Poppe, 1887)
    Type. *Sarcoptes musculinus* Koch, 1844
14. *Neolabidocarpus* Gunther, 1942
    Type. *Labidocarpus buloloensis* Gunther, 1940
15. *Olabidocarpus* Lawrence, 1948
    Type. *Labidocarpus belsorum* van Eyndhoven, 1940
16. *Prolabidocarpus* Lawrence, 1948
    Type. *Prolabidocarpus canadensis* Lawrence, 1948
17. *Schizocarpus* Trouessart, 1896 (= *Haptosoma* Kramer, 1896)
    Type. *Schizocarpus mingaudi* Trouessart, 1896
18. *Schizocoptes* Lawrence, 1944
    Type. *Schizocoptes conjugatus* Lawrence, 1944
19. *Trichoecius* Canestrini, 1899 (= *Trichobius* Canestrini, 1897 *nom. praeocc.*)
    Type. *Myocoptes brevipes* Canestrini and Trouessart, 1895

Discussion: Gunther 1942 divided the group into four subfamilies based on the type of clasping organs. Womersley 1943 keys them as follows:

Key to the Listrophoridae

1. Legs ɪ and ɪɪ modified as claspers   2

   Legs ɪɪɪ and ɪv modified as claspers   Myocoptinae

   Maxillae modified as claspers   Listrophorinae

2. Legs ɪ and ɪɪ with caruncles, not highly modified, sometimes with accessory claspers   Atopomelinae

   Legs ɪ and ɪɪ without caruncles, highly modified, without accessory claspers   Labidocarpinae

These mites are found in the hair of small to medium-sized mammals and only rarely in the feathers of birds (*Chirodiscus*). *Myocoptes musculinus* (Koch) produces a type of mange on laboratory white mice for which the name "Myocoptic mange" has been proposed. This species is common throughout the world. A listrophorid mite likely to be encountered is *Chirodiscoides caviae* Hirst which is attached to the dorsal hairs of the guinea pig; the legs of this species are flattened to grasp the hairs of the host. *Labidocarpus nasicolus* Lawrence has been collected on the vibrissae on or near the nose leaf of the bat, each being attached near the base of one of these tactile hairs. Lawrence 1938 says: "Like *Myobia* this mite is unable to move readily from place to place on account of the remarkable modifications of its anterior legs. It seems probable therefore that it descends the hair to which it is attached to feed on the secretions liberated by the sebaceous glands at its base. The nose leaf of *Rhinolophus* (bat) itself is unusually well supplied with these fat secreting glands, enabling its surface to be kept perpetually moist and thus more sensitive to currents of air. It is significant that these mites have hitherto been found only on the nose-leaved group of bats of the suborder Microchiroptera. Hexapod larvae have been observed in the body cavity of the ovigerous female of *Labidocarpus rollinati* and *L. nasicolus.*"

References:

Gunther, C. 1942. Notes on the Listrophoridae (Acarina: Sarcoptoidea). Proc. Linn. Soc. N. S. Wales 67(3, 4):109–110.

Lawrence, R. F. 1938. A new acarine parasite of bats. Parasitol. 30(3): 309–313.

——. 1948. Studies on some parasitic mites from Canada and South Africa. J. Parasitol. 34(5):364–379.

Womersley, H. 1943. Australian species of Listrophoridae Canest. (Acarina) with notes on the new genera. Trans. Roy. Soc. South Australia 67(1):10–19.

Analgesidae Trouessart, 1915

Figure 306

Diagnosis: The analgesids are feather mites. As a rule, the females lack plates on the hysterosoma (exception *Mesalges*). They have an undivided, rounded, posterior margin. Legs I and II usually have latero-ventral, triangular, cufflike projections. Legs III or IV, or both, of the male are more developed than the others and often are highly developed.

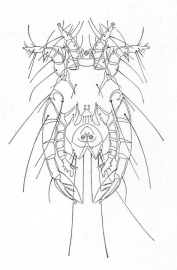

Figure 306 *Megninia columbae* Buchholz. Venter of male. (After Hirst 1922)

Genera:

1. *Analges* Nitzsch, 1818
   Type. *Analges passerinus* Nitzsch, 1818
2. *Analgopsis* Trouessart, 1919
   Type. *Acarus passerinus* Linnaeus, 1758 (= DeGeer, 1778)
3. *Berlesella* Trouessart, 1919
   Type. *Berlesella alata* Trouessart, 1919
4. *Hemialges* Trouessart, 1888
   Type. *Megninia pappus* Trouessart and Neumann, 1888
5. *Hyperalges* Trouessart, 1915
   Type. *Megninia magnifica* Trouessart, 1895
6. *Ingrassia* Oudemans, 1905
   Type. *Megninia veliger* Oudemans, 1904
7. *Megninia* Berlese, 1881
   Type. *Dermaleichus cubitalis* Mégnin, 1877
8. *Mesalges* Trouessart, 1888
   Type. *Dermaleichus abbreviatus* Buchholz, 1869
9. *Metanalges* Trouessart, 1919
   Type. *Megninia elongata* Trouessart, 1886
10. *Nealges* Trouessart, 1886
    Type. *Nealges poppei* Trouessart, 1886

11. *Plesialges* Trouessart, 1919
     Type. *Plesialges mimus* Trouessart, 1919
12. *Protalges* Trouessart, 1885 (= *Hartingia* Oudemans, 1897)
     Type. *Protalges robini* Trouessart, 1885
13. *Psoroptoides* Trouessart, 1919
     Type. *Megninia psoroptopus* Trouessart, 1885
14. *Pteralloptes* Trouessart, 1884 (= *Analloptes* Trouessart, 1885)
     Type. *Dermaleichus stellaris* Buchholz, 1869
15. *Varchia* Oudemans, 1905
     Type. *Pteralloptes gambettae* Oudemans, 1904
16. *Xolalges* Trouessart, 1885
     Type. *Xolalges scaurus* Trouessart, 1885

References:

Gaud, J. and M. L. Petitot. 1948. Sarcoptides plumicoles des oiseaux du
     Maroc. Ann. de Parasit. 23(1–2):35–46.
──────. 1948. Sarcoptides plumicoles des oiseaux d'Indochine. Ann. de
     Parasit. 23(5–6):337-347.

Dermoglyphidae Mégnin and Trouessart, 1883

(= Falculiferidae Oudemans, 1908;
Pterolichidae Trouessart, 1915;
Syringobiidae Berlese, 1907)

Figures 307–309

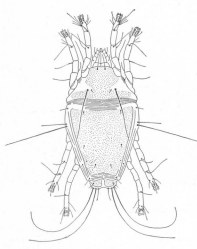

Figure 307 *Pterolichus obtusus* Robin.
Dorsum of female. (After Hirst 1922)

Diagnosis: The dermoglyphids are feather mites. Both sexes have at least a propodosomal shield and often other dorsal plates as well. The posterior of the body is either round or slightly emarginate. A pair of vertical setae is present on the propodosoma. Legs III and IV are often thicker than the others and occasionally legs I or II or both are much thicker than the others. Apodemes of legs I and II are either united or end freely. Heteromorphic males may be present in which monstrous deviations from the normal are to be found in legs IV and the chelicerae (*Bdellorhynchus*), or in legs I and II and the chelicerae (*Falculifer*), or in the palpi (*Cheiloceras*), or in legs III and IV (*Protolichus*).

The families Falculiferidae, Pterolichidae, and Syringobiidae are included under the Dermoglyphidae since at the present time characters of familial rank cannot be found and, with the characters used by Vitzthum, the families are difficult to key out and are not constant in structure.

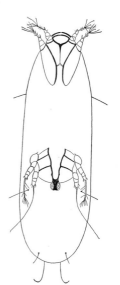

Figure 308 *Falculifer rostratus* (Buchholz). Hypopial nymph. (After Hirst 1922)

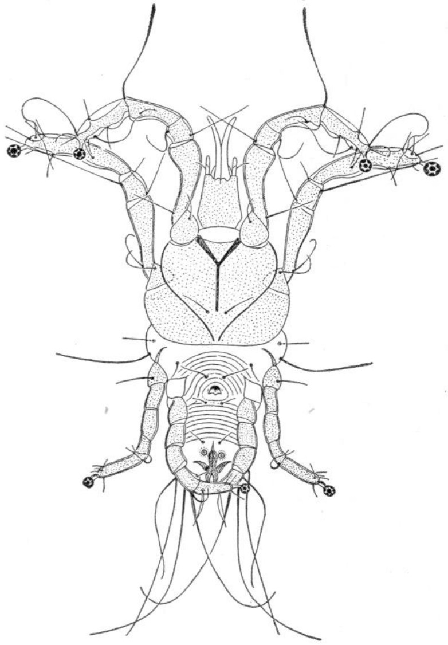

Figure 309 *Falculifer rostratus* (Buchholz). Venter of male.

Genera:

1. *Dermoglyphus* Mégnin, 1877
   Type. *Dermaleichus elongatus* Mégnin, 1877
2. *Anasicudion* Trouessart and Neumann, 1888
   Type. *Dermaleichus landoisii* Buchholz, 1869
3. *Anoplonotus* Trouessart, 1915
   Type. *Pterolichus semaphorus* Trouessart, 1886
4. *Avenzoaria* Oudemans, 1905
   Type. *Dermaleichus totani* Canestrini, 1878
5. *Bdellorhynchus* Trouessart, 1885
   Type. *Bdellorhynchus polymorphus* Trouessart, 1885

6. *Bonnetella* Trouessart, 1934 (= *Buchholzia* Trouessart, 1915 *nom. praeocc.*)
   Type. *Analges fuscus* Nitzsch, 1818
7. *Ceratothrix* Trouessart, 1915
   Type. *Pterolichus corniger* Trouessart and Neumann, 1888
8. *Chauliacia* Oudemans, 1905
   Type. *Pterolichus securiger* Robin, 1877
9. *Cheiloceras* Trouessart, 1898
   Type. *Cheiloceras cervus* Trouessart, 1898
10. *Cheylabis* Trouessart, 1885
    Type. *Cheylabis latus* Trouessart, 1885
11. *Columellaia* Oudemans, 1904
    Type. *Dermoglyphus varians* Trouessart, 1886
12. *Eustathia* Oudemans, 1905
    Type. *Pterolichus cultrifer* Robin, 1868
13. *Falculifer* Railliet, 1896
    Type. *Dermaleichus rostratus* Buchholz, 1869
14. *Freyana* Haller, 1877
    Type. *Dermaleichus anatinus* Koch, 1841
15. *Gabucinia* Oudemans, 1905
    Type. *Pterolichus delibatus* Tobin, 1877
16. *Halleria* Trouessart and Mégnin, 1885
    Type. *Freyana* (*Halleria*) *hirsutirostris* Trouessart and Mégnin
17. *Kramerella* Trouessart, 1915 (= *Crameria* Haller, 1878 *nom. praeocc.*)
    Type. *Crameria lunulata* Haller, 1878
18. *Michaelichus* Trouessart and Mégnin (= *Michaelia* Trouessart, 1885, *sed non* = *Michaelia* Berlese, 1884)
    Type. *Dermaleichus heteropus* Michael, 1881
19. *Microchelys* Trouessart, 1915
    Type. *Freyana* (*Microspalax*) *delicatula* Trouessart, 1898
20. *Microspalax* Mégnin and Trouessart, 1884
    Type. *Freyana* (*Microspalax*) *manicata* Mégnin and Trouessart, 1884
21. *Neumanniella* Trouessart, 1915 (= *Neumannia* Trouessart and Neumann, 1888 *nom. praeocc.*)
    Type. *Neumannia chelifer* Trouessart and Neumann, 1888
22. *Oustaletia* Trouessart, 1885
    Type. *Pterolichus* (*Oustaletia*) *pegasus* Trouessart, 1885
23. *Paralges* Trouessart, 1885
    Type. *Paralges pachycnemis* Trouessart, 1885
24. *Plutarchia* Oudemans, 1904
    Type. *Plutarchia chelopus* Oudemans, 1904 (*partim* = *Syringobia chelopus* Trouessart and Neumann, 1888)

25. *Protolichus* Trouessart, 1884
    Type. *Pterolichus (Protolichus) brachiatus* Trouessart, 1884
26. *Protonyssus* Trouessart, 1915
    Type. *Protalges larva* Trouessart, 1885
27. *Pseudogiebelia* Radford, 1950 (= *Giebelia* Trouessart, 1915, *nom. praeocc.*)
    Type. *Dermaleichus puffini* Buchholz, 1869
28. *Pterolichus* Robin, 1868
    Type. *Pterolichus obtusus* Robin, 1868
29. *Pteronyssus* Robin, 1868
    Type. *Pteronyssus striatus* Robin, 1877
30. *Pseudalloptes* Trouessart and Mégnin, 1884
    Type. *Pterolichus bisubulatus* Robin, 1877
31. *Sammonica* Oudemans, 1904
    Type. *Syringobia ovalis* Trouessart, 1898
32. *Sphaerogastra* Trouessart, 1897
    Type. *Sphaerogastra thylacodes* Trouessart, 1897
33. *Syringobia* Trouessart and Neumann, 1888
    Type. *Syringobia chelopus* Trouessart and Neumann, 1888
34. *Thecarthra* Trouessart, 1896
    Type. *Pterolichus theca* Mégnin and Trouessart, 1884
35. *Xoloptes* Canestrini, 1879
    Type. *Pterolichus claudicans* Robin, 1877

Discussion: Oudemans 1922 has outlined the life cycle of the feather mites as follows. There are two types of eggs, a hard-shelled one and a thin-shelled one. The thin-shelled eggs contain larvae while still within the mother and thus the female mite may be either ovoviparous or viviparous. There is a six-legged larva which hatches from the egg to molt into the eight-legged nymph, the protonymph. The protonymph molts and the deutonymph emerges. The sexes in this stage can be distinguished in that the female possesses a copulatory opening. Both forms give rise to the eight-legged adults. When mating takes place the male always copulates with the female deutonymph. Spurlock and Emlen 1942 have studied the nymphal form of a feather mite which they called *Hypodectes chapini* and which was found in a red-shafted flicker, *Colaptes cafer collaris,* in California. These mites were "loosely encysted in the connective tissue surrounding the trachea, and to a lesser extent, the esophagus. The greatest concentration was near the point of entrance of the trachea into the buccal cavity, but the area of infection extended from the lungs to the tongue. No movement was visible with the cysts as far as could be determined, and there was no apparent pathology in the host tissue at the site of infection." In reviewing the literature Spurlock and Emlen state the following on *Falculifer rostratus* (Buchholz): "The normal nymph molts into the hypopial stage during adverse environmental conditions, as during the molting of birds, etc. The hypopial forms migrate internally through the feather follicles or respiratory organs of the bird host and come to lie in subcutaneous or tracheal tissue, there to live and grow until such times as external conditions become normal when they return to the outside and take on their original form. This deviation of the normal life cycle is supposed by these authors (i.e., Robin and Mégnin) to be a means of saving the colony from destruction."

Pterolichus obtusus Robin occurs on several species of birds such as fowl and French partridge. *P. bicaudatus* Gervais is to be found on ostriches in South Africa and California. *Dermoglyphus elongatus* Mégnin and *D. minor* Norner are to be found inside the quills of fowls.

References:

Oudemans, A. C. 1922. Ueber die metamorphose der vogelbewohnenden Acaridiae. Tijdschr. v. Ent. 65:184–191.

Spurlock, G. M., and J. T. Emlen. 1942. *Hypodectes chapini* n. sp. (Acarina) from the red-shafted flicker. J. Parasitol. 28(4):341–344.

Vitzthum, H. 1933. Die endoparasitische Deutonymphe von *Pterolichus nisi*. Zeitschrift f. Parasitenkunde 6(2):151–169.

Proctophyllodidae Mégnin and Trouessart, 1883

Figures 310, 311

Diagnosis: The proctophyllodids are feather mites. Both sexes have dorsal and dorso-lateral propodosomal shields, a hysterosomal shield, and several other small shields. The rear of the female body is tapering, bilobate, and has sword-shaped or bristle-like appendages on each lobe. The posterior margin of the male is often bilobate, too, and often has leaf-shaped appendages. No vertical setae appear on the propodosoma. Rodlike, distally blunt tactile setae are found on tibiae I and II. All tarsi have caruncles.

Genera:

1. *Proctophyllodes* Robin, 1868
   Type. *Dermaleichus glandarinus* Koch, 1840
2. *Alloptes* G. Canestrini, 1879
   Type. *Dermaleichus crassipes* Canestrini, 1878

3. *Favettea* Trouessart, 1915
   Type. *Favettea heteroclyta* Trouessart, 1915
4. *Monojoubertia* Radford, 1950 (= *Joubertia* Oudemans, 1905, *nom praeocc.*)
   Type. *Peterodectes microphyllus* Robin and Mégnin, 1877
5. *Montesauria* Oudemans, 1905
   Type. *Pterodectes cylindricus* Robin, 1868

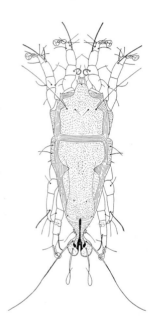 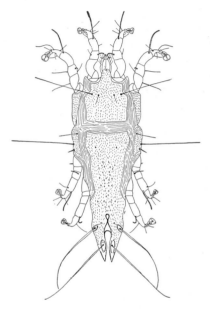

Figure 310 *Trouessartia rosteri* Berlese. Dorsum of male.

Figure 311 *Trouessartia rosteri* Berlese. Dorsum of female.

6. *Pseudalges* Trouessart, 1885 (= *Allanalges* Trouessart, 1886)
   Type. *Pterocolus analgoides* Trouessart, 1885
7. *Pterodectes* Robin, 1868
   Type. *Pterodectes rutilus* Robin, 1868
8. *Pterophagus* Mégnin, 1877
   Type. *Pterophagus strictus* Mégnin, 1877
9. *Trouessartia* Canestrini, 1899 (= *Pterocolus* Haller, 1878, *nom. praeocc.*)
   Type. *Dermaleichus corvinus* Koch, 1840

Discussion: These are feather-inhabiting mites and are similar in habits to the Analgesidae and Dermoglyphidae.

Reference:

Vitzthum, H. 1929. Acari. Die Tierwelt Mitteleuropas 3(3):1–112.

CHAPTER VIII

Oribatei Dugès, 1833

THE gnathosoma is usually concealed within a camerostome. Stigma and tracheae may be present, opening into porose areas. Pseudostigmatic organs are generally present on the propodosoma. The body is usually strongly sclerotized, dark in color, and when not thusly armored the skin is leathery. The coxal apodemes are sunk beneath the skin but are still visible, although not as strongly so as in the Acaridiae. The tarsi have one to three claws and are without caruncles. The palpi usually have five movable segments. The two sexes are similar. Three pairs of genital suckers are present; the males do not possess adanal suckers; and both sexes generally have the genital and anal openings covered by lidlike shields.

The Oribatei, although divided into many larger groups by European workers, can be easily separated into two distinct groups—the Aptyctima and the Ptyctima—in that in the former the propodosoma is not movably hinged with the hysterosoma, whereas it is hinged in the latter group.

Within the Aptyctima we find several natural groups based on the genital-anal plate arrangement, and possession or lack of pteromorphs or wings. Because of the complexity and uncertainty of these divisions the reader is referred to Vitzthum, Willmann, and Sellnick. A rather comprehensive study of these mites as a whole will have to be made before these characters can be properly weighed and evaluated.

The oribatid mites, once considered as of taxonomic interest only, have gained economic importance owing to the discovery that many of them have been found to be hosts of various tapeworms. In studies of soil fauna there is an indication that these mites, which constitute a high percentage of the fauna, are important factors in promoting soil fertility through breaking down organic matter by digestion, as do the earthworms. These two factors alone, the second possibly of really great importance, are enough to warrant more extensive study of the bionomics of this large, soil-inhabiting group. Jacot, in the United States, had made a start toward this goal before he died but had accomplished little; Trägårdh, in Sweden, in his study of forest soils has contributed some knowledge; and Marie Hammer and S. L. Tuxen are at present doing extensive work on the soil fauna, especially on the oribatid mites, in Denmark. As can be seen, much remains to be done. It is in the study of the soil fauna that the sampling funnels— Berlese, Tullgren, and others, and their modifications—have come into use, and through these one can gain an insight into the tremendous amount of material which can be found in the soil.

Kates and Runkel 1948 have reviewed the literature on the oribatids as vectors of the sheep tapeworm, *Moniezia expansa,* and also report on the other species of tapeworm which are known to utilize the oribatid mites as intermediate hosts. Apparently there are no taxonomic units of mites that are vectors; rather it appears that the determining factor is which species is dominant in the sheep pasture and which is able to swallow the eggs of the tapeworm. Many mites are present in pastures but are too small to be vectors; other mites capable of being the intermediate host under laboratory conditions will be found to be forest-humus-inhabiting mites, not pasture forms, and therefore of no importance in transmitting the tapeworm. To date, mites in the families Galumnidae, Oribatulidae, Carabodidae, Notaspididae, Pelopidae, Liacaridae, and Haplozetidae have been found to be vectors of various tapeworms. The species involved will be listed under their respective families. This list is by no means to be considered complete, but merely an indication of the number of mites which will probably be found to be vectors upon future study.

To obtain a background for the study of the oribatids, it is necessary to have available the early papers by H. E. Ewing, which covered the taxonomy of these mites in the Illinois region; the various papers by A. P. Jacot, which can be found listed in his obituary in the "Florida Entomologist," Vol. XXIV, No. 2, pp. 43-47, 1941; the beautifully illustrated papers by François Grandjean of France; A. D. Michael's two volumes, "British Oribatidae," Vol. 1, 1881 and Vol. 2, 1883; and the two excellent German publications, one by Carl Willmann, "Moosmilben oder Oribatiden (Oribatei), Tierwelt Deutschland," Vol. 22, pp. 79-200, 1931, and the other by Max Sellnick, "Formenkreiss: Hornmilben, Oribatei, Die Tierwelt Mitteleuropas," Vol. 3, pp.

1-42, 1929. There are many other papers in the literature which will have to be studied before critical work can be done on the group, but the above list will give a beginner an idea of the group. At the time of this writing very little work has been done on the fauna west of the Mississippi River and this region remains practically unknown. Eastern North America, especially the northeastern region, has been studied to a certain extent by A. P. Jacot who found an influx of some European species. One of these [for example, *Scheloribates laevigatus* (Koch)] has been reported by Kates and Runkel 1948 from as far west as North Dakota. This species is a well-known German one and is also to be found in Russia. Thus some care must be taken when studying the western forms, and they should be compared with eastern and European species. This holds true for all mites, both free-living and parasitic.

Since, as a whole, very little is known of the habits of the oribatids, nothing will be given under the family headings on biology unless definitely known. It is at present sufficient to say that they are generally soil and debris livers and are also to be found on tree trunks, in moss, lichens, and similar habitats, where they feed on the organic matter. *Hydrozetes* is an exception in that it lives in water.

Because of the complexities of the divisions created by the European workers (cohorts, phalanges, etc.) the group is here presented as a single large unit divided into families only. A few of the families are not so distinct as desired and may, in future time, be recombined. In a few cases certain families have been suppressed but, as a whole, the present family arrangement has been kept, even though morphological characters do not always appear to warrant the divisions.

Key to the Oribatei [1]

1. Mouth parts not visible from above; soft- or hard-bodied   2

    Mouths parts visible from above; soft-bodied   Palaeacaridae

2. Prosoma and opisthosoma not hinged together   3

    Prosoma and opisthosoma hinged together (armadillo-like)   32

3. Genital and anal openings not in common ventral plate; the boundary separating these openings close behind genital plates, and anal opening at posterior end of hysterosoma   4

    Genital and anal openings in common ventral plate   5

[1] Based on keys by Sellnick and Willmann.

4. Hysterosoma cylindrical; genital opening small, far to rear and in front of anal opening   Eulohmanniidae

   Hysterosoma pouchlike or baglike; genital opening far to front; space between anal and genital openings equal to length of anal opening   Nanhermanniidae

   Genital and anal openings each lying in separate ventral plate   Epilohmanniidae

5. Genital and anal opening large, touching each other and covering entire length of opisthosoma   6

   Genital and anal opening moderately small, more or less trapezoid shape or oval, separated from each other by distinct section of ventral plate   13

6. Genital and anal opening in common, narrow frame   7

   Genital and anal opening not in narrow frame, but in broad, common, ventral plate that reaches to lateral margins of hysterosoma 10

7. Hysterosoma with flat venter and dorsum either flat or weakly arched   8

   Hysterosoma cylindrical   .   Lohmanniidae

8. Dorsum of hysterosoma lightly arched   9

   Dorsum of hysterosoma flat, usually with raised margin or sunken dorsal surface   Camisiidae

9. With pseudostigmata and pseudostigmatic organs; with or without transverse sutures on hysterosoma   Hypochthoniidae

   Without pseudostigmata or pseudostigmatic organs and in their place only simple setae; no transverse sutures   Malaconothridae

10. Adults bearing cast skins of immature stages on dorsum   11

    Adults not bearing cast skins on dorsum of hysterosoma which is strongly arched   Hermanniidae

11. Without tubelike or other projections on lateral margins of hysterosoma   12

    With tubelike or other projections on lateral margin of hysterosoma   Hermanniellidae

12. Dorsum of hysterosoma flat or weakly arched; genital plates divided by transverse suture   Neoliodidae

    Dorsum of hysterosoma flat; body and legs covered by thick layer of secretion; genital plates not divided by transverse suture   Plateremaeidae

13. Hysterosoma without pteromorphs or wings 14

Hysterosoma with distinct, although at times small, pteromorphs or wings 21

14. Chelicerae of usual shape—chelate—for chewing 15

Chelicerae long, narrow, knifelike, toothed on distal end   Gustaviidae

15. Fourth, and all, legs normal, not adapted for jumping 16

Fourth pair of legs adapted for jumping; in death leg directed forward   Zetorchestidae

16. Lateral and posterior margins of dorsal shield not bent ventrally 17

Lateral and posterior margins of dorsal shield bent ventrally, so that large part of dorsal shield to be seen on ventral side   Cymbaeremaeidae

17. Legs III and IV on lateral margins of venter or not far from them 18

Legs III and IV beneath venter and fairly distant from lateral margins   Liacaridae

18. Legs of usual structure, shorter than body or not beadlike; propodosoma with lamellae-like, ridged, or bladelike prominences 19

Legs long, usually longer than body, or when not as long then constricted in form of beadlike necklace, each segment strikingly bulblike, swollen   Belbidae

19. With or without suture between propodosoma and hysterosoma; with pseudostigmata and pseudostigmatic organs 20

Without suture between propodosoma and hysterosoma; no pseudostigmata or pseudostigmatic organs; no tectopedia II and III   Ameronothridae

20. Dorsum of hysterosoma smooth or weakly punctate; femora I and II never with strikingly long petiole   Eremaeidae

Dorsum of hysterosoma usually with strong sculpturing or weak punctations; femora I and II frequently with thin stalk or petiole and swollen distally   Carabodidae

21. Pteromorphs not movably hinged 22

Pteromorphs movably hinged to body 28

22. Pteromorphs attached to hysterosoma only; not covering large portion of propodosoma 23

Pteromorphs attached to both hysterosoma and propodosoma, covering pseudostigmata and even pseudostigmatic organs and good portion of propodosoma; with small pteromorphs not directed ventrally; with two pairs of genital setae   Oripodidae

23. Pteromorphs extending well past anterior margin of hysterosoma 24

    Pteromorphs not extending past anterior margin of hysterosoma 25

24. Pteromorphs extending anteriorly but not ventrally from place of insertion; lamellae may be large but not spectacularly so
                                                              Tenuialidae

    Pteromorphs extending well anteriorly past anterior margin of hysterosoma and strongly curving ventrally; lamellae cover propodosoma   Notaspididae

25. Pteromorphs not large nor curving ventrally   26
    Pteromorphs large and curving ventrally; lamellae cover propodosoma   Oribatellidae

26. Lamellae not covering most of propodosoma; chelicerae normal, without processes   27

    Lamellae covering most of propodosoma; fixed chela of chelicerae with forward-directed hornlike process   Microzetidae

27. Pteromorphs in one plane only, not curving ventrally; with four pairs of genital setae in adults   Oribatulidae

    Pteromorphs curving ventrally; with six pairs of genital setae in adults   Ceratozetidae

28. Pteromorphs not extending anterior or posterior to line of attachment (hinge) to body   29

    Pteromorphs extending anteriorly and posteriorly to line of attachment to body   30

29. Genital plates with five pairs of setae (occasionally four according to Vitzthum); chelicerae normal, strong; interlamellar setae normal   Haplozetidae

    Genital plates with six pairs of setae; chelicerae (except in *Propelops*) long, slender, with minute shears; interlamellar setae may be normal, missing, or spatulate   Pelopidae

30. Lamellae not covering much of propodosoma   31

    Lamellae covering most of propodosoma; genital plates with five pairs of setae; anterior pair of circumanal setae next to anterior end of anal opening   Epactozetidae

31. Genital plates with six pairs of setae; anterior pair of circumanal
setae laterad of anal plates   Galumnidae

     Genital plates with five pairs of setae; anterior pair of circumanal
setae anterior to anal plate   Parakalummidae

32. Hysterosoma not segmented   33

     Hysterosoma segmented   Protoplophoridae

33. Genital and anal openings lying in large plate and separated from
each other   Mesoplophoridae

     Genital and anal openings not lying in large plate and touching
each other   Phthiracaridae

Palaeacaridae Grandjean, 1932

Figures 312–315

Diagnosis: These mites have a very thin cuticle without special
sclerotization. Their body is divided into a propodosoma and a hysterosoma with a neck-shaped constriction between both. The propo-

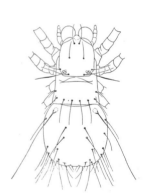

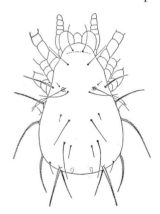

Figure 312 *Grandjeanacarus araneola*
Grandjean. Dorsum of female.
(After Grandjean 1932)

Figure 313 *Acaronychus trägårdhi*
Grandjean. Dorsum of female. (After
Grandjean 1932)

dosoma has five pairs of setae (the rostral, lamellar, interlamellar, exo-
stigmatic, and angular setae). Pseudostigmatic organs are filiform or
lanceolate and are inserted into simple, cuplike pseudostigmata. The
chelicerae are large, uncovered, project far in front of the rostral plate,
and have dentate chelae adapted for chewing vegetable substances.

Composed of five segments, the palpi are simple. The maxillae have two pairs of appendages: the exterior maxillary lobes are strongly sclerotized, dentate at the tip, and two-segmented; the inner, thin maxillary plates have three pairs of setae. The legs are five- or six-segmented. Transverse sutures and transverse rows of setae may or may not be present on the hysterosoma. The respiratory system consists of stigmata on the exterior side of the base of the chelicerae and has short tracheae (according to Trägårdh).

Although Grandjean 1932 divided this group into three distinct families—the Palaeacaridae, Acaronychidae, and Parhypochthonidae—it is thought best for the present to keep these mites in one family—the Palaeacaridae—with subfamily divisions. Trägårdh 1932 erected a new suborder for these, calling it Palaeacariformes; Grandjean 1932 argued that these mites were primitive oribatids and

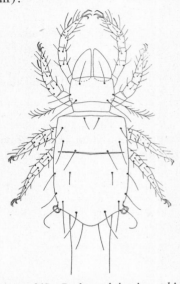

Figure 314 *Acaronychus trägårdhi* Grandjean. Lateral view of female. (After Grandjean 1932)

Figure 315 *Parhypochthonius aphidinus* Berlese. Dorsum of female. (After Berlese 1904)

did not constitute a separate group whereas Zakhvatkin 1945, 1946, without further amplification, stated that his studies warranted the suborder rank given them by Trägårdh. The present classification, that of being the most primitive family of oribatids, is used more or less arbitrarily and, as in many cases, final decision will have to await further work on the part of the specialists interested in these primitive forms.

Key to the Palaeacaridae

1. With six free leg segments   2

   With five free leg segments; hysterosoma with transverse sutures and separated from propodosoma by suture   Parhypochthoniinae

2. Hysterosoma with transverse suture; suture between propodosoma and hysterosoma; two or three pairs of genital suckers   Palaeacarinae

Hysterosoma without transverse sutures; no true segmentation between propodosoma and hysterosoma; with three pairs of genital suckers and peculiar genital armature of spinelike processes
Acaronychinae

Palaeacarinae Grandjean, 1932

Genera:

1. *Palaeacarus* Trägårdh, 1932
   Type. *Palaeacarus hystricinus* Trägårdh, 1932
2. *Aphelacarus* Grandjean, 1932
   Type. *Parhypochthoninus acarinus* Berlese, 1910
3. *Archeonothrus* Trägårdh, 1906
   Type. *Archeonothrus natalensis* Trägårdh, 1906
4. *Beklemishevia* Zakhvatkin, 1945
   Type. *Beklemishevia galeodula* Zakhvatkin, 1945
5. *Grandjeanacarus* Zakhvatkin, 1945
   Type. *Palaeacarus araneola* Grandjean, 1932
6. *Trägårdhacarus* Zakhvatkin, 1945
   Type. *Trägårdhacarus lapshovi* Zakhvatkin, 1945

Acaronychinae Grandjean, 1932

Genus:

Acaronychus Grandjean, 1932
Type. *Acaronychus trägårdhi* Grandjean, 1932

Parhypochthoniinae Grandjean, 1932

Genera:

1. *Parhypochthonius* Berlese, 1904
   Type. *Parhypochthonius aphidinus* Berlese, 1904
2. *Gehypochthonius* Jacot, 1936
   Type. *Gehypochthonius rhadamantus* Jacot, 1936

Discussion: These mites are little known and have been seen by only a few acarologists. They live in forest soil and debris and will probably be found to be more common than suspected when more thorough collections are made.

References:

Grandjean, F. 1932. Au sujet des *Palaeacariformes* Trägårdh. Bull. Paris Mus. d'Hist. Nat. Ser. 2, 4(4):411–426.

Jacot, A. P. 1936. Some primitive moss-mites of North Carolina. J. Elisha Mitchell Sci. Soc. 52(1):20–26, Pl. 1.

——. 1936. More primitive moss-mites of North Carolina. J. Elisha Mitchell Sci. Soc. 52(2):247–353, Pl. 20.

——. 1938. More primitive moss-mites of North Carolina—III. J. Elisha Mitchell Sci. Soc. 54(1):127–137, Pls. 12, 12.

Trägårdh, I. 1932. Palaeacariformes, a new suborder of Acari. Arkiv. för Zoologi, 24 B(2):1–6.

Zakhvatkin, A. 1945. On the discovery of Palaeacariformes (Acarina) in the U.S.S.R. Comptes Rendus (Doklady) de l'Academie des Sciences de l'U.S.S.R. 47(9):673–676 (English text).

——. 1945. Étude morphologique sur *Beklemishevia galeodula* n. g. et n. sp.—representant nouveau des Palaeacariformes (Acarina). Moskov. Obshch. Isp. Prirody, Otd. Biol. Biul. (Soc. Nat. de Moscou, Sect. Biol. Bul.) an. 116, 50:60–71 (French summary, Russian text).

Eulohmanniidae Grandjean, 1931

Figure 316

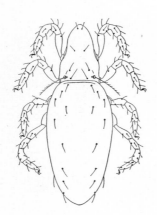

Diagnosis: The eulohmanniids are slender, elongated mites whose propodosoma and hysterosoma are connected by a thin membrane. The hysterosoma is cylindrical. Genital plates are placed far towards the rear and are separated from the anal plates by the hysterosomal plate suture.

Figure 316   *Eulohmannia ribagai* Berlese. Dorsum of female. (After Berlese 1910)

Genera:

1. *Eulohmannia* Berlese, 1910 (= *Arthronothrus* Trägårdh, 1910)
   Type. *Lohmannia* (*Eulohmannia*) *ribagai* Berlese, 1910
2. *Collohmannia* Sellnick, 1922
   Type. *Collohmannia gigantea* Sellnick, 1922
3. *Perlohmannia* Berlese, 1916
   Type. *Lohmannia insignis* Berlese, 1904

Discussion: *Collohmannia* and *Perlohmannia* are placed here tentatively until more critical study can be made.

Nanhermanniidae Sellnick, 1924

Figures 317, 318

Diagnosis: These mites are elongated, narrow, and have a pouchlike hysterosoma. Anal plates are placed on the venter at the rear; genital plates are located anteriorly and are separated from the anal opening

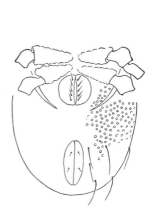 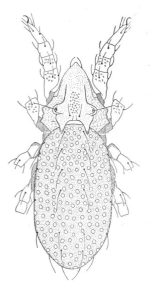

Figure 317 *Nanhermannia nana* (Nicolet). Venter of hysterosoma showing division line between genital and anal plates.

Figure 318 *Nanhermannia elegantula* Berlese. Dorsum of female. (After Berlese 1913)

by a suture between the dorsum and the venter of the hysterosoma. The suture has moved forward on the venter so as not to include the anal opening which actually lies in a ventral portion of the dorsal shield.

Genus:

 Nanhermannia Berlese, 1913
 Type. *Nothrus nanus* Nicolet, 1855

Reference:

Hartman, A. G. 1949. A new species of Nanhermannia with notes on the genus. Proc. Ent. Soc. Wash. 51(4):169–171.

Epilohmanniidae Oudemans, 1923

Figures 319, 320

Diagnosis: These mites are small and have two ventral plates, one behind the other, each with a posterior indentation which encloses the genital, or, respectively, the anal plates. There are no lamellae or tec-

Figure 319 *Epilohmannia cylindrica* (Berlese). Venter of female showing divisions of plates. (After Oudemans 1915)

Figure 320 *Epilohmannia cylindrica* (Berlese). Venter of larva showing the organ of Claparède between coxae I and II (see *Rhizoglyphus echinopus* larva). (After Grandjean 1946)

topedia. The last four segments of the legs are almost equal in length and there is one claw. The palpus is two-segmented and the mouth parts are hidden from above. The larval form of *Epilohmannia cylindrica* (Berlese) possesses the Claparède organ.

Genera:

1. *Epilohmannia* Berlese, 1916 (= *Lesseria* Oudemans, 1916)
   Type. *Lohmannia cylindrica* Berlese, 1904
2. *Archegozetes* Grandjean, 1931
   Type. *Epilohmannia* (?) *magna* Sellnick, 1925

Lohmanniidae Grandjean, 1931

Figures 321, 322

Diagnosis: The lohmanniids have a cylindrical hysterosoma which is broadly attached to the propodosoma. The genital and anal plates are contiguous. The palpi have four movable segments.

 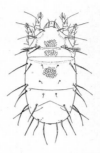

Figure 321 *Torpacarus omittens* Grandjean. Venter of female. (After Grandjean 1950)

Figure 322 *Torpacarus omittens* Grandjean. Dorsum of female. (After Grandjean 1950)

Genera:

1. *Lohmannia* Michael, 1898 (= *Michaelia* Haller, 1884, *nom. prae-occ.*)
   Type. *Michaelia paradoxa* Haller, 1884
2. *Annectacarus* Grandjean, 1950
   Type. *Annectacarus mucronatus* Grandjean, 1950
3. *Cryptacarus* Grandjean, 1950
   Type. *Cryptacarus promecus* Grandjean, 1950
4. *Meristacarus* Grandjean, 1934
   Type. *Meristacarus porcula* Grandjean, 1934
5. *Thamnacarus* Grandjean, 1950
   Type. *Lohmannia deserticola* Grandjean, 1934
6. *Torpacarus* Grandjean, 1950
   Type. *Torpacarus omittens* Grandjean, 1950

Discussion: Grandjean 1950 has limited the family to the above genera, stating that they are an isolated, homogeneous group with primitive characters. They lack tracheae, lateral-hysterosomal glands, and have a gradual development in which the larval, three nymphal, and adult stages resemble one another.

Reference:

Grandjean, F. 1950. Étude sur les Lohmanniidae (Oribates, Acariens). Archiv. Zool. Exper. et Generale 87(2):95–161.

Hypochthoniidae Berlese, 1910

Figures 323–326

Diagnosis: None, one, or several transverse sutures divide the dorsum of the hysterosoma into several sections. The body is weakly sclerotized. The genital plates are usually broader than the anal plates.

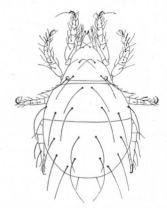

Figure 323   *Pterochthonius angelus* (Berlese). Dorsum of female, detail of propodosomal seta, palpus, clawlike set of ovapositor, and chelicera. (After Grandjean 1950)

Figure 324   *Hypochthonius rufulus* var. *paucipectinatus* Jacot. Dorsum of female.

Only one egg develops at a time except in *Trhypochthonius* and *Trhypochthoniellus* where four to six eggs may mature simultaneously. These two genera have been placed in a distinct subfamily—Trhypochthoniinae—by Willmann, and into a family by Vitzthum. Grandjean 1946 divided the Hypochthoniidae into the Hypochthoniidae, Brachychthoniidae, Cosmochthoniidae, and Sphaerochthoniidae, these being based upon the number and location of the transverse sutures; in 1950 he erected the family Pterochthoniidae for *Pterochthonius angelus* (Berlese), basing it upon the primitive chelicerae, the retention of the preanal segment, the clawlike ovipositor setae, and the large, ornate body setae. This is a primitive mite to be found in west-

ern Europe and the mountains of Mexico. Sellnick placed all the gen-·
era under one family and his grouping is being retained, although
future work will probably corroborate Grandjean's findings.

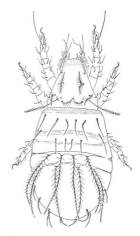

Figure 325 *Cosmochthonius plumatus*
Berlese. Dorsum of female.

Figure 326 *Eniochthonius pallidulus*
(Michael). Ventral plates of female.
(After Grandjean 1933)

Genera:

1. *Hypochthonius* Koch, 1836 (= *Hypochthoniella* Berlese, 1910
   = *Arthrochthonius* Ewing, 1917)
   Type. *Hypochthonius rufulus* Koch, 1836
2. *Amnemochthonius* Grandjean, 1948
   Type. *Amnemochthonius taeniophorus* Grandjean, 1948
3. *Atopochthonius* Grandjean, 1948
   Type. *Atopochthonius artiodactylus* Grandjean, 1948
4. *Brachychochthonius* Jacot, 1938
   Type. *Brachychochthonius jugatus* Jacot, 1938
5. *Brachychthonius* Berlese, 1910
   Type. *Hypochthonius brevis* Michael, 1887
6. *Cosmochthonius* Berlese, 1910
   Type. *Hypochthonius lanatus* Michael, 1887
7. *Eniochthonius* Grandjean, 1933
   Type. *Hypochthonius pallidulus* Michael, 1887
8. *Eobrachychthonius* Jacot, 1936
   Type. *Eobrachychthonius sexnotatus* Jacot, 1936
9. *Eohypochthonius* Jacot, 1938
   Type. *Hypochthonius gracilis* Jacot, 1936

· 10. *Epilohmannoides* Jacot, 1936
   Type. *Epilohmannoides terrae* Jacot, 1936
11. *Haplochthonius* Willmann, 1930
   Type. *Haplochthonius simplex* Willmann, 1930
12. *Heterochthonius* Berlese, 1910
   Type. *Cosmochthonius (Heterochthonius) gibbus* Berlese, 1910
13. *Malacoangelia* Berlese, 1913
   Type. *Malacoangelia remigera* Berlese, 1910
14. *Poecilochthonius* Balogh, 1943
   Type. *Brachychthonius italicus* Berlese, 1910
15. *Pterochthonius* Berlese, 1913
   Type. *Cosmochthonius angelus* Berlese, 1910
16. *Sphaerochthonius* Berlese, 1910
   Type. *Hypochthonius splendidus* Berlese, 1904
17. *Trhypochthoniellus* Willmann, 1928
   Type. *Trhypochthoniellus setosus* Willmann, 1928
18. *Trhypochthonius* Berlese, 1904 (= *Tumidalvus* Ewing, 1908)
   Type. *Hypochthonius tectorum* Berlese, 1896

References:

Grandjean, F. 1928. Sur un oribatidé pourvu d'yeux. Bull. Soc. Zool. France 53(4):235–242.
——. 1946. Les *Enarthronota* (Acariens) 1 serie. Annales Sciences Naturelles ser. Botanique et Zoologie, 11 Ser., 8:213–248.
——. 1948. Les *Enarthronota* (Acariens) 2 serie. Annales Sciences Naturelles ser. Botanique et Zoologie, 11 Ser., 10:29–58.
——. 1950. Les *Enarthronota* (Acariens) 3 serie. Annales Sciences Naturelles ser. Botanique et Zoologie, 11 Ser., 12:85–107.
Jacot, A. P. See references under Palaeacaridae.
Womersley, H. 1945. Australian Acarina. The genera *Brachychthonius* Berl. and *Cosmochthonius* Berl. (Hypochthonidae-Oribatoidea). Records South Austral. Mus. 8:(2):219–223.

Malaconothridae Berlese, 1916

Figure 327

Diagnosis: These mites are generally grayish-
or yellowish-brown in color. The dorsum of the
body is slightly convex. There are no true pseudostigmata or pseudostigmatic organs but there
is a simple bristle instead.

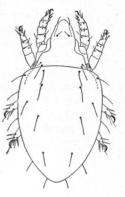

Figure 327 *Malaconothrus egregia* Berlese. Dorsum
of female. Note lack of pseudostigmatic organs. (After
Berlese 1905)

Genera:

1. *Malaconothrus* Berlese, 1905
   Type. *Nothrus monodactylus* Michael, 1888
2. *Mucronothrus* Trägårdh, 1931
   Type. *Mucronothrus rostratus* Trägårdh, 1931
3. *Trimalaconothrus* Berlese, 1916
   Type. *Malaconothrus* (*Trimalaconothrus*) *indusiatus* Berlese, 1916

Camisiidae Sellnick, 1928

Figure 328

Diagnosis: The genital and anal openings are contiguous. Small, sclerotic strips or plates lie close to the genital and
anal openings; the anal opening is closed by a
pair of striplike, sclerotic plates. The pseudostigmatic organs are either funnel- or shell-
shaped. Usually with raised margins, the dorsum
of the hysterosoma is flat. Many of the species
of *Camisia* have characteristic elongated processes on the posterior margin of the body.

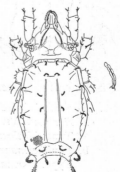

Figure 328 *Camisia segnis* (Hermann). Dorsum of female and dorsal seta enlarged. (After Grandjean 1936)

Genera:

1. *Camisia* v. Heyden, 1826
   Type. *Notaspis segnis* Hermann, 1804
2. *Acronothrus* Berlese, 1916
   Type. *Nothrus cophinarius* Michael, 1907
3. *Heminothrus* Berlese, 1913
   Type. *Nothrus targionii* Berlese, 1885
4. *Nothrus* Koch, 1836 (= *Angelia* Berlese, 1885 = *Gymnonothrus* Ewing, 1917)
   Type. *Nothrus palustris* Koch, 1839
5. *Platynothrus* Berlese, 1913
   Type. *Nothrus peltifer* Koch, 1839
6. *Uronothrus* Berlese, 1913
   Type. *Nothrus segnis* Koch, 1839

Hermanniidae Sellnick, 1928

Figures 329–331

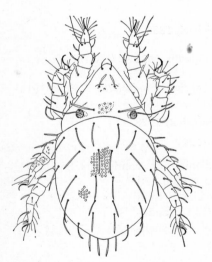

Diagnosis: The hermanniids have a strongly convex hysterosoma. Their genital and anal plates are contiguous in the common ventral plate.

Figure 329 *Hermannia gibba* (Koch). Dorsum of female.

Genera and subgenera:

1. *Hermannia* Nicolet, 1855
   a. *Hermannia* s. str.
      Type. *Nothrus gibbus* Koch, 1839
   b. *Phyllhermannia* Berlese, 1916
      Type. *Hermannia phyllophora* Michael, 1908

2. *Masthermannia* Berlese, 1913
Type. *Angelia mammillaris* Berlese, 1904

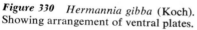

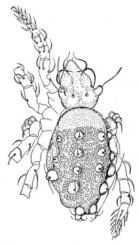

Figure 330 *Hermannia gibba* (Koch). Showing arrangement of ventral plates.

Figure 331 *Masthermannia mammillaris* (Berlese). Showing bizzare structures occasionally found in mites. (After Berlese 1913)

Neoliodidae Willmann, 1913

Figures 332, 333

Diagnosis: The lateral and posterior margins of the dorsal shields are bent angularly toward the venter so that a considerable portion of the dorsal shield lies ventrally. The dorsum of the hysterosoma is completely covered with cast skins (which lie one on the other) of the young stages. Each flap of the genital opening is divided into two parts by a transverse suture.

Genera:

1. *Neoliodes* Berlese, 1888 (= *Liodes* Heyden, 1826, *nom. praeocc.* = *Udetaliodes* Jacot, 1929)
   Type. *Notaspis theleproctus* Hermann, 1804
2. *Embolacarus* Sellnick, 1918 (fossil)
   Type. *Embolacarus pergratus* Sellnick, 1918 (according to Vitzthum the systematic position of this genus is uncertain)
3. *Platyliodes* Berlese, 1916
   Type. *Nothrus doderleinii* Berlese, 1883

4. *Poroliodes* Grandjean, 1934
   Type. *Nothrus theleproctus* Michael, 1888
5. *Teleioliodes* Grandjean, 1934
   Type. *Teleioliodes madininensis* Grandjean, 1934

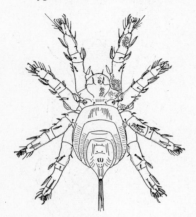 

Figure 332 *Teoliodes madininensis* Grandjean. Dorsum of female. (After Grandjean 1934)

Figure 333 *Neoliodes* sp. Venter, showing arrangement of ventral plates.

Cymbaeremaeidae Willmann, 1931

Figures 334, 335

 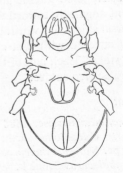

Figure 334 *Cymbaeremaeus* (*Scapheremaeus*) *marginalis* (Banks). Dorsum of female.

Figure 335 *Cymbaeremaeus* (*Scapheremaeus*) *marginalis* (Banks). Venter of female showing arrangement of shields and plates.

Diagnosis: Apterogasterina. The dorsal shield is turned under toward the venter so that when it is seen from below a large part of the dorsal armor can also be seen. The body is variously sculptured.

Genera and subgenera:

1. *Cymbaeremaeus* Berlese, 1896
   a. *Cymbaeremaeus* s. str.
      Type. *Eremaeus cymba* Nicolet, 1855
   b. *Scapheremaeus* Berlese, 1910 (= *Mulvius* Sellnick, 1918, fossil)
      Type. *Eremaeus cymba* Berlese, 1886
2. *Eremella* Berlese, 1913
   Type. *Eremella vestita* Berlese, 1913
3. *Micreremus* Berlese, 1908
   Type. *Eremaeus brevipes* Michael, 1888
4. *Tectocymba* Sellnick, 1918, fossil
   Type. *Tectocymba rara* Sellnick, 1918

Belbidae Willmann, 1931

Figures 336–338

Diagnosis: Apterogasterina. Their chelic-erae are normal as is the dorsal plate which does not curve ventrally. Legs III and IV are placed on or near the edge of the body. Usually these are large mites

Figure 336 *Belba* sp. Leg I.

with legs which are longer than their body; smaller species have legs in which the shape of the segments gives a beaded effect. Sometimes they carry cast skins of immature stages on the dorsum.

Genera and subgenera:

1. *Belba* v. Heyden, 1826
   Type. *Notaspis corynopus* Hermann, 1804
2. *Allodamaeus* Banks, 1947
   Type. *Allodamaeus ewingi* Banks, 1947
3. *Amerus* Berlese, 1896
   a. *Amerus* s. str.
      Type. *Belba troisii* Berlese, 1883
   b. *Neamerus* Willmann, 1939
      Type. *Amerus (Neamerus) lundbladi* Willmann, 1939
4. *Damaeus* Koch, 1836
   Type. *Damaeus auritus* Koch, 1836

5. *Dameobelba* Sellnick, 1928
   Type. *Oribata minutissimus* Sellnick, 1920
6. *Gymnodamaeus* Kulczynski, 1902
   Type. *Damaeus bicostatus* Koch, 1836

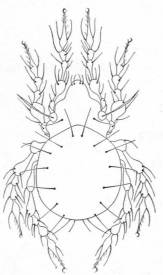

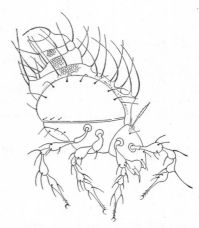

Figure 337 *Belba jacoti* Wilson. Dorsum of female without cast skins on dorsum. (After Wilson 1936)

Figure 338 *Belba jacoti* Wilson. Female with cast nymphal skins on back. (After Wilson 1936)

7. *Jacotella* Banks, 1947
   Type. *Gymnodamaeus quadricaudiculus* Jacot, 1937
8. *Porobelba* Grandjean, 1936
   Type. *Oribata spinosus* Sellnick, 1920

Eremaeidae Willmann, 1931

Figures 339, 340

Diagnosis: The lateral and posterior margins of the hysterosoma are not turned under. Legs III and IV are articulated at the lateral margin of the ventral surface or only a short distance from it. The legs are shorter than the body and of ordinary structure. Femora I and II lack a conspicuous stalk or projecting scapular angles. The propodosoma has ledgelike or leaflike lamellae and the dorsum of the hysterosoma is either smooth or weakly punctate.

Genera and subgenera:

1. *Eremaeus* Koch, 1836
   Type. *Eremaeus hepaticus* Koch, 1836
2. *Amerobelba* Berlese, 1908
   Type. *Amerobelba decedens* Berlese, 1908
3. *Autogneta* Hull, 1916
   Type. *Notaspis longilamellata* Michael, 1888

 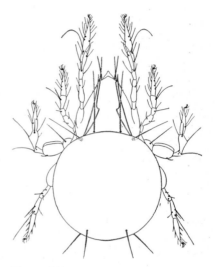

Figure 339 *Lucoppia* sp. Venter of female showing leg attachment.

Figure 340 *Ceratoppia bipilis* (Hermann). Dorsum of female.

4. *Caleremaeus* Berlese, 1910
   Type. *Notaspis monilipes* Michael, 1882
5. *Calvoppia* Jacot, 1934
   Type. *Calvoppia perkinsi* Jacot, 1934
6. *Ceratoppia* Berlese, 1908
   Type. *Notaspis bipilis* Hermann, 1804
7. *Conoppia* Berlese, 1908
   Type. *Oppia microptera* Berlese, 1885
8. *Damaeolus* Paoli, 1908
   Type. *Damaeosoma aperatum* Berlese, 1903
9. *Dampfiella* Sellnick, 1931
   Type. *Dampfiella procera* Sellnick, 1931
10. *Dolicheremaeus* Jacot, 1938
    Type. *Dolicheremaeus rubripedes* Jacot, 1938

11. *Eremobelba* Berlese, 1908
    Type. *Eremaeus leporosus* Haller, 1884
12. *Eremulus* Berlese, 1908
    a. *Eremulus* s. str.
    Type. *Eremulus flagellifer* Berlese, 1908
    b. *Epieremulus* Berlese, 1916
    Type. *Eremulus (Epieremulus) geometricus* Berlese, 1916
13. *Gradidorsum* Sellnick, 1918, fossil
    Type. *Gradidorsum asper* Sellnick, 1918
14. *Gymnodampia* Jacot, 1937
    Type. *Amerobelba setata* Berlese, 1916
15. *Imparatoppia* Jacot, 1934
    Type. *Imparatoppia imparata* Jacot, 1934
16. *Halozetes* Berlese, 1916
    Type. *Notaspis marina* Lohmann, 1907
17. *Lawrencoppia* Jacot, 1934
    Type. *Lawrencoppia mauritius* Jacot, 1934
18. *Hydrozetes* Berlese, 1902
    Type. *Notaspis lacustris* Michael, 1882
19. *Licneremaeus* Paoli, 1908
    Type. *Notaspis licnophorus* Michael, 1882
20. *Licnobelba* Grandjean, 1931
    Type. *Licnobelba alestensis* Grandjean, 1931
21. *Licnodamaeus* Grandjean, 1931
    Type. *Licneremaeus undulatus* Paoli, 1908
22. *Licnoliodes* Grandjean, 1931
    Type. *Licnoliodes andrei* Grandjean, 1931
23. *Lucoppia* Berlese, 1908
    a. *Lucoppia* s. str.
    Type. *Zetes lucorum* Koch, 1840
    b. *Phauloppia* Berlese, 1908
    Type. *Oppia conformis* Berlese, 1895
24. *Metrioppia* Grandjean, 1931
    Type. *Metrioppia helvetica* Grandjean, 1931
25. *Nasozetes* Sellnick, 1930
    Type. *Nasozetes sumatrensis* Sellnick, 1930
26. *Oppia* Koch, 1836 (= *Dameosoma* Berlese, 1892 = *Amolops* Hull, 1916 = *Dissorhina* Hull, 1916 = *Zetobelba* Hull, 1916)
    Type. *Oppia nitens* Koch, 1836
27. *Oppiella* Jacot, 1937
    Type. *Dameosoma corrugatum* Berlese, 1904
28. *Oribata* Latreille, 1802
    Type. *Acarus geniculatus* Linnaeus, 1758

29. *Paraliodes* Hall, 1911
    Type. *Paraliodes incurvata* Hall, 1911
30. *Oribella* Berlese, 1908
    Type. *Notaspis pectinata* Michael, 1885
31. *Peloppia* Sellnick, 1931
    Type. *Peloppia serrata* Sellnick, 1931
32. *Phyllotegeus* Berlese, 1913
    Type. *Leiosoma palmicinctum* Michael, 1883
33. *Polypterozetes* Berlese, 1916
    Type. *Polyterozetes cherubin* Berlese, 1916
34. *Rhynchoribates* Grandjean, 1929
    Type. *Rhynchoribates rostratus* Grandjean, 1929
35. *Strieremaeus* Sellnick, 1918, fossil
    Type. *Strieremaeus illibatus* Sellnick, 1918
36. *Suctobelba* Paoli, 1908
    Type. *Notaspis trigona* Michael, 1888
37. *Suctobelbella* Jacot, 1937
    Type. *Suctobelbella serratirostrum* Jacot, 1937
38. *Suctobelbila* Jacot, 1937
    Type. *Suctobelbila punctillata* Jacot, 1937
39. *Tricheremaeus* Berlese, 1908
    Type. *Notaspis serrata* Michael, 1885
40. *Trizetes* Berlese, 1904
    Type. *Trizetes pyramidalis* Berlese, 1904
41. *Tuberemaeus* Sellnick, 1930
    Type. *Tuberemaeus singularis* Sellnick, 1930

Peloppia and *Metrioppia* have been placed into a separate family—Peloppiidae Balogh, 1943—on the basis of the long, slender chelicerae such as is to be found in many of the Pelopidae. The present, more conservative arrangement is followed here.

References:

Grandjean, F. 1948. Sur les Hydrozetes (Acariens) de l'Europe Occidentale. Bull. Paris Mus. d'Hist. Nat., Ser. 2, 20(4):328–335.

Newell, I. M. 1945. *Hydrozetes* Berlese (Acari, Oribatoidea): The occurrence of the genus in North America, and the phenomenon of levitation. Trans. Conn. Acad. Arts and Sci. 36:253–275.

Strenzke, K. 1950. Bestimmungstabelle der holsteinischen *Suctobelba*-Arten (Acarina: Oribatei). Archiv. für Hydrobiologie 44:340–343.

Carabodidae Willmann, 1931

Figure 341

Diagnosis: The lateral and posterior margins of the hysterosoma are not turned under ventrally. Usually the dorsum of the hysterosoma is coarsely sculptured or at least distinctly punctate. Legs III and IV are articulated at the lateral margin of the ventral surface or very close to it. The legs are of normal structure and are shorter than the body. Femora I and II frequently have a thin stalk and are greatly swollen distally. The propodosoma has lamellae-like protuberances, ledges, or small leaves or shelves.

Figure 341 *Cepheus mirabiloides* Jacot. Dorsum of female.

Genera and subgenera:

1. *Carabodes* Koch, 1836
   a. *Carabodes* s. str.
      Type. *Carabodes coriaceus* Koch, 1836
   b. *Carabocepheus* Berlese, 1910
      Type. *Carabodes (Carabocepheus) lounsburyi* Berlese, 1910
   c. *Otocepheus* Berlese, 1904
      Type. *Carabodes (Otocepheus) longior* Berlese, 1904
2. *Carabodoides* Jacot, 1937
   Type. *Carabodoides saccharomycetoides* Jacot, 1937
3. *Cepheus* Koch, 1836 (= *Tegeocranus* Nicolet, 1855)
   a. *Cepheus* s. str.
      Type. *Cepheus latus* Koch, 1836
   b. *Chaunoproctus* Pearse, 1906
      Type. *Chaunoproctus cancellatus* Pearse, 1906 (poorly described and position uncertain)
   c. *Microtegeus* Berlese, 1916
      Type. *Tegeocranus (Microtegeus) undulatus* Berlese, 1916
   d. *Oribatodes* Banks, 1895
      Type. *Oribatodes mirabilis* Banks, 1895
   e. *Protocepheus* Jacot, 1928
      Type. *Tegeocranus hericius* Michael, 1887

4. *Cerocpheus* Trägårdh, 1931

Type. *Cerocpheus mirabilis* Trägårdh, 1931

5. *Charassobates* Grandjean, 1929

Type. *Charassobates cavernosus* Grandjean, 1929

6. *Eremaeozetes* Berlese, 1913

Type. *Eremaeozetes tuberculatus* Berlese, 1913

7. *Eremobodes* Jacot, 1937

Type. *Eremobodes pectinatus* Jacot, 1937

8. *Eupterotegaeus* Berlese, 1916

Type. *Tegeocranus ornatissimus* Berlese, 1908

9. *Eutegaeus* Berlese, 1916

Type. *Oribata bostocki* Michael, 1908

10. *Neocepheus* Willmann, 1936

Type. *Neocepheus hummelincki* Willmann, 1936

11. *Niphocepheus* Balogh, 1943

Type. *Cepheus nivalis* Schweizer, 1922

12. *Ommatocepheus* Berlese, 1913

Type. *Cepheus ocellatus* Michael, 1882

13. *Passalozetes* Grandjean, 1932

Type. *Passalozetes africanus* Grandjean, 1932

14. *Plategeocranus* Sellnick, 1918, fossil

Type. *Nothrus sulcatus* Karsch, 1884

15. *Pseudocepheus* Jacot, 1928

Type. *Cepheus vulgaris* Nicolet, 1855

16. *Scutoribates* Sellnick, 1918, fossil

Type. *Scutoribates perornatus* Sellnick, 1918

17. *Scutovertex* Michael, 1879

Type. *Scutovertex sculptus* Michael, 1879

18. *Tectocepheus* Berlese, 1913

Type. *Tegeocranus velatus* Michael, 1880

19. *Tegeocranellus* Berlese, 1913

Type. *Tegeocranus laevis* Berlese, 1905

20. *Tritegeus* Berlese, 1913

Type. *Cepheus bifidatus* Nicolet, 1855

21. *Xenillus* Robineau-Desvoidy, 1839 ($=$ *Cepheus* Nicolet, 1855 $=$ *Banksia* Voigts and Oudemans, 1905)

Type. *Notaspis tegeocranus* Hermann, 1804 ($=$ *Xenillus clypeator* Robineau-Desvoidy, 1839)

Discussion: Several species of Carabodidae are known to be vectors of tapeworms. They are *Scutovertex minutus,* vector of *Bertiella studeri, Cittotaenia ctenoides,* and *C. denticulata* in Germany; *Xenillus tegeocranus,* vector of *Cittotaenia ctenoides* and *C. denticulata* in Germany; *Cepheus cepheiformis,* vector of *C. ctenoides* and *C. denticulata* in Germany; and *Carabodidae* sp., vector of *Anoplocephala perfoliata* in the U.S.S.R.

Ameronothridae Willmann, 1931

Figure 342

Diagnosis: A sclerotized formation bridges the propodosoma and the hysterosoma and no true dividing suture is present. The skin is leather-like. There are no pseudostigmata, sensory setae, or tectopodia II and III.

Figure 342 *Ameronothrus schneideri* (Oudemans). Dorsum of female showing lack of suture between propodosoma and hysterosoma. (After Oudemans 1905)

Genus:

Ameronothrus Berlese, 1896
a. *Ameronothrus* s. str.
Type. *Eremaeus lineatus* Thorell, 1871
b. *Hygroribates* Jacot, 1934
Type. *Nothrus* (?) *marinus* Banks, 1896

Discussion: The species belonging to this genus live close to the seashore, usually in the tidal zone. A few are known from Europe. *Ameronothrus* (*Hygroribates*) *marinus* (Banks) was found on rocks in the tidal zone at Sea Cliff, N. Y. Jacot 1934 subsequently found it in restricted areas along the New York coast and Grandjean 1947 collected it on the French coast. Jacot states: "it is evident that this species is distinctly marine though mostly restricted to estuaries and harbors, i.e., where there is not too much sand scour, and thus where growths of films of unicellular algae may develop. It would therefore not be expected on the exposed headlands between the bays where algal coated rocks are rare or absent. I also suspect that it would be rare or absent where rocks are without crannies and fissures. The rougher the rock (as schist) the better. Another factor limiting the spread of the species is that of viviparity. This means that there are no eggs for dissemination by water currents, but that the young are born on the parental stone."

The figure shown is from Oudemans and although lacking in details it does illustrate the family characters. Jacot 1934 gives more detailed studies for the North American form but no general drawing.

References:

Grandjean, F. 1947. Observations sur les Oribates (17e serie). Bull. d'Hist. Nat. Ser. 2, 19(2):165–172.

Jacot, A. P. 1934. An introduced moss mite in America. J. N. Y. Ent. Soc. 42:329–337.

Hermanniellidae Grandjean, 1934

Figures 343–345

Diagnosis: These mites have a small tube which contains the mouth of the oil gland projecting forward on each side of the opisthosoma. If this tube is lacking a strong sclerotized leaflike or wartlike outgrowth appears in its place.

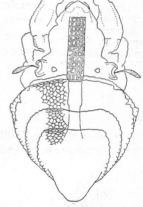

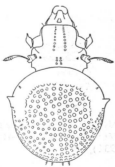

Figure 343 *Plasmobates pagoda* Grandjean. Female carrying cast skins on back and with secretions on legs. (After Grandjean 1929)

Figure 344 *Plasmobates pagoda* Grandjean. Female with cast skins and secretions removed. (After Grandjean 1929)

Figure 345 *Plasmobates pagoda* Grandjean. Chelicera. (After Grandjean 1929)

Genera:

1. *Hermanniella* Berlese, 1908
   Type. *Hermannia granulata* Nicolet, 1855
2. *Plasmobates* Grandjean, 1929
   Type. *Plasmobates pagoda* Grandjean, 1929
3. *Solenozetes* Grandjean, 1931
   Type. *Plasmobates cribratus* Grandjean, 1929

Plateremaeidae Trägårdh, 1931

Figures 346–348

Figure 346 *Platere-maeus vestitus* Trägårdh. Showing articulation between tibia and tarsus IV, femur and genu III, and genu and tibia III. (After Trägårdh 1931)

Diagnosis: The hysterosoma is flat and is covered with four concentrically arranged skins (one larval and three nymphal exuviae). The body and legs are covered with a thick secretion. Terminal ends of the femur, genu, and tibia are narrow, articulating in the sockets of the genu, tibia, and tarsus respectively. Three claws appear on the tip of the small peduncle.

Genus:

Plateremaeus Berlese, 1908
Type. *Damaeus ornatissimus* Berlese, 1888

Figure 347 *Plateremaeus vestitus* Trägårdh. Dorsum of female. (After Trägårdh 1931)

Figure 348 *Plateremaeus vestitus* Trägårdh. Venter of female. (After Trägårdh 1931)

Reference:

Trägårdh, I. 1931. Acarina from the Juan Fernandez Islands. The Natural History of Juan Fernandez and Easter Islands, III. 553–628.

Liacaridae Willmann, 1931

Figures 349, 350

Diagnosis: Lateral and posterior margins of the hysterosoma are not bent ventrally. Legs III and IV are located ventrally, usually far removed from the lateral margins.

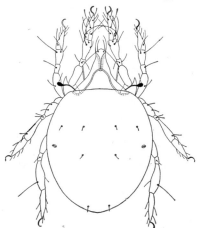

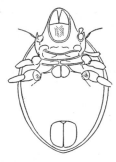

Figure 349 *Cultroribula divergens* Jacot. Dorsum of female.

Figure 350 *Liacarus coracinus* (Koch). Venter of female showing coxal attachments.

Genera:

1. *Liacarus* Michael, 1898 (= *Leiosoma* Nicolet, 1855, *nom. praeocc.*)
   Type. *Oribata nitens* Gervais, 1844
2. *Adoristes* Hull, 1916
   Type. *Oribates ovatus* Koch, 1840
3. *Astegistes* Hull, 1916 (= *Cultrozetes* Sellnick, 1922)
   Type. *Acarus muscorum* Scopoli, 1763 (= *Zetes pilosus* Koch, 1840)
4. *Cultroribula* Berlese, 1908
   Type. *Notaspis juncta* Michael, 1885

Discussion: Three species belonging to this family are known to be vectors of various tapeworms. *Liacarus coracinus* (Koch) is the intermediate host of *Cittotaenia ctenoides* and *C. denticulata* in Germany; *Adoristes ovatus* (Koch) is the intermediate host of a *Moniezia* sp. in Russia; and a *Liacarus* sp. is the intermediate host of *Anoplocephala perfoliata* in Russia.

Zetorchestidae Michael, 1898

Figures 351, 352

Diagnosis: Leg IV is adapted for jumping. This leg is directed forward when the mite is dead. There are no pteromorphs.

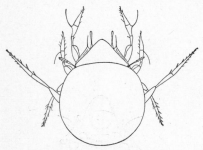 

Figure 351 *Zetorchestes micronychus* Berlese. Dorsum of female. (After Berlese 1883)

Figure 352 *Zetorchestes micronychus* Berlese. Venter of female showing leg IV arrangement. (After Berlese 1883)

Genera:

1. *Zetorchestes* Berlese, 1888
   Type. *Carabodes micronychus* Berlese, 1883
2. *Zetorchella* Berlese, 1916
   Type. *Zetorchella pedestris* Berlese, 1916

Gustaviidae Willmann, 1931

Figures 353, 354

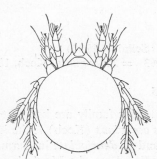 

Diagnosis: The chelicerae are long, narrow, knifelike, and sawlike on the distal end. There are no pteromorphs.

Figure 353 *Gustavia microcephala* (Nicolet). Dorsum of female. (After Berlese 1884)

Figure 354 *Gustavia microcephala* (Nicolet). Chelicera. (After Berlese 1884)

Genus:

Gustavia Kramer, 1879 (= *Serrarius* Michael, 1883)
Type. *Leiosoma microcephala* Nicolet, 1855 (= *Gustavia sol* Kramer, 1879)

Oripodidae Jacot, 1925

Figure 355

Diagnosis: These mites belong in the Pterogasterina. Pteromorphs are strongly developed anteriorly and combined with each other along the anterior edge of the opisthosoma. A coalesced portion of the pteromorphs forms a bridge over the propodosoma and covers the basal part, or all, of the pseudostigmatic setae and interlamellar setae; this bridge may or may not be coalesced with propodosoma. Two or three pairs of genital setae may be present.

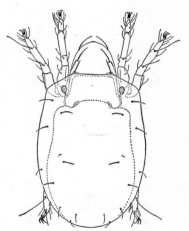

Figure 355 *Oripoda elongata* Banks. Dorsum of female.

Genera:

1. *Oripoda* Banks, 1904
   Type. *Oripoda elongata* Banks, 1904
2. *Cryptoribatula* Jacot, 1934
   Type. *Cryptoribatula taishanensis* Jacot, 1934
3. *Gymnobates* Banks, 1902
   Type. *Gymnobates glaber* Banks, 1902
4. *Jurabates* Jacot, 1929
   Type. *Oribata pseudofusiger* Schweizer, 1922

Reference:

Banks, N. 1904. A treatise on the Acarina, or mites. Proc. U. S. Nat. Mus. 28(1382):71.

Tenuialidae Jacot, 1929

Figure 356

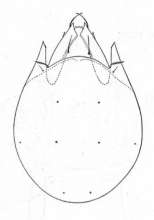

Diagnosis: The chelicerae are broad with strong shears. The lamellae are not especially developed. Prolonged anteriorly as plates the pteromorphs extend the length of the opisthosoma without interruptions. Jacot's conception of the pteromorphs places this family into the Pterogasterina.

Figure 356 *Tenuiala nuda* Ewing. Dorsum of female, legs omitted.

Genera:

1. *Tenuiala* Ewing, 1913
   Type. *Tenuiala nuda* Ewing, 1913
2. *Hafenrefferia* Oudemans, 1906
   Type. *Oribates gilvipes* Koch, 1840

Oribatulidae Jacot, 1929

(= *Scheloribatidae* Grandjean, 1933)

Figures 357, 358

Diagnosis: This family belongs with the Pterogasterina. The pteromorphs lie in one plane only and do not bend ventrally to protect the legs. When seen from above the anterior edge of the pteromorph curves backward. Each genital plate has four setae (an exception is an undescribed species from Panama, which has only the two anterior setae left on each plate).

Grandjean 1933 created the family Scheloribatidae for those mites which differed in the anal setal formula in the immature forms in having 0-2-3-4-4 in the larval, proto-, deuto-, tritonymphal, and adult stages. Oribatulidae has one seta in the larval stage. When the two groups are considered side by side it is difficult to separate them and so the two are included as one unit here.

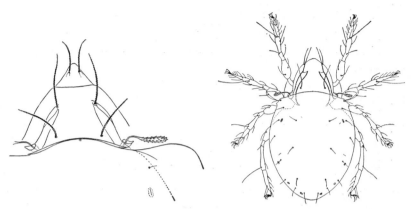

Figure 357   *Protoschelobates seghettii* Runkel and Kates. Anterior dorsal portion of female showing pteromorphs, pseudostigma and pseudostigmatic organs, lamellae, and setal arrangement.

Figure 358   *Oribatula minuta* (Ewing). Dorsum of female.

Genera and subgenera:

1. *Oribatula* Berlese, 1896
   a. *Oribatula* s. str.
      Type. *Notaspis tibialis* Nicolet, 1855
   b. *Zygoribatula* Berlese, 1916 (= *Neoribatula* Ewing, 1917)
      Type. *Oribatula connexa* Berlese, 1916
   c. *Hemileius* Berlese, 1916
      Type. *Protoribates* (*Scheloribates*) *initialis* Berlese, 1908
2. *Cardioribates* Jacot, 1934
   Type. *Oribata oriformis* Pearse, 1910
3. *Drymobates* Grandjean, 1930
   Type. *Drymobates silvicola* Grandjean, 1930
4. *Drymobatoides* Jacot, 1936
   Type. *Drymobatoides mauritius* Jacot, 1936
5. *Eporibatula* Sellnick, 1928
   Type. *Eremaeus rauschensis* Sellnick, 1928
6. *Exoribatula* Jacot, 1936
   Type. *Exoribatula biundatus* Jacot, 1936
7. *Liebstadia* Oudemans, 1906
   Type. *Notaspis similis* Michael, 1888

8. *Protoschelobates* Jacot, 1934
   Type. *Murcia insularis* Oudemans, 1917
9. *Scheloribates* Berlese, 1908
   a. *Scheloribates* s. str.
      Type. *Zetes latipes* Koch, 1844
   b. *Paraschelobates* Jacot, 1934
      Type. *Scheloribates* (*Paraschelobates*) *mumfordi* Jacot, 1934
10. *Styloribates* Jacot, 1934
    Type. *Styloribates pectinatus* Jacot, 1934
11. *Unguizetes* Sellnick, 1925
    Type. *Oribates sphaerula* Berlese, 1905
12. *Zetomimus* Hull, 1916
    Type. *Oribata furcata* Warburton and Pearse, 1905
13. *Zetomotrichus* Grandjean, 1934
    Type. *Zetomotrichus lacrimans* Grandjean, 1934

Discussion: In the family Oribatulidae, *Scheloribates laevigatus* (Koch) is the principal vector of the various tapeworms. To date, four other species are also involved. *S. laevigatus* is the intermediate host of *Moniezia expansa* in the United States and Russia; of *M. benedeni* in Russia; of *Bertiella studeri, Cittotaenia ctenoides,* and *C. denticulata* in Germany; and of *Anoplocephala perfoliata, A. magna* and *Thysaniezia giardi* in Russia. *Scheloribates latipes* (Koch) is the intermediate host of *Anoplocephala perfoliata* and *Thysaniezia giardi* in Russia. *Protoschelobates seghettii* Runkel and Kates and *Oribatula minuta* (Ewing) are intermediate hosts of *Moniezia expansa* in the United States. *Liebstadia similis* (Michael) is the vector of *Cittotaenia ctenoides* in Germany. Kates and Runkel 1948 give an excellent review of the biology and distributions of the oribatid mites which are vectors of the tapeworms and their work should be consulted for further details.

References:

Grandjean, F. 1933. Étude sur le développement des Oribates. Bull. Soc. Zool. France 58(1):30–61.

Kates, K. C. and C. E. Runkel. 1948. Observations on oribatid mite vectors of *Moniezia expansa* on pastures, with a report of several new vectors from the United States. Proc. Helminth. Soc. Wash. 15(1):18–33.

Ceratozetidae Jacot, 1925

Figure 359

Diagnosis: The ceratozetids belong with the Pterogasterina. They
have small pteromorphs which do
not project beyond the anterior
portion of the opisthosoma. The
inner margin of the lamellae is
fastened to the propodosoma and
the anterior portion projects freely. There may or may not be trans-
lamellae. Genital plates have six
pairs of setae.

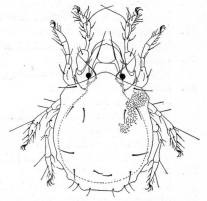

Figure 359 *Jugatala tuberosa* Ewing.
Dorsum of female.

Genera and subgenera:

1. *Ceratozetes* Berlese, 1908
    a. *Ceratozetes* s. str.
        Type. *Oribata gracilis* Michael, 1884
    b. *Allozetes* Berlese, 1913
        Type. *Ceratozetes (Allozetes) pusillus* Berlese, 1913
2. *Alloribates* Banks, 1947
    Type. *Alloribates singularis* Banks, 1947
3. *Balzania* Jacot, 1929
    Type. *Oribata microptera* Canestrini, 1896
4. *Banksinus* Jacot, 1938
    Type. *Oribata arborea* Banks, 1895
5. *Calyptozetes* Thor, 1929
    Type. *Oribata sarekensis* Trägårdh, 1910
6. *Chamobates* Hull, 1916
    Type. *Oribata cuspidata* Michael, 1884
7. *Diapterobates* Grandjean, 1936
    Type. *Sphaerozetes (Trichoribates) numerosus* Sellnick, 1924
8. *Edwardzetes* Berlese, 1914
    Type. *Oribata edwardsii* Nicolet, 1855
9. *Frischia* Oudemans, 1915
    Type. *Frischia elongata* Oudemans, 1915

10. *Globozetes* Sellnick, 1928
    Type. *Globozetes longipilus* Sellnick, 1928
11. *Hammeria* Sellnick, 1944
    Type. *Hammeria groenlandica* Sellnick, 1944
12. *Humerobates* Sellnick, 1928
    Type. *Notaspis humeralis* Hermann, 1804
13. *Iugoribates* Sellnick, 1944
    Type. *Iugoribates gracilis* Sellnick, 1944
14. *Jugatala* Ewing, 1913
    Type. *Jugatala tuberosa* Ewing, 1913
15. *Limnozetes* Hull, 1916
    a. *Limnozetes* s. str.
       Type. *Acarus ciliatus* Schrank, 1803 (= *Oribata sphagni* Michael, 1884)
    b. *Mycobates* Hull, 1916
       Type. *Oribata parmeliae* Michael, 1884
16. *Melanozetes* Hull, 1916
    Type. *Oribates mollicomus* Koch, 1840
17. *Minunthozetes* Hull, 1916
    Type. *Zetes simirufus* Koch, 1840 (= *Oribata fusigera* Michael, 1884)
18. *Mochlozetes* Grandjean, 1930
    Type. *Mochlozetes penetrabilis* Grandjean, 1930
19. *Nesiotizetes* Jacot, 1934
    Type. *Nesiotizetes adamsoni* Jacot, 1934
20. *Oromurcia* Thor, 1930
    Type. *Oromurcia bicuspidata* Thor, 1930
21. *Propeschelobates* Jacot, 1936
    Type. *Oribata albida* Ewing, 1907
22. *Sphaerobates* Sellnick, 1928
    Type. *Sphaerozetes* (?) *gratus* Sellnick, 1921
23. *Sphaerozetes* Berlese, 1885 (= *Euzetes* Berlese, 1908)
    Type. *Oribates orbicularis* Koch, 1836
24. *Storkania* Jacot, 1929
    Type. *Oribata simplex* Storkán, 1925
25. *Svalbardia* Thor, 1930
    Type. *Svalbardia paludicola* Thor, 1930
26. *Tegeozetes* Berlese, 1913
    Type. *Tegeozetes tunicatus* Berlese, 1913
27. *Terrazetes* Jacot, 1936
    Type. *Oribates sphaerula* Berlese, 1905
28. *Trachyoribates* Berlese, 1908
    a. *Trachyoribates* s. str.
       Type. *Oribates ampulla* Berlese, 1904

b. *Indoribates* Jacot, 1929
Type. *Protoribates punctulatus* Sellnick, 1925
29. *Trichoribates* Berlese, 1910
a. *Trichoribates* s. str.
Type. *Murcia trimaculata* Koch, 1836
b. *Sphaerozetella* Jacot, 1929
Type. *Oribates orbicularis* Berlese, 1883 (*non* C. L. Koch 1836)

Discussion: *Trichoribates incisellus* (Kramer) is known to be the vector of *Cittotaenia ctenoides* in Germany.

References:

Hammer, Marie. 1944. Studies on the oribatids and collemboles of Greenland. Meddelelser om Gronland 141(3):1–210.
———. 1946. The zoology of East Greenland. Meddelelser om Gronland 122(1):1–39.

Oribatellidae Jacot, 1925

Figure 360

Diagnosis: This family also belongs with the Pterogasterina. The pteromorphs do not extend anteriorly past the opisthosoma. The lamellae are attached only by their rear margin to the propodosoma and as a rule they are large, covering a considerable part of the propodosoma. Many species are striking in appearance.

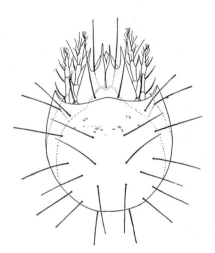

Figure 360 *Oribatella magniseta* Ewing. Dorsum of female.

Genera and subgenera:

1. *Oribatella* Banks, 1895
Type. *Oribatella quadridentata* Banks, 1895
2. *Anachipteria* Grandjean, 1932
Type. *Anachipteria deficiens* Grandjean, 1932

3. *Joelia* Oudemans, 1906 (= *Coggiella* Berlese, 1916)
   Type. *Oribates fiorii* Coggi, 1898
4. *Tectoribates* Berlese, 1910
   a. *Tectoribates* s. str.
      Type. *Oribata tecta* Michael, 1883
   b. *Unduloribates* Balogh, 1943
      Type. *Tectoribates undulatus* Berlese, 1915

Microzetidae Grandjean, 1936

Figures 361, 362

Diagnosis: These mites are included in the Pterogasterina. Their chelicerae have a forward-directed horn dorsally on the fixed chela. Tectopedium I has a large leaf or plate which is a continuation of the side wall of the propodosoma.

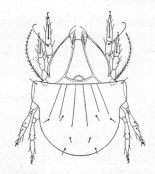

Figure 361 *Phylacozetes membranulifer* Grandjean. Cheliceral tip showing horn. (After Grandjean 1936)

Figure 362 *Microzetes appalachicola* Jacot. Dorsum of female.

The free margin of the tectopedium is of a complicated form with large flaps separated from one another by deep incisions; these flaps are so rolled that the tectopedium is convexly arched on the line of the body axis. The lamellae are always very large, hinged, or joined at the base and are not connected with one another; they can be of various shapes and can be folded lengthwise. The legs can be withdrawn under the lamellae and into these folds if the mite takes a position of protection. From the paraxial side of the lamellae arises a membranous flap which may be simple, harpoon-like, or have strong teeth. The podosoma and opisthosoma are separated ventrally by a broad, dark-colored band, a thickening of apodeme IV; above this can be seen a fine transverse suture which joins the anterior lateral corner of the genital opening with the sclerotized area surrounding the leg. The podosoma is larger than the opisthosoma.

Genera:

1. *Microzetes* Berlese, 1913
   Type. *Sphaerozetes mirandus* Berlese, 1908
2. *Acaroceras* Grandjean, 1936
   Type. *Acaroceras odontotus* Grandjean, 1936
3. *Nellacarus* Grandjean, 1936
   Type. *Nellacarus petrocoriensis* Grandjean, 1936
4. *Phylacozetes* Grandjean, 1936
   Type. *Phylacozetes membranulifer* Grandjean, 1936

Reference:

Grandjean, F. 1936. Les Microzetidae n. fam. (Oribates). Bull. Soc. Zool. de France 61(2):60–93.

Notaspididae Oudemans, 1900

Figure 363

Diagnosis: Belonging with the Pterogasterina these mites have pteromorphs with an anteriorly projecting point which reaches almost to the tip of the rostrum. Lamellae, which cover almost the entire propodosoma, are hinged posteriorly and are attached to each other in a small central area.

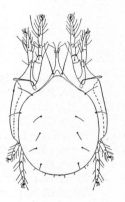

Figure 363 *Notaspis magnus Sellnick.* Dorsum of female.

Genera:

1. *Notaspis* Hermann, 1804 (= *Achipteria* Berlese, 1885)
   Type. *Acarus coleoptratus* Linnaeus, 1758
2. *Achipterina* Berlese, 1916
   Type. *Achipteria (Achipterina) oribatelloides* Berlese, 1916
3. *Cerachipteria* Grandjean, 1935
   Type. *Cerachipteria digitata* Grandjean, 1935
4. *Fuscozetes* Sellnick, 1928
   Type. *Oribata fuscipes* Koch, 1844

Discussion: *Notaspis coleoptratus* (L.) is a vector of *Bertiella studeri* and *Cittotaenia ctenoides* in Germany, whereas *Achipteria* (*Notaspis*) sp. is a vector of *Anoplocephala perfoliata* in Russia.

Haplozetidae Grandjean, 1936

Figure 364

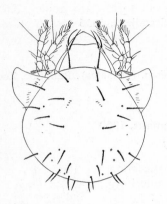

Diagnosis: The haplozetids have movable, hinged pteromorphs. Tectopedium IV is lengthened by a leaflike extension. The genital plates have five pairs of setae. Grandjean 1936 says there are occasionally four pairs of genital setae in certain species.

Figure 364 *Peloribates curtipilus* Jacot. Dorsum of female.

Genera:

1. *Haplozetes* Willmann, 1935
   Type. *Peloribates vindobonensis* Willmann, 1935
2. *Neogymnobates* Ewing, 1917
   Type. *Oribata multipilosa* Ewing, 1907
3. *Peloribates* Berlese, 1908 (= *Parazetes* Willmann, 1930 = *Euryparazetes* Radford, 1950)
   Type. *Oribata peloptoides* Berlese, 1888
4. *Protoribates* Berlese, 1908
   Type. *Oribata monodactyla* Haller, 1884
5. *Rostrozetes* Sellnick, 1925
   Type. *Rostrozetes foveolatus* Sellnick, 1925
6. *Xylobates* Jacot, 1929
   Type. *Oribata lophothrichus* Berlese, 1904

Discussion: A single species, *Peloribates curtipilus* Jacot, has been found as a vector of the sheep tapeworm, *Moniezia expansa*.

Reference:

Grandjean, F. 1936. Observations sur les Oribates (10 serie). Bull. Paris Mus. d'Hist. Nat. Ser. 2, 8(3):246–249.

Pelopidae Ewing, 1917

Figures 365, 366

Diagnosis: Classed with the Pterogasterina the pelopids have large, movable, hinged pteromorphs which reach out anteriorly but not posteriorly over the line of attachment (except in *Peloptulus* and *Galumnella* where the posterior end is drawn out to a sharp point). The middle part of the anterior margin of the hysterosoma (between pteromorphs) reaches out anteriorly over the borderline between the pro-

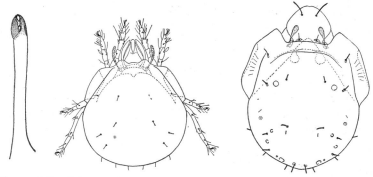

Figure 365 *Pelops sylvestris* Jacot. Chelicera and dorsum of female.

Figure 366 *Lepidozetes singularis* Berlese. Female.

podosoma and the hysterosoma, sometimes extending further than the anterior end of the pteromorphs. Interlamellar setae are either spatulalike (*Pelops, Eupelops, Tectopelops, Parapelops*), or normally hairlike (*Peloptulus, Pelopsis, Propelops*), or lacking (*Galumnella, Galumnopsis*). The chelicerae are broad at the base and suddenly narrow to make a long, slender segment with minute shears (except in *Propelops* which has normal chelicerae). There are six pairs of genital setae.

Genera and subgenera:

1. *Pelops* Koch, 1836
   Type. *Notaspis hirsutus* Koch, 1836
2. *Eupelops* Ewing, 1917
   Type. *Pelops uraceus* Koch, 1840
3. *Galumnella* Berlese, 1916
   Type. *Galumnella paradoxa* Berlese, 1916

4. *Galumnopsis* Grandjean, 1931
   Type. *Galumnopsis holoscripta* Grandjean, 1931
5. *Lepidozetes* Berlese, 1910
   a. *Lepidozetes* s. str.
      Type. *Lepidozetes singularis* Berlese, 1910
   b. *Tegoribates* Ewing, 1917 (= *Lepidoribates* Sellnick, 1920)
      Type. *Tegoribates subniger* Ewing, 1917
6. *Parapelops* Jacot, 1938
   Type. *Pelops bifurcatus* Ewing, 1909
7. *Pelopsis* Hall, 1911
   Type. *Pelopsis undiuscula* Hall, 1911
8. *Peloptulus* Berlese, 1908
   Type. *Pelops phaeonotus* Koch, 1844
9. *Propelops* Jacot, 1937
   Type. *Propelops pinicus* Jacot, 1937
10. *Tectopelops* Jacot, 1929
    Type. *Pelops laevigatus* Nicolet, 1855

Discussion: Two species, *Pelops tardus* Koch and *P. planicornis* (Schrank), are known as vectors of the tapeworm *Cittotaenia ctenoides* in Germany.

The genus *Lepidozetes* is not typical of this group and may warrant subfamily or family rank. It differs mainly in having large, coalesced lamellae covering the entire propodosoma. The interlamellar setae are small, the hysterosoma overlaps the propodosoma, there are six pairs of genital setae, and the chelicerae are normal.

Galumnidae Grandjean, 1936

Figures 367, 368

Diagnosis: Of the Pterogasterina these mites have large, movable, hinged, winglike pteromorphs; the rounded anterior and posterior ends project far over the line where they join the body. A suture between the propodosoma and the hysterosoma may or may not be present. The lamellae are weakly developed or lacking. Each genital plate has six setae; the first anterior pair of circumanal setae is on the lateral anterior margin of the anal opening.

Genera and subgenera:

1. *Galumna* v. Heyden, 1826 (= *Zetes* Koch, 1836 = *Centroribates* Berlese, 1914)

a. *Galumna* s. str.
Type. *Notaspis alatus* Hermann, 1804
b. *Pergalumna* Grandjean, 1936
Type. *Oribates nervosus* Berlese, 1914
c. *Stictozetes* Berlese, 1916
Type. *Oribates* (*Stictozetes*) *scaber* Berlese, 1916
d. *Vaghia* Oudemans, 1917
Type. *Oribates* (*Stictozetes*) *stupendus* Berlese, 1916
2. *Allogalumna* Grandjean, 1936
Type. *Galumna alamellae* Jacot, 1935
3. *Holokalumma* Jacot, 1929
Type. *Holokalumma coloradensis* Jacot, 1929
4. *Pilizetes* Sellnick, 1937
Type. *Pilizetes africanus* Sellnick, 1937
5. *Psamnogalumna* Balogh, 1943
Type. *Stictozetes hungaricus* Sellnick, 1925

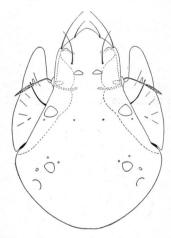

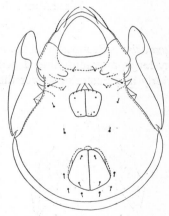

Figure 367 *Galumna virginiensis*
Jacot. Dorsum of female. (After Jacot
1934)

Figure 368 *Galumna virginiensis*
Jacot. Venter of female. (After Jacot
1934)

Discussion: The Galumnidae, or large-winged mites, are rather bizarre forms which possess large, movable pteromorphs. Several species are known to be vectors of tapeworms. *Galumna virginiensis* Jacot is the vector of *Moniezia expansa* in the United States; *G. nervosus* (Berlese) of *Cittotaenia ctenoides* in the United States and of *Anoplocephala perfoliata* in Russia; *G. obvius* (Berlese) of *Moniezia expansa, M. benedeni, Anoplocephala perfoliata,* and *Paranoplocephala mamillana* in Russia and of *Cittotaenia ctenoides* in Germany; *G. emarginatum* (Banks) and *G. nigra* (Ewing) of *Moniezia expansa* in the United States; *Galumna* sp. of *Moniezia expansa* in the United States and of *Bertiella studeri* in Germany. *Allogalumna longipluma* (Berlese) is a vector of *Paranoplocephala mamillana* in Russia.

References:

Jacot, A. P. 1929. American oribatid mites of the subfamily Galumninae. Bull. Mus. Compar. Zool. 69(1):1–37.

———. 1933. The primitive Galumninae (Oribatoidea-Acarina) of the Middle West. Amer. Midland Nat. 14(6):680–703.

———1934. The Galumnas (Oribatoidea-Acarina) of the northeastern United States. J. N. Y. Ent. Soc. 42:87–125.

———. 1935. The large-winged mites of Florida. Florida Ent. 19(1): 1–15; 19(2):17–31; 19(3):43–47.

Parakalummidae Grandjean, 1936

Figures 369, 370

Diagnosis: Grouped with the Pterogasterina the parakalummids have very large, movable, hinged, winglike pteromorphs, which extend anteriorly and posteriorly over the line of attachment to the body. The

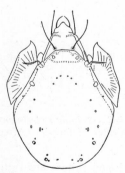
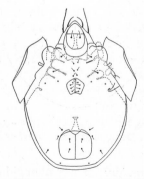
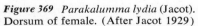

Figure 369 *Parakalumma lydia* (Jacot). Dorsum of female. (After Jacot 1929)

Figure 370 *Parakalumma lydia* (Jacot). Venter of female. (After Jacot 1929)

propodosoma and hysterosoma are separated by a suture. The lamellae are weakly developed or lacking. Each genital plate has five setae; the anterior pair of circumanal setae lies in front of the anal opening.

Genera:

1. *Parakalumma* Jacot, 1929
   Type. *Neoribates lydia* Jacot, 1923
2. *Holozetes* Jacot, 1929
   Type. *Galumna texana* Banks, 1906
3. *Kratzensteinia* Oudemans, 1917
   Type. *Oribata rugifrons* Stoll, 1891
4. *Neoribates* Berlese, 1914
   Type. *Oribates roubali* Berlese, 1900
5. *Neorizetes* Jacot, 1933
   Type. *Oribata rugosala* Ewing, 1909
6. *Protokalumma* Jacot, 1929
   Type. *Oribata depressa* Banks, 1905
7. *Sandenia* Oudemans, 1917
   Type. *Galumna georgiae* Oudemans, 1914

Reference:

Grandjean, F. 1936. Les Oribates de Jean Frédéric Hermann et de son Père. Ann. Soc. Ent. de France 105:27–110.

Epactozetidae Grandjean, 1936

Figure 371

Diagnosis: These mites belong with the Pterogasterina and have large, movable, hinged, winglike pteromorphs which extend far back and in front of the line of joining to the body. The propodosoma and hysterosoma are separated by a suture and there are very large lamellae which cover the greatest part of the propodosoma. Five pairs of setae are present on the genital plates; the anterior pair of circumanal setae is next to the anterior end of the anal opening.

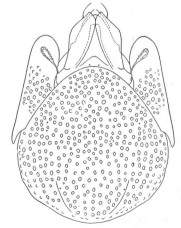

Figure 371 *Epactozetes imitator* Grandjean. Dorsum of female. (After Grandjean 1936)

Genus:

Epactozetes Grandjean, 1930

Type. *Epactozetes imitator* Grandjean, 1930

Reference:

Grandjean, F. 1936. Les Oribates de Jean Frédéric Hermann et de son Père. Ann. Soc. Ent. de France 105:27–110.

Protoplophoridae Jacot, 1923

Figure 372

Diagnosis: These mites are capable of closing up like an armadillo, protecting the mouth parts and legs. When the mite is closed, only the anal aperture is visible and the genital opening, legs, and gnathosoma are covered by the aspis. The body proper is divided into four

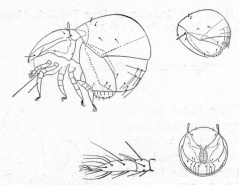

Figure 372 *Aedoplophora glomerata* Grandjean. Lateral view of female; lateral view of contracted female; detail of tarsus I; anterior view of contracted female. (After Grandjean 1932)

parts: the anterior dorsal or pronotaspis; the dorsal posterior plate or metanotaspis or pygidium; and two lateral, symmetrical plates—the pleuraspis—which cover a large part of the venter of the hysterosoma. The pygidium is movable and can sink entirely into the pronotaspis or can be fully withdrawn. Genital plates are immediately behind the coxae IV; the anal plates are directly behind the genital plates and between the pleuraspis.

Genera:

1. *Protoplophora* Berlese, 1910
   Type. *Protoplophora palpalis* Berlese, 1910
2. *Aedoplophora* Grandjean, 1932
   Type. *Aedoplophora glomerata* Grandjean, 1932
3. *Arthroplophora* Berlese, 1910
   Type. *Arthroplophora paradoxa* Berlese, 1910
4. *Cryptoplophora* Grandjean, 1932
   Type. *Cryptoplophora abscondita* Grandjean, 1932
5. *Prototritia* Berlese, 1916
   Type. *Arthroplophora* (*Prototritia*) *armadillo* Berlese, 1916

Discussion: These mites live in humus and rotten roots. There are only a few known species, probably owing to the difficulty in collecting them, as well as insufficient collecting.

Reference:

Grandjean, F. 1932. La Famille des Protoplophoridae (Acariens). Bull. Soc. Zool. de France 58(1):10–36.

Mesoplophoridae Jacot, 1923

Figures 373, 374

Diagnosis: The hysterosoma is not divided into segments. The genital opening and anal opening lie in a large ventral plate which is connected with the dorsal shield.

 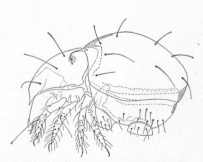

Figure 373 *Mesoplophora michaeliana* Berlese. Venter of female. (After Berlese 1904)

Figure 374 *Mesoplophora pulchra* Sellnick. Lateral view of female. (After Grandjean 1933)

Genus:

Mesoplophora Berlese, 1904
Type. *Mesoplophora michaeliana* Berlese, 1904

Reference:

Grandjean, F. 1933. Oribates de l'Afrique du Nord. Bull. Soc. d'Hist. Nat.
de l'Afrique du Nord 24:308–323.

Phthiracaridae Perty, 1841

Figures 375–377

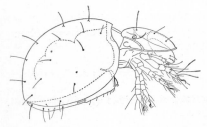

Figure 375 *Pseudotritia ardua* (Koch).
Lateral view of female. (After Jacot 1930)

Diagnosis: The hysterosoma is not divided by transverse sutures. Genital and anal plates lie in a large ventral plate which is not connected with the dorsal shield.

Jacot 1930 states: "The outstanding character of the Phthiracaridae is the ability to withdraw the cephalothorax and legs within the vault of the notogaster, a development which so much recalls the box turtle, armadillo and others. One often reads that the aspis is hinged to the abdomen and capable of folding down like the hinged lid of a box. This is highly erroneous. There is no hinge. The cephalo-

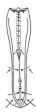

Figure 376 *Pseudotritia ardua* (Koch).
Genital-anal region. (After Jacot 1930)

Figure 377 *Phthiracarus setosellum*
Jacot. Propodosoma and legs (dotted) withdrawn into cavity in upper part of hysterosoma and with aspis covering the opening. (After Jacot 1930)

thorax is merely drawn into the upper part of the cavity of the abdomen and between the legs, which spread out four on each side. This is done in such a way that a chitinous shield or aspis, borne on top of the head (with the visor forward) closes the opening like a lid on a kettle. The ends of the feet (tarsus and claws) fit into the anterior end of this lid, i.e., under the visor."

Key to the Phthiracaridae

1. Genital and anal plates short and broad; ventral hysterosomal plate broadly surrounding anal opening to rear   Phthiracarinae

   Genital and anal plates long and narrow; ventral hysterosomal plate narrowly surrounding anal opening to rear   Euphthiracarinae

Phthiracarinae Perty, 1841

Genera and subgenera:

1. *Phthiracarus* Perty, 1841
   a. *Phthiracarus* s. str.
      Type. *Acarus piger* Scolpoli, 1763 (= *Phthiracarus contractilis* Perty, 1841)
   b. *Tropacarus* Ewing, 1917 (= *Calhoplophora* Berlese, 1923)
      Type. *Hoplophora carinata* Koch, 1841
   c. *Trachyhoplophora* Berlese, 1923
      Type. *Hoplophora magna* Nicolet, 1855
   d. *Hoplophorella* Berlese, 1923
      Type. *Hoplophora cucullatum* Ewing, 1909
2. *Steganacarus* Ewing, 1917
   Type. *Hoplophora anomala* Berlese, 1883
3. *Hoplophthiracarus* Jacot, 1933
   Type. *Hoploderma histricinum* Berlese, 1908
4. *Atropacarus* Ewing, 1917
   Type. *Hoplophora stricula* Koch, 1836
5. *Ginglymacarus* Ewing, 1917
   Type. *Hoplophora dasypus* Dugès, 1834
6. *Hoploderma* Michael, 1898 (= *Hoplophora* Koch, 1836, *nom. prae-occ.*)
   Type. *Hoplophora laevigata* Koch, 1844

Euphthiracarinae Jacot, 1930

Genera and subgenera:

1. *Oribotritia* Jacot, 1924 (= *Tritia* Berlese, 1883, *nom. praeocc.*)
   Type. *Hoplophora decumana* Koch, 1836
2. *Indotritia* Jacot, 1928
   Type. *Tritia krakatauensis* Sellnick, 1924

3. *Pseudotritia* Willmann, 1920
   a. *Pseudotritia* s. str.
      Type. *Tritia monodactyla* Willmann, 1919
   b. *Phtiracarulus* Berlese, 1920
      Type. *Phtiracarus (Phtiracarulus) perexiguus* Berlese, 1920
4. *Euphthiracarus* Ewing, 1917
   Type. *Phthiracarus flavus* Ewing, 1908
5. *Hummelia* Oudemans, 1916
   Type. *Hummelia karpellesi* Oudemans, 1916 (= *Hoplophora ardua* Karpelles, 1893)
6. *Peridromotritia* Jacot, 1923
   Type. *Phthiracarus rotundus* Ewing, 1908
7. *Acrotritia* Jacot, 1923
   Type. *Phthiracarus americanus* Ewing, 1909

Reference:

Jacot, A. P. 1930. Oribatid mites of the subfamily Phthiracarinae of the northeastern United States. Proc. Boston Soc. Nat. Hist. 36(6):209–261.

INDEX